Teacher Edition

Eureka Math
Grade 4
Module 3

Special thanks go to the Gordon A. Cain Center and to the Department of Mathematics at Louisiana State University for their support in the development of *Eureka Math*.

For a free *Eureka Math* Teacher
Resource Pack, Parent Tip
Sheets, and more please
visit www.Eureka.tools

Printed in the U.S.A.

This book may be purchased from the publisher at eureka-math.org

10 9 8 7 6

ISBN 978-1-63255-372-0

Eureka Math: A Story of Units **Contributors**

Katrina Abdussalaam, Curriculum Writer

Tiah Alphonso, Program Manager—Curriculum Production

Kelly Alsup, Lead Writer / Editor, Grade 4

Catriona Anderson, Program Manager—Implementation Support

Debbie Andorka-Aceves, Curriculum Writer

Eric Angel, Curriculum Writer

Leslie Arceneaux, Lead Writer / Editor, Grade 5

Kate McGill Austin, Lead Writer / Editor, Grades PreK–K

Adam Baker, Lead Writer / Editor, Grade 5

Scott Baldridge, Lead Mathematician and Lead Curriculum Writer

Beth Barnes, Curriculum Writer

Bonnie Bergstresser, Math Auditor

Bill Davidson, Fluency Specialist

Jill Diniz, Program Director

Nancy Diorio, Curriculum Writer

Nancy Doorey, Assessment Advisor

Lacy Endo-Peery, Lead Writer / Editor, Grades PreK–K

Ana Estela, Curriculum Writer

Lessa Faltermann, Math Auditor

Janice Fan, Curriculum Writer

Ellen Fort, Math Auditor

Peggy Golden, Curriculum Writer

Maria Gomes, Pre-Kindergarten Practitioner

Pam Goodner, Curriculum Writer

Greg Gorman, Curriculum Writer

Melanie Gutierrez, Curriculum Writer

Bob Hollister, Math Auditor

Kelley Isinger, Curriculum Writer

Nuhad Jamal, Curriculum Writer

Mary Jones, Lead Writer / Editor, Grade 4

Halle Kananak, Curriculum Writer

Susan Lee, Lead Writer / Editor, Grade 3

Jennifer Loftin, Program Manager—Professional Development

Soo Jin Lu, Curriculum Writer

Nell McAnelly, Project Director

This page intentionally left blank

Mathematics Curriculum

4
GRADE

Table of Contents

GRADE 4 • MODULE 3

Multi-Digit Multiplication and Division

Grade 4 • Module 3

Multi-Digit Multiplication and Division

OVERVIEW

In this 43-day module, students use place value understanding and visual representations to solve multiplication and division problems with multi-digit numbers. As a key area of focus for Grade 4, this module moves slowly but comprehensively to develop students' ability to reason about the methods and models chosen to solve problems with multi-digit factors and dividends.

Students begin in Topic A by investigating the formulas for area and perimeter. They then solve multiplicative comparison problems including the language of *times as much as* with a focus on problems using area and perimeter as a context (e.g., "A field is 9 feet wide. It is 4 times as long as it is wide. What is the perimeter of the field?"). Students create diagrams to represent these problems as well as write equations with symbols for the unknown quantities (**4.OA.1**). This is foundational for understanding multiplication as scaling in Grade 5 and sets the stage for proportional reasoning in Grade 6. This Grade 4 module, beginning with area and perimeter, allows for new and interesting word problems as students learn to calculate with larger numbers and interpret more complex problems (**4.OA.2**, **4.OA.3**, **4.MD.3**).

In Topic B, students use place value disks to multiply single-digit numbers by multiples of 10, 100, and 1,000 and two-digit multiples of 10 by two-digit multiples of 10 (**4.NBT.5**). Reasoning between arrays and written numerical work allows students to see the role of place value units in multiplication (as pictured below). Students also practice the language of units to prepare them for multiplication of a single-digit factor by a factor with up to four digits and multiplication of two two-digit factors.

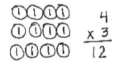

In preparation for two-digit by two-digit multiplication, students practice the new complexity of multiplying two two-digit multiples of 10. For example, students have multiplied 20 by 10 on the place value chart and know that it shifts the value one place to the left, 10 × 20 = 200. To multiply 20 by 30, the associative property allows for simply tripling the product, 3 × (10 × 20), or multiplying the units, 3 tens × 2 tens = 6 hundreds (alternatively, (3 × 10) × (2 × 10) = (3 × 2) × (10 × 10)). Introducing this early in the module allows students to practice during fluency so that, by the time it is embedded within the two-digit by two-digit multiplication in Topic H, understanding and skill are in place.

EUREKA MATH™

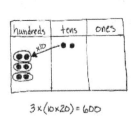

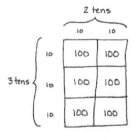

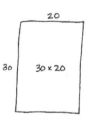

Building on their work in Topic B, students begin in Topic C decomposing numbers into base ten units in order to find products of single-digit by multi-digit numbers. Students use the distributive property and multiply using place value disks to model. Practice with place value disks is used for two-, three-, and four-digit by one-digit multiplication problems with recordings as partial products. Students bridge partial products to the recording of multiplication via the standard algorithm.[1] Finally, the partial products method, the standard algorithm, and the area model are compared and connected by the distributive property (**4.NBT.5**).

$$1,423 \times 3$$

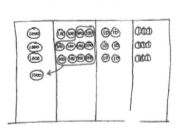

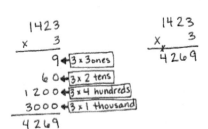

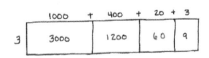

Topic D gives students the opportunity to apply their new multiplication skills to solve multi-step word problems (**4.OA.3**, **4.NBT.5**) and multiplicative comparison problems (**4.OA.2**). Students write equations from statements within the problems (**4.OA.1**) and use a combination of addition, subtraction, and multiplication to solve.

In Topic E, students synthesize their Grade 3 knowledge of division types (*group size unknown* and *number of groups unknown*) with their new, deeper understanding of place value.

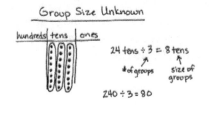

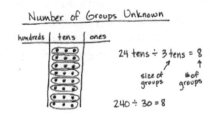

---

[1]Students become fluent with the standard algorithm for multiplication in Grade 5 (5.NBT.5). Grade 4 students are introduced to the standard algorithm in preparation for fluency and as a general method for solving multiplication problems based on place value strategies, alongside place value disks, partial products, and the area model. Students are not assessed on the standard algorithm in Grade 4.

Students focus on interpreting the remainder within division problems, both in word problems and long division (**4.OA.3**). A remainder of 1, as exemplified below, represents a leftover flower in the first situation and a remainder of 1 ten in the second situation.[2]

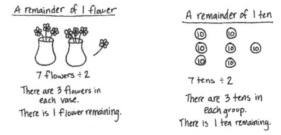

While we have no reason to subdivide a remaining flower, there are good reasons to subdivide a remaining ten. Students apply this simple idea to divide two-digit numbers unit by unit: dividing the tens units first, finding the remainder (the number of tens unable to be divided), and decomposing remaining tens into ones to then be divided. Students represent division with single-digit divisors using arrays and the area model before practicing with place value disks. The standard division algorithm[3] is practiced using place value knowledge, decomposing unit by unit. Finally, students use the area model to solve division problems, first with and then without remainders (**4.NBT.6**).

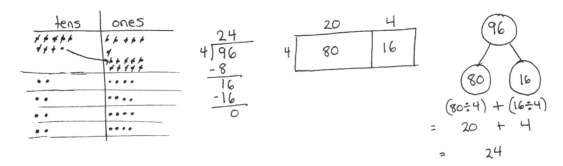

In Topic F, armed with an understanding of remainders, students explore factors, multiples, and prime and composite numbers within 100 (**4.OA.4**), gaining valuable insights into patterns of divisibility as they test for primes and find factors and multiples. This prepares them for Topic G's work with multi-digit dividends.

Topic G extends the practice of division with three- and four-digit dividends using place value understanding. A connection to Topic B is made initially with dividing multiples of 10, 100, and 1,000 by single-digit numbers. Place value disks support students visually as they decompose each unit before dividing. Students then practice using the standard algorithm to record long division. They solve word problems and make connections to the area model as was done with two-digit dividends (**4.NBT.6, 4.OA.3**).

---

[2]Note that care must be taken in the interpretation of remainders. Consider the fact that $7 \div 3$ is not equal to $5 \div 2$ because the remainder of 1 is in reference to a different whole amount ($2\frac{1}{3}$ is not equal to $2\frac{1}{2}$).

[3]Students become fluent with the standard division algorithm in Grade 6 (**6.NS.2**). For adequate practice in reaching fluency, students are introduced to, but not assessed on, the division algorithm in Grade 4 as a general method for solving division problems.

EUREKA MATH™

The module closes as students multiply two-digit by two-digit numbers. Students use their place value understanding and understanding of the area model to empower them to multiply by larger numbers (as pictured to the right). Topic H culminates at the most abstract level by explicitly connecting the partial products appearing in the area model to the distributive property and recording the calculation vertically (**4.NBT.5**). Students see that partial products written vertically are the same as those obtained via the distributive property: 4 twenty-sixes + 30 twenty-sixes = 104 + 780 = 884.

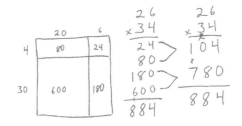

As students progress through this module, they are able to apply the multiplication and division algorithms because of their in-depth experience with the place value system and multiple conceptual models. This helps to prepare them for fluency with the multiplication algorithm in Grade 5 and the division algorithm in Grade 6. Students are encouraged in Grade 4 to continue using models to solve when appropriate.

Notes on Pacing for Differentiation

Within this module, if pacing is a challenge, consider the following omissions. In Lesson 1, omit Problem 1 if you embedded it into Module 2, and omit Problem 4, which can be used for a center activity. In Lesson 8, omit the drawing of models in Problems 2 and 4 of the Concept Development and in Problem 2 of the Problem Set. Instead, have students think about and visualize what they would draw. Omit Lesson 10 because the objective for Lesson 10 is the same as that for Lesson 9. Omit Lesson 19, and instead, embed discussions of interpreting remainders into other division lessons. Omit Lesson 21 because students solve division problems using the area model in Lesson 20. Using the area model to solve division problems with remainders is not specified in the Progressions documents. Omit Lesson 31, and instead, embed analysis of division situations throughout later lessons. Omit Lesson 33, and embed into Lesson 30 the discussion of the connection between division using the area model and division using the algorithm.

Look ahead to the Pacing Suggestions for Module 4. Consider partnering with the art teacher to teach Module 4's Topic A simultaneously with Module 3.

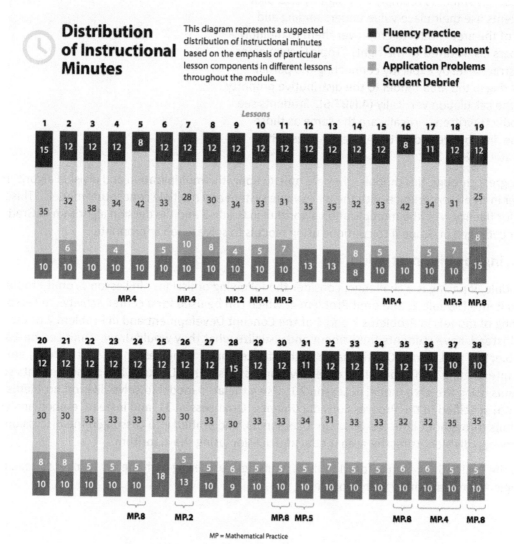

Focus Grade Level Standards

Use the four operations with whole numbers to solve problems.

4.OA.1   Interpret a multiplication equation as a comparison, e.g., interpret $35 = 5 \times 7$ as a statement that 35 is 5 times as many as 7 and 7 times as many as 5. Represent verbal statements of multiplicative comparisons as multiplication equations.

4.OA.2   Multiply or divide to solve word problems involving multiplicative comparison, e.g., by using drawings and equations with a symbol for the unknown number to represent the problem, distinguishing multiplicative comparison from additive comparison. (See CCLS Glossary, Table 2.)

EUREKA MATH

4.OA.3   Solve multistep word problems posed with whole numbers and having whole-number answers using the four operations, including problems in which remainders must be interpreted. Represent these problems using equations with a letter standing for the unknown quantity. Assess the reasonableness of answers using mental computation and estimation strategies including rounding.

Gain familiarity with factors and multiples.

4.OA.4   Find all factor pairs for a whole number in the range 1–100. Recognize that a whole number is a multiple of each of its factors. Determine whether a given whole number in the range 1–100 is a multiple of a given one-digit number. Determine whether a given whole number in the range 1–100 is prime or composite.

Use place value understanding and properties of operations to perform multi-digit arithmetic.[4]

4.NBT.5   Multiply a whole number of up to four digits by a one-digit whole number, and multiply two two-digit numbers, using strategies based on place value and the properties of operations. Illustrate and explain the calculation by using equations, rectangular arrays, and/or area models.

4.NBT.6   Find whole-number quotients and remainders with up to four-digit dividends and one-digit divisors, using strategies based on place value, the properties of operations, and/or the relationship between multiplication and division. Illustrate and explain the calculation by using equations, rectangular arrays, and/or area models.

Solve problems involving measurement and conversion of measurements from a larger unit to a smaller unit.[5]

4.MD.3   Apply the area and perimeter formulas for rectangles in real world and mathematical problems. *For example, find the width of a rectangular room given the area of the flooring and the length, by viewing the area formula as a multiplication equation with an unknown factor.*

Foundational Standards

3.OA.3   Use multiplication and division within 100 to solve word problems in situations involving equal groups, arrays, and measurement quantities, e.g., by using drawings and equations with a symbol for the unknown number to represent the problem. (See CCLS Glossary, Table 2.)

3.OA.4   Determine the unknown whole number in a multiplication or division equation relating three whole numbers. *For example, determine the unknown number that makes the equation true in each of the equations 8 × ? = 48, 5 = _ ÷ 3, 6 × 6 = ?.*

---

[4]4.NBT.4 is addressed in Module 1 and is then reinforced throughout the year.
[5]4.MD.1 is addressed in Modules 2 and 7; 4.MD.2 is addressed in Modules 2, 5, 6, and 7.

3.OA.5   Apply properties of operations as strategies to multiply and divide. (Students need not use formal terms for these properties.) *Examples: If 6 × 4 = 24 is known, then 4 × 6 = 24 is also known. (Commutative property of multiplication.) 3 × 5 × 2 can be found by 3 × 5 = 15, then 15 × 2 = 30, or by 5 × 2 = 10, then 3 × 10 = 30. (Associative property of multiplication.) Knowing that 8 × 5 = 40 and 8 × 2 = 16, one can find 8 × 7 as 8 × (5 + 2) = (8 × 5) + (8 × 2) = 40 + 16 = 56. (Distributive property.)*

3.OA.6   Understand division as an unknown-factor problem. *For example, find 32 ÷ 8 by finding the number that makes 32 when multiplied by 8.*

3.OA.7   Fluently multiply and divide within 100, using strategies such as the relationship between multiplication and division (e.g., knowing that 8 × 5 = 40, one knows 40 ÷ 5 = 8) or properties of operations. By the end of Grade 3, know from memory all products of two one-digit numbers.

3.OA.8   Solve two-step word problems using the four operations. Represent these problems using equations with a letter standing for the unknown quantity. Assess the reasonableness of answers using mental computation and estimation strategies including rounding. (This standard is limited to problems posed with whole numbers and having whole-number answers; students should know how to perform operations in the conventional order when there are no parentheses to specify a particular order, i.e., Order of Operations.)

3.NBT.3   Multiply one-digit whole numbers by multiples of 10 in the range 10–90 (e.g., 9 × 80, 5 × 60) using strategies based on place value and properties of operations.

3.MD.7   Relate area to the operations of multiplication and addition.

3.MD.8   Solve real world and mathematical problems involving perimeters of polygons, including finding the perimeter given the side lengths, finding an unknown side length, and exhibiting rectangles with the same perimeter and different areas or with the same area and different perimeters.

Focus Standards for Mathematical Practice

MP.2   **Reason abstractly and quantitatively.** Students solve multi-step word problems using the four operations by writing equations with a letter standing in for the unknown quantity.

MP.4   **Model with mathematics.** Students apply their understanding of place value to create area models and rectangular arrays when performing multi-digit multiplication and division. They use these models to illustrate and explain calculations.

MP.5   **Use appropriate tools strategically.** Students use mental computation and estimation strategies to assess the reasonableness of their answers when solving multi-step word problems. They draw and label bar and area models to solve problems as part of the RDW process. Additionally, students select an appropriate place value strategy when solving multiplication and division problems.

MP.8   **Look for and express regularity in repeated reasoning.** Students express the regularity they notice in repeated reasoning when they apply place value strategies in solving multiplication and division problems. They move systematically through the place values, decomposing or composing units as necessary, applying the same reasoning to each successive unit.

Overview of Module Topics and Lesson Objectives

Standards		Topics and Objectives	Days
4.OA.1 **4.OA.2** **4.MD.3** 4.OA.3	A	**Multiplicative Comparison Word Problems** Lesson 1: Investigate and use the formulas for area and perimeter of rectangles. Lesson 2: Solve multiplicative comparison word problems by applying the area and perimeter formulas. Lesson 3: Demonstrate understanding of area and perimeter formulas by solving multi-step real world problems.	3
4.NBT.5 4.OA.1 4.OA.2 4.NBT.1	B	**Multiplication by 10, 100, and 1,000** Lesson 4: Interpret and represent patterns when multiplying by 10, 100, and 1,000 in arrays and numerically. Lesson 5: Multiply multiples of 10, 100, and 1,000 by single digits, recognizing patterns. Lesson 6: Multiply two-digit multiples of 10 by two-digit multiples of 10 with the area model.	3
4.NBT.5 4.OA.2 4.NBT.1	C	**Multiplication of up to Four Digits by Single-Digit Numbers** Lesson 7: Use place value disks to represent two-digit by one-digit multiplication. Lesson 8: Extend the use of place value disks to represent three- and four-digit by one-digit multiplication. Lessons 9–10: Multiply three- and four-digit numbers by one-digit numbers applying the standard algorithm. Lesson 11: Connect the area model and the partial products method to the standard algorithm.	5
4.OA.1 **4.OA.2** **4.OA.3** **4.NBT.5**	D	**Multiplication Word Problems** Lesson 12: Solve two-step word problems, including multiplicative comparison. Lesson 13: Use multiplication, addition, or subtraction to solve multi-step word problems.	2
		Mid-Module Assessment: Topics A–D (review 1 day, assessment ½ day, return ½ day)	2

©2015 Great Minds. eureka-math.org
G4-M3-TE-B2-1.3.1-01.2016

Standards		Topics and Objectives	Days
4.NBT.6 4.OA.3	E	**Division of Tens and Ones with Successive Remainders**	8
		Lesson 14: Solve division word problems with remainders.	
		Lesson 15: Understand and solve division problems with a remainder using the array and area models.	
		Lesson 16: Understand and solve two-digit dividend division problems with a remainder in the ones place by using place value disks.	
		Lesson 17: Represent and solve division problems requiring decomposing a remainder in the tens.	
		Lesson 18: Find whole number quotients and remainders.	
		Lesson 19: Explain remainders by using place value understanding and models.	
		Lesson 20: Solve division problems without remainders using the area model.	
		Lesson 21: Solve division problems with remainders using the area model.	
4.OA.4	F	**Reasoning with Divisibility**	4
		Lesson 22: Find factor pairs for numbers to 100, and use understanding of factors to define prime and composite.	
		Lesson 23: Use division and the associative property to test for factors and observe patterns.	
		Lesson 24: Determine if a whole number is a multiple of another number.	
		Lesson 25: Explore properties of prime and composite numbers to 100 by using multiples.	
4.OA.3 **4.NBT.6** 4.NBT.1	G	**Division of Thousands, Hundreds, Tens, and Ones**	8
		Lesson 26: Divide multiples of 10, 100, and 1,000 by single-digit numbers.	
		Lesson 27: Represent and solve division problems with up to a three-digit dividend numerically and with place value disks requiring decomposing a remainder in the hundreds place.	
		Lesson 28: Represent and solve three-digit dividend division with divisors of 2, 3, 4, and 5 numerically.	

©2015 Great Minds. eureka-math.org
G4-M3-TE-B2-1.3.1-01.2016

EUREKA
MATH™

Standards		Topics and Objectives		Days
		Lesson 29:	Represent numerically four-digit dividend division with divisors of 2, 3, 4, and 5, decomposing a remainder up to three times.	
		Lesson 30:	Solve division problems with a zero in the dividend or with a zero in the quotient.	
		Lesson 31:	Interpret division word problems as either *number of groups unknown* or *group size unknown*.	
		Lesson 32:	Interpret and find whole number quotients and remainders to solve one-step division word problems with larger divisors of 6, 7, 8, and 9.	
		Lesson 33:	Explain the connection of the area model of division to the long division algorithm for three- and four-digit dividends	
4.NBT.5 4.OA.3 4.MD.3	H	**Multiplication of Two-Digit by Two-Digit Numbers**		5
		Lesson 34:	Multiply two-digit multiples of 10 by two-digit numbers using a place value chart.	
		Lesson 35:	Multiply two-digit multiples of 10 by two-digit numbers using the area model.	
		Lesson 36:	Multiply two-digit by two-digit numbers using four partial products.	
		Lessons 37–38:	Transition from four partial products to the standard algorithm for two-digit by two-digit multiplication.	
		End-of-Module Assessment: Topics A–H (review 1 day, assessment ½ day, return ½ day, remediation or further applications 1 day)		3
Total Number of Instructional Days				**43**

Terminology

New or Recently Introduced Terms

- Associative property (e.g., $96 = 3 \times (4 \times 8) = (3 \times 4) \times 8$)
- Composite number (positive integer having three or more whole number factors)
- Distributive property (e.g., $64 \times 27 = (60 \times 20) + (60 \times 7) + (4 \times 20) + (4 \times 7)$)
- Divisible
- Divisor (the number by which another number is divided)
- Formula (a mathematical rule expressed as an equation with numbers and/or variables)
- Long division (process of dividing a large dividend using several recorded steps)

- Partial product (e.g., 24 × 6 = (20 × 6) + (4 × 6) = 120 + 24)
- Prime number (positive integer greater than 1 having whole number factors of only 1 and itself)
- Remainder (the number left over when one integer is divided by another)

Familiar Terms and Symbols[6]

- Algorithm (steps for base ten computations with the four operations)
- Area (the amount of two-dimensional space in a bounded region)
- Area model (a model for multiplication and division problems that relates rectangular arrays to area, in which the length and width of a rectangle represent the factors for multiplication, and for division, the width represents the divisor and the length represents the quotient)
- Array (a set of numbers or objects that follow a specific pattern, a matrix)
- Bundling, grouping, renaming, changing (compose or decompose a 10, 100, etc.)
- Compare (to find the similarity or dissimilarity between)
- Distribute (decompose an unknown product in terms of two known products to solve)
- Divide, division (e.g., 15 ÷ 5 = 3)
- Equation (a statement that the values of two mathematical expressions are equal using the = sign)
- Factors (numbers that can be multiplied together to get other numbers)
- Mixed units (e.g., 1 ft 3 in, 4 lb 13 oz)
- Multiple (product of a given number and any other whole number)
- Multiply, multiplication (e.g., 5 × 3 = 15)
- Perimeter (length of a continuous line forming the boundary of a closed geometric figure)
- Place value (the numerical value that a digit has by virtue of its position in a number)
- Product (the result of multiplication)
- Quotient (the result of division)
- Rectangular array (an arrangement of a set of objects into rows and columns)
- Rows, columns (e.g., in reference to rectangular arrays)
- ___ *times as many* ___ *as* ___ (multiplicative comparative sentence frame)

---

[6]These are terms and symbols students have used or seen previously.

Suggested Tools and Representations

- Area model
- Grid paper
- Number bond
- Place value disks: suggested minimum of 1 set per pair of students (18 ones, 18 tens, 18 hundreds, 18 thousands, 1 ten thousand)

Area Model

Number Bond

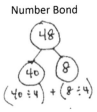

Place Value Disks

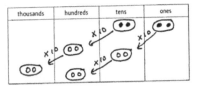

Thousands Place Value Chart

- Tape diagram
- Ten thousands place value chart (Lesson 7 Template)
- Thousands place value chart (Lesson 4 Template)

Scaffolds[7]

The scaffolds integrated into *A Story of Units* give alternatives for how students access information as well as express and demonstrate their learning. Strategically placed margin notes are provided within each lesson elaborating on the use of specific scaffolds at applicable times. They address many needs presented by English language learners, students with disabilities, students performing above grade level, and students performing below grade level. Many of the suggestions are organized by Universal Design for Learning (UDL) principles and are applicable to more than one population. To read more about the approach to differentiated instruction in *A Story of Units,* please refer to "How to Implement *A Story of Units*."

---

[7]Students with disabilities may require Braille, large print, audio, or special digital files. Please visit the website www.p12.nysed.gov/specialed/aim for specific information on how to obtain student materials that satisfy the National Instructional Materials Accessibility Standard (NIMAS) format.

Assessment Summary

Type	Administered	Format	Standards Addressed
Mid-Module Assessment Task	After Topic D	Constructed response with rubric	4.OA.1 4.OA.2 4.OA.3 4.NBT.5 4.MD.3
End-of-Module Assessment Task	After Topic H	Constructed response with rubric	4.OA.1 4.OA.2 4.OA.3 4.OA.4 4.NBT.5 4.NBT.6 4.MD.3

Mathematics Curriculum

4
GRADE

Topic A

Multiplicative Comparison Word Problems

4.OA.1, 4.OA.2, 4.MD.3, 4.OA.3

Focus Standards:	4.OA.1	Interpret a multiplication equation as a comparison, e.g., interpret 35 = 5 × 7 as a statement that 35 is 5 times as many as 7 and 7 times as many as 5. Represent verbal statements of multiplicative comparisons as multiplication equations.
	4.OA.2	Multiply or divide to solve word problems involving multiplicative comparison, e.g., by using drawings and equations with a symbol for the unknown number to represent the problem, distinguishing multiplicative comparison from additive comparison. (See CCLS Glossary, Table 2.)
	4.MD.3	Apply the area and perimeter formulas for rectangles in real world and mathematical problems. *For example, find the width of a rectangular room given the area of the flooring and the length, by viewing the area formula as a multiplication equation with an unknown factor.*
Instructional Days:	3	
Coherence -Links from:	G3–M4	Multiplication and Area
	G3–M7	Geometry and Measurement Word Problems
-Links to:	G5–M5	Addition and Multiplication with Volume and Area

Students begin Topic A by investigating the formulas for area and perimeter. In Lesson 1, they use those formulas to solve for area and perimeter and to find the measurements of unknown lengths and widths. In Lessons 2 and 3, students use their understanding of the area and perimeter formulas to solve multiplicative comparison problems including the language of *times as much as* with a focus on problems using area and perimeter as a context (e.g., *A field is 9 feet wide. It is 4 times as long as it is wide. What is the perimeter of the field?*) (**4.OA.2, 4.MD.3**). Students create diagrams to represent these problems as well as write equations with symbols for the unknown quantities.

Problem 2: The width of David's tent is 5 feet.
The length is twice the width.
David's rectangular air mattress measures 3 feet by 6 feet.
If David puts the air mattress in the tent, how many square feet of floor space will be available for the rest of his things?

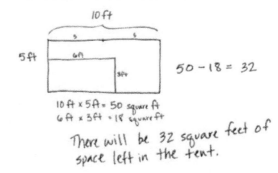

Multiplicative comparison is foundational for understanding multiplication as scaling in Grade 5 and sets the stage for proportional reasoning in Grade 6. Students determine, using *times as much as,* the length of one side of a rectangle as compared to its width. Beginning this Grade 4 module with area and perimeter allows students to review their multiplication facts, apply them to new and interesting word problems, and develop a deeper understanding of the area model as a method for calculating with larger numbers.

A Teaching Sequence Toward Mastery of Multiplicative Comparison Word Problems
Objective 1: Investigate and use the formulas for area and perimeter of rectangles. (Lesson 1)
Objective 2: Solve multiplicative comparison word problems by applying the area and perimeter formulas. (Lesson 2)
Objective 3: Demonstrate understanding of area and perimeter formulas by solving multi-step real-world problems. (Lesson 3)

Lesson 1

Objective: Investigate and use the formulas for area and perimeter of rectangles.

Suggested Lesson Structure

- ■ Fluency Practice   (15 minutes)
- ■ Concept Development   (35 minutes)
- ■ Student Debrief   (10 minutes)
- **Total Time**   **(60 minutes)**

Fluency Practice (15 minutes)

- Perimeter and Area **4.MD.3**   (3 minutes)
- Multiply a Number by Itself **4.MD.3**   (5 minutes)
- Group Counting **4.OA.4**   (3 minutes)
- Find the Unknown Factor **4.OA.4**   (4 minutes)

Perimeter and Area (3 minutes)

Materials: (T) Grid paper (with ability to project or enlarge grid paper)

Note: This fluency activity prepares students for this lesson's Concept Development.

   T: (Project grid paper with a rectangle of 5 units by 2 units shaded.) What's the length of the longest side?

   S: 5 units.

   T: (Write *5 units*. Point to the opposite side.) What's the length of the opposite side?

   S: 5 units.

   T: (Write *5 units*.) What's the sum of the rectangle's two longest sides?

   S: 10 units.

   T: What's the length of the shortest side?

   S: 2 units.

   T: (Write *2 units*. Point to the unknown side.) What's the length of the unknown side?

   S: 2 units.

   T: (Write *2 units*.) What's the sum of the rectangle's two shortest sides?

   S: 4 units.

   T: What's the perimeter?

   S: 14 units.

©2015 Great Minds. eureka-math.org
G4-M3-TE-B2-1.3.1-01.2016

T: How many square units are in one row?

S: 5 square units.

T: How many rows of 5 square units are there?

S: 2 rows.

T: Let's find how many square units there are in the rectangle, counting by fives.

S: 5, 10.

T: What's the area?

S: 10 square units.

Repeat the process for 3 × 4 and 7 × 3 rectangles.

Multiply a Number by Itself (5 minutes)

Note: Multiplying a number by itself helps students quickly compute the areas of squares.

T: (Project 1 × 1 = ____.) Say the complete multiplication equation.

S: 1 × 1 = 1.

Repeat the process for 2, 3, 4, 5, 6, 7, 8, 9, and 10.

T: I'm going to call out a number. You say the answer when it's multiplied by itself. 2.

S: 4.

Repeat the process for this possible sequence: 1, 10, 5, 3, 6, 8, 4, 7, and 9.

Group Counting (3 minutes)

Note: Group counting helps review multiples and factors that students need to recall during the lesson.

Direct students to count forward and backward, occasionally changing the direction of the count, using the following sequence: threes to 24, fours to 24, and sixes to 24.

T: Count by threes. Ready? (Use a familiar signal to indicate counting up or counting down.)

S: 3, 6, 9, 12, 9, 12, 9, 12, 15, 18, 21, 18, 21, 18, 21, 24, 21, 18, 21, 18, 15, 12, 9, 12, 9, 6, 3.

Find the Unknown Factor (4 minutes)

Materials: (S) Personal white board

Note: Finding the unknown factor in isolation prepares students to solve *unknown side* problems when given the area.

T: (Project 3 × ____ = 12.) On your personal white boards, write the unknown factor.

S: (Write 4.)

T: Say the multiplication sentence.

S: 3 × 4 = 12.

Repeat the process with the following possible sequence: 4 × ____ = 12, 4 × ____ = 24, 3 × ____ = 24, 6 × ____ = 12, 6 × ____ = 24, and 3 × ____ = 18.

Lesson 1:   Investigate and use the formulas for area and perimeter of rectangles.

EUREKA MATH™

©2015 Great Minds. eureka-math.org
G4-M3-TE-B2-1.3.1-01.2016

Concept Development (35 minutes)

Materials: (T) Grid paper (with ability to project or enlarge grid paper), chart paper (S) Grid paper, personal white board

Problem 1: Review and compare perimeter and area of a rectangle.

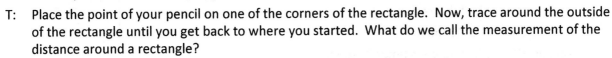

T: Draw a rectangle on your grid paper that is four units wide and seven units long.

S: (Draw the rectangle on grid paper.)

T: (Monitor to see that students have drawn the rectangle correctly.) Tell your partner what you notice about your rectangle.

S: The opposite sides are the same length. → It has four right angles. → The area of the rectangle is 28 square units. → The perimeter of the rectangle is 22 units.

T: Place the point of your pencil on one of the corners of the rectangle. Now, trace around the outside of the rectangle until you get back to where you started. What do we call the measurement of the distance around a rectangle?

S: The perimeter.

T: Trace the perimeter again. This time, count the units as you trace them. What is the perimeter of the rectangle?

S: 22 units.

T: When we know the measurements of the length and width of a rectangle, is there a quicker way to determine the perimeter than to count the units while tracing?

S: We could add the measurements of all four sides of the rectangle.

T: Take your pencil and count all of the squares within your rectangle. These squares represent the area of the rectangle. How do I find the area of the rectangle?

S: You count the squares. → You can multiply the length times the width of the rectangle. → Four units times 7 units is 28 square units.

Problem 2: Use the formula 2 × (*l* + *w*) to solve for perimeter and to find an unknown side length of a rectangle.

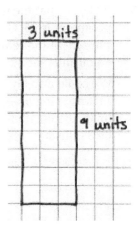

T: Draw a rectangle on your graph paper that is 3 units wide and 9 units long. (Draw and display the rectangle.) Watch as I label the length and width of the rectangle. Now, label the length and width of your rectangle. How can I find the perimeter?

S: Add up the lengths of all of the sides. 3 + 9 + 3 + 9 = 24. The perimeter is 24 units. → You could also add 3 + 3 + 9 + 9. The answer is still 24 units. The order doesn't matter when you are adding.

T: Use your pencil to trace along one width and one length. Along how many units did you trace?

S: 12 units.

T: How does 12 relate to the length and width of the rectangle?

S: It's the sum of the length and width.

T: How does the sum of the length and width relate to finding the perimeter of the rectangle?

S: It's halfway around. → I can double the length and double the width to find the perimeter instead of adding all the sides ($2l + 2w$). → I could also add the length and the width and double that sum, $2 \times (l + w)$. → Both of those work since the opposite sides are equal.

T: You have just mentioned many **formulas**, like counting along the sides of the rectangle or adding sides or doubling, to find the perimeter. Let's create a chart to keep track of the formulas for finding the perimeter of a rectangle. Talk to your partner about the most efficient way to find the perimeter.

S: If I draw the shape on grid paper, I can just count along the edge. → I am good at adding, so I will add all four sides. → It is faster to double the sum of the length and width. It's only two steps.

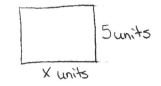

Formulas for Perimeter

$P = L + w + L + w$

$P = 2L + 2w$

$P = 2 \times (L + w)$

T: We can write the formula as $P = 2 \times (l + w)$ on our chart, meaning we add the length and width first and then multiply that sum by 2. What is the length plus width of this rectangle?

S: 3 plus 9 equals 12. 12 units.

T: 12 units doubled, or 12 units times 2, equals …?

S: 24 units.

T: Now, draw a rectangle that is 2 units wide and 4 units long. Find the perimeter by using the formula I just mentioned. Then, solve for the perimeter using a different formula to check your work.

S: $2 + 4 = 6$ and $6 \times 2 = 12$. The perimeter is 12 units. → Another way is to double 2, double 4, and then add the doubles together. 4 plus 8 is 12 units. Both formulas give us the same answer.

Repeat with a rectangle that is 5 units wide and 6 units long.

Instruct students to sketch a rectangle with a width of 5 units and a perimeter of 26 units on their personal white boards, not using graph paper.

(sketch of rectangle labeled 5 units on the right and x units below)

T: Label the width as 5 units. Label the length as an unknown of *x* units. How can we determine the length? Discuss your ideas with a partner.

S: If I know that the width is 5, I can label the opposite side as 5 units since they are the same. If the perimeter is 26, I can take away the widths to find the sum of the other two sides. $26 - 10 = 16$. If the sum of the remaining two sides is 16, I know that each side must be 8 since I know that they are equal and that $8 + 8 = 16$, so $x = 8$ (shows sketch to demonstrate her thinking).

S: We could also find the length another way. I know that if I add the length and the width of the rectangle together, I will get half of the perimeter. In this rectangle, because the perimeter is 26 units, the length plus the width equals 13 units. If the width is 5, that means that the length has to be 8 units because $5 + 8 = 13$. → $26 \div 2 = 13$, $x + 5 = 13$ or $13 - 5 = x$, so $x = 8$.

Repeat for P = 28 cm, l = 8 cm.

Lesson 1:   Investigate and use the formulas for area and perimeter of rectangles.

Problem 3: Use the area formula (*l* × *w*) to solve for area and to solve for the unknown side length of a rectangle.

T: Look back at the rectangle with the width of 3 units and the length of 9 units. How can we find the area of the rectangle?

S: We can count all of the squares. → We could also count the number of squares in one row and then skip-count that number for all of the rows. → That's just multiplying the number of rows by the number in each row. → A quicker way is to multiply the length times the width. Nine rows of 3 units each is like an array. We can just multiply 9 × 3.

T: Talk to your partner about the most efficient way to find the area of a rectangle.

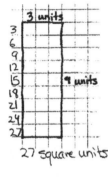
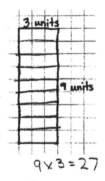

Discuss how to find the area for the 2 × 4 rectangle and the 5 × 6 rectangle drawn earlier in the lesson. Encourage students to multiply length times width to solve. Ask students to tell how the area of each rectangle needs to be labeled and why.

T: We discussed a formula for finding the perimeter of a rectangle. We just discovered a formula for finding the area of a rectangle. If we use *A* for area, *l* for length, and *w* for width, how could we write the formula?

S: $A = l \times w$.

T: (Sketch a rectangle on the board, and label the area as 50 square centimeters.) If we know that the area of a rectangle is 50 square centimeters and that the length of the rectangle is 10 centimeters, how can we determine the measurement of the width of the rectangle?

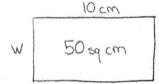

S: I can use the area formula. 50 square centimeters is equal to 10 centimeters times the width. 10 times 5 equals 50, so the width is 5 centimeters. → The area formula says 50 = 10 × ____. I can solve that with division! So, 50 square centimeters divided by 10 centimeters is 5 centimeters.

Repeat for *A* = 32 square m, *l* = 8 m and for *A* = 63 square cm, *w* = 7 cm.

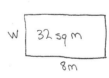
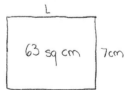

Problem 4: Given the area of a rectangle, find all possible whole number combinations of the length and width, and then calculate the perimeter.

- T: If a rectangle has an area of 24 square units, what whole numbers could be the length and width of the rectangle? Discuss with your partner.

- S: The length is 3 units, and the width is 8 units. → Yes, but the length could also be 4 units and the width 6 units. Or, the other way around: length of 6 units and width of 4 units. → There are many combinations of length and width to make a rectangle with an area of 24 square units.

- T: With your partner, draw and complete a table similar to mine until you have found all possible whole number combinations for the length and width.

Circulate, checking to see that students are using the length times width formula to find the dimensions. Complete the table with all combinations as a class.

- T: Now, sketch each rectangle, and solve for the perimeter using the perimeter formula.

Circulate, checking to see that students draw rectangles to scale and solve for perimeter using the formula. Check answers as a class.

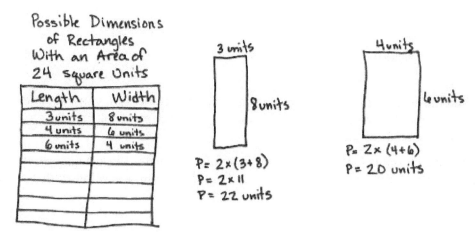

Problem Set (10 minutes)

Students should do their personal best to complete the Problem Set within the allotted 10 minutes. Some problems do not specify a method for solving. This is an intentional reduction of scaffolding that invokes MP.5, Use Appropriate Tools Strategically. Students should solve these problems using the RDW approach used for Application Problems.

For some classes, it may be appropriate to modify the assignment by specifying which problems students should work on first. With this option, let the purposeful sequencing of the Problem Set guide your selections so that problems continue to be scaffolded. Balance word problems with other problem types to ensure a range of practice. Consider assigning incomplete problems for homework or at another time during the day.

Lesson 1:   Investigate and use the formulas for area and perimeter of rectangles.

©2015 Great Minds. eureka-math.org
G4-M3-TE-B2-1.3.1-01.2016

EUREKA MATH™

Student Debrief (10 minutes)

Lesson Objective: Investigate and use the formulas for area and perimeter of rectangles.

The Student Debrief is intended to invite reflection and active processing of the total lesson experience.

Invite students to review their solutions for the Problem Set. They should check work by comparing answers with a partner before going over answers as a class. Look for misconceptions or misunderstandings that can be addressed in the Debrief. Guide students in a conversation to debrief the Problem Set and process the lesson.

Any combination of the questions below may be used to lead the discussion.

- What is a **formula** for solving for perimeter? What formula is most efficient?

- Compare the units used to measure perimeter and the units used to measure area (length units and square units).

- What was challenging about solving Problems 6(a) and 6(b)? How did the process of solving Problems 4 and 5 help you to figure out how to solve Problems 6(a) and 6(b)?

- The perimeters of the rectangles in Problems 2(a) and 2(b) are the same. Why are the areas different?

- The areas of the rectangles in Problems 6(a) and 6(b) are the same. Why are the perimeters different?

- How did you find the answer for the length of the unknown side, x, in Problems 4(a) and 4(b)?

- What was your strategy for finding the length of the unknown side, x, in Problems 5(a) and 5(b)? Discuss with your partner.

- What significant math vocabulary did we use today to communicate precisely?

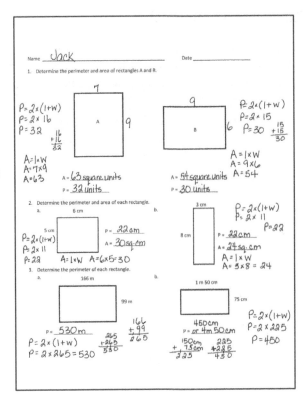

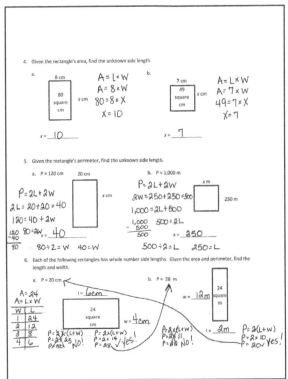

EUREKA MATH™

Lesson 1:   Investigate and use the formulas for area and perimeter of rectangles.

23

©2015 Great Minds. eureka-math.org
G4-M3-TE-B2-1.3.1-01.2016

Exit Ticket (3 minutes)

After the Student Debrief, instruct students to complete the Exit Ticket. A review of their work will help with assessing students' understanding of the concepts that were presented in today's lesson and planning more effectively for future lessons. The questions may be read aloud to the students.

EUREKA
MATH™

Name _____   Date _____

1. Determine the perimeter and area of rectangles A and B.

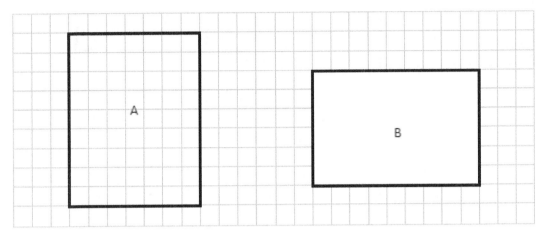

a. A = _____

b. P = _____

A = _____

P = _____

2. Determine the perimeter and area of each rectangle.

a.

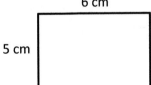

6 cm

5 cm

P = _____

A = _____

b.

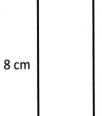

3 cm

8 cm

P = _____

A = _____

EUREKA
MATH™

3. Determine the perimeter of each rectangle.

a.

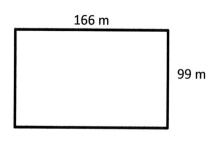

166 m

99 m

P = _____

b.

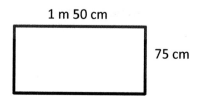

1 m 50 cm

75 cm

P = _____

4. Given the rectangle's area, find the unknown side length.

a.

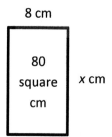

8 cm

80 square cm

x cm

x = _____

b.

7 cm

49 square cm

x cm

x = _____

Lesson 1:   Investigate and use the formulas for area and perimeter of rectangles.

EUREKA
MATH™

5. Given the rectangle's perimeter, find the unknown side length.

a. P = 120 cm

20 cm

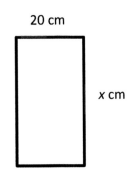

x cm

x = _____

b. P = 1,000 m

x m

250 m

x = _____

6. Each of the following rectangles has whole number side lengths. Given the area and perimeter, find the length and width.

a. P = 20 cm

l = _____

24
square
cm

w = _____

b. P = 28 m

w = _____

24
square
m

l = _____

Name _____   Date _____

1. Determine the area and perimeter of the rectangle.

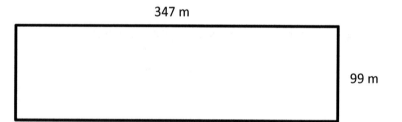

8 cm

2 cm

2. Determine the perimeter of the rectangle.

347 m

99 m

Lesson 1:   Investigate and use the formulas for area and perimeter of rectangles.

©2015 Great Minds. eureka-math.org
G4-M3-TE-B2-1.3.1-01.2016

EUREKA
MATH™

Name _____   Date _____

1. Determine the perimeter and area of rectangles A and B.

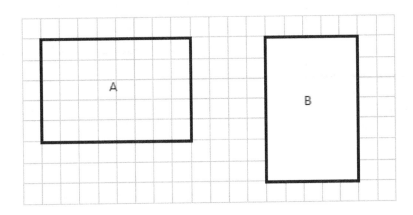

a. A = _____   A = _____

b. P = _____   P = _____

2. Determine the perimeter and area of each rectangle.
   a.   b.   4 cm

   7 cm
                    P = _____
   3 cm
                    A = _____   9 cm   P = _____

                                                           A = _____

3. Determine the perimeter of each rectangle.

a.

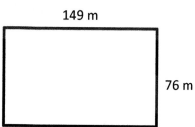

P = _____

b.

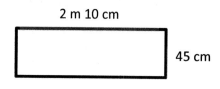

P = _____

4. Given the rectangle's area, find the unknown side length.

a.

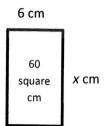

x = _____

b.

5 m

| 25 square m | x m |

x = _____

EUREKA
MATH™

5. Given the rectangle's perimeter, find the unknown side length.

a.   P = 180 cm

40 cm

x cm

x = _____

b.   P = 1,000 m

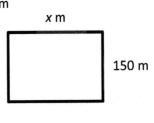

x m

150 m

x = _____

6. Each of the following rectangles has whole number side lengths. Given the area and perimeter, find the length and width.

a.   A = 32 square cm
     P = 24 cm

l = _____

32 square cm

w = _____

b.   A = 36 square m
     P = 30 m

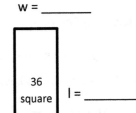

w = _____

36 square m

l = _____

EUREKA
MATH™

Lesson 1:   Investigate and use the formulas for area and perimeter of rectangles.

31

©2015 Great Minds. eureka-math.org
G4-M3-TE-B2-1.3.1-01.2016

Lesson 2

Objective: Solve multiplicative comparison word problems by applying the area and perimeter formulas.

Suggested Lesson Structure

■ Fluency Practice   (12 minutes)
■ Application Problem   (6 minutes)
□ Concept Development   (32 minutes)
■ Student Debrief   (10 minutes)
  Total Time   **(60 minutes)**

Fluency Practice (12 minutes)

- Multiply a Number by Itself **4.MD.3**   (2 minutes)
- Rename the Unit **4.NBT.1**   (4 minutes)
- Find the Area and Perimeter **4.MD.3**   (6 minutes)

Multiply a Number by Itself (2 minutes)

Materials: (S) Personal white board

Note: Multiplying a number by itself helps students quickly compute the areas of squares.

Repeat the process from Lesson 1, using more choral response.

Rename the Unit (4 minutes)

Materials: (S) Personal white board

Note: Renaming units helps prepare students for Topic B.

   T: (Project 7 tens = _____.) Fill in the blank to make a true number sentence using standard form.
   S: 7 tens = 70.

Repeat the process for 9 tens, 10 tens, 11 tens, and 12 tens.

   T: (Project 17 tens = _____.) Fill in the blank to make a true number sentence using standard form.
   S: (Show 17 tens = 170.)

Repeat with the following possible sequence: 17 hundreds, 17 thousands, 13 tens, 13 hundreds, and 13 thousands.

Lesson 2:   Solve multiplicative comparison word problems by applying the area
              and perimeter formulas.

EUREKA MATH™

Find the Area and Perimeter (6 minutes)

Materials: (S) Personal white board

Note: This fluency activity reviews Lesson 1.

  T: (Project a rectangle with a length of 4 cm and a width of 3 cm.) On your personal white boards, write a multiplication sentence to find the area.

  S: (Write 4 cm × 3 cm = 12 square cm.)

  T: Use the formula for perimeter to solve.

  S: (Write 2 × (4 cm + 3 cm) = 14 cm.)

Repeat the process for a rectangle with dimensions of 6 cm × 4 cm.

  T: (Project a square with a length of 2 m.) This is a square. Say the length of each side.

  S: 2 meters.

  T: On your boards, write a multiplication sentence to find the area.

  S: (Write 2 m × 2 m = 4 square m.)

  T: Write the perimeter.

  S: 2 × (2 m + 2 m) = 8 m.

Repeat the process for squares with lengths of 3 cm and 9 cm.

  T: (Project a rectangle with an area of 12 square cm, length of 2 cm, and x for the width.) On your boards, write a division sentence to find the width.

  S: (Write 12 square cm ÷ 2 cm = 6 cm.)

Repeat the process for 12 square cm ÷ 4 cm, 18 square cm ÷ 3 cm, and 25 square cm ÷ 5 cm.

Application Problem (6 minutes)

Tommy's dad is teaching him how to make tables out of tiles. Tommy makes a small table that is 3 feet wide and 4 feet long. How many square-foot tiles does he need to cover the top of the table? How many feet of decorative border material will his dad need to cover the edges of the table?

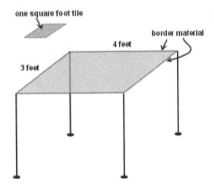

Extension: Tommy's dad is making a table 6 feet wide and 8 feet long. When both tables are placed together, what will their combined area be?

Lesson 2:   Solve multiplicative comparison word problems by applying the area and perimeter formulas.

33

©2015 Great Minds. eureka-math.org
G4-M3-TE-B2-1.3.1-01.2016

Note: This Application Problem builds from **3.MD.5**, **3.MD.6**, and **3.MD.8** and bridges back to the Concept Development of Lesson 1, during which students investigated and used the formulas for the area and perimeter of rectangles.

4ft

$A = 3ft \times 4ft$
$A = 12$ square ft

$P = 2 \times (4+3)$
$P = 2 \times 7 ft$
$P = 14 ft$

Tommy will need 12 square foot tiles and his dad will need 14 feet of border material.

8ft

6ft

$A = 6 \times 8$
$A = 48$ square ft
$48 + 12 = 60$

Both tables together will give 60 square feet of area.

Concept Development (32 minutes)

Materials: (T) Chart of formulas for perimeter and area from Lesson 1 (S) Personal white board, square-inch tiles

Problem 1: A rectangle is 1 inch wide. It is 3 times as long as it is wide. Use square tiles to find its length.

T: Place 3 square-inch tiles on your personal white board. Talk to your partner about what the width and length of this rectangle are.

S: (Discuss.)

T: I heard Alyssa say that the width is 1 inch and the length is 3 inches. Now, make it 2 times as long. (Add 3 more square tiles.) It's now 6 inches long. Three times as long (add 3 more tiles) would be 9 inches. Using the original length of 3 inches, tell your partner how to determine the current length that is three times as many.

S: I multiply the original length times 3. → Three times as long as 3 inches is the same as 3 times 3 inches.

Repeat using tiles to find a rectangle that is 3 inches wide and 3 times as long as it is wide.

Lesson 2: Solve multiplicative comparison word problems by applying the area and perimeter formulas.

EUREKA MATH™

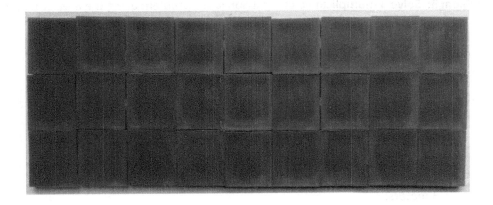

$W = 3in$
$L = 3 \times 3in = 9in$

Problem 2: A rectangle is 2 meters wide. It is 3 times as long as it is wide. Draw to find its length.

T: The rectangle is 2 meters wide. (Draw a vertical line and label it as 2 meters.)

T: It is 3 times as long as it is wide. That means the length can be thought of as three segments, or short lines, each 2 meters long. (Draw the horizontal lines to create a square 2 meters by 2 meters.)

T: Here is the same length, 2 times as long, 3 times as long. (Extend the rectangle as shown.) What is the length when there are 3 segments, each 2 meters long?

S: 6 meters.

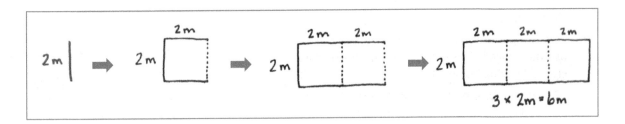

T: With your partner, draw this rectangle and label the length and width. What is the length? What is the width?

S: The length is 6 meters, and the width is 2 meters.

T: What is the perimeter? Use the chart of formulas for perimeters from Lesson 1 for reference.

S: Doubling the sum of 6 meters and 2 meters gives us 16 meters.

T: What is the area?

S: 6 meters times 2 meters is 12 square meters.

Repeat with a rectangle that is 3 meters long and 4 times as wide as it is long.

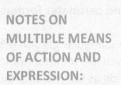

NOTES ON MULTIPLE MEANS OF ACTION AND EXPRESSION:

Ease the task of drawing by offering students the choice of tracing the concrete tiles. Alternatively, reduce the small motor demands by providing a template, grid paper, or computer software for drawing.

Lesson 2: Solve multiplicative comparison word problems by applying the area
and perimeter formulas.

©2015 Great Minds. eureka-math.org
G4-M3-TE-B2-1.3.1-01.2016

35

Problem 3: Solve a multiplicative comparison word problem using the area and perimeter formulas.

Christine painted a mural with an area of 18 square meters and a length of 6 meters. What is the width of her mural? Her next mural will be the same length as the first but 4 times as wide. What is the perimeter of her next mural?

Display the first two statements of the problem.

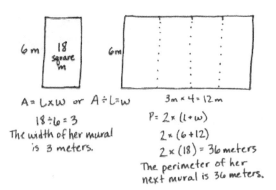

- T: With your partner, determine the width of the first mural.

- S: The area is 18 square meters. 18 square meters divided by 6 meters is 3 meters. The width is 3 meters.

- T: True. (Display the last two statements of the problem.) Using those dimensions, draw and label Christine's next mural. Begin with the side length you know, 6 meters. How many copies of Christine's first mural will we see in her next mural? Draw them.

- S: Four copies. (Draw.)

- T: Tell me a multiplication sentence to find how wide her next mural will be.

- S: 3 meters times 4 equals 12 meters.

- T: Finish labeling the diagram.

- T: Find the perimeter of Christine's next mural. For help, use the chart of formulas for perimeter that we created during Lesson 1.

- S: 12 meters plus 6 meters is 18 meters. 18 meters doubled is 36 meters. The perimeter is 36 meters.

Problem 4: Observe the relationship of area and perimeter while solving a multiplicative comparison word problem using the area and perimeter formulas.

Sherrie's rectangular garden is 8 square meters. The longer side of the garden is 4 meters. Nancy's garden is twice as long and twice as wide as Sherrie's rectangular garden.

Display the first two statements.

- T: With your partner, draw and label a diagram of Sherrie's garden.

- S: (Draw and label Sherrie's garden.)

- T: What is the width of Sherrie's garden?

- S: Two meters because 8 square meters divided by 4 meters is 2 meters.

> **NOTES ON MULTIPLE MEANS OF ENGAGEMENT:**
>
> English language learners may benefit from frequent checks for understanding as the word problem is read aloud. Explain how the term *square meters* denotes the garden's area. Instead of *twice*, say *two times*. Use gestures and illustrations to clarify the meaning. In addition, after students discover the relationship between area and perimeter, challenge them to explore further. Ask, "If you draw another rectangle with a different length, will a similar doubling of the perimeter and quadrupling of the area result?"

Lesson 2:   Solve multiplicative comparison word problems by applying the area and perimeter formulas.

©2015 Great Minds. eureka-math.org
G4-M3-TE-B2-1.3.1-01.2016

T: (Display the next statement.) Help me draw Nancy's garden. Twice as long as 4 meters is how many meters?

S: 8 meters.

T: Twice as wide as 2 meters is how many meters?

S: 4 meters.

T: Draw Nancy's garden and find the perimeters of both gardens.

S: (Draw and solve to find the perimeters.)

T: Tell your partner the relationship between the two perimeters.

S: Sherrie's garden has a perimeter of 12 meters. Nancy's garden has a perimeter of 24 meters. → The length doubled, and the width doubled, so the perimeter doubled! 12 meters times 2 is 24 meters.

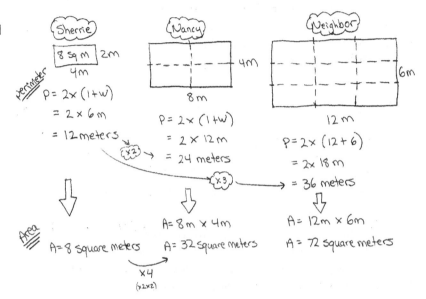

T: If Sherrie's neighbor had a garden 3 times as long and 3 times as wide as her garden, what would be the relationship of the perimeter between those gardens?

S: The perimeter would triple!

T: Solve for the area of Nancy's garden and the neighbor's garden. What do you notice about the relationship among the perimeters and areas of the three gardens?

S: Nancy's garden has an area of 32 square meters. The neighbor's garden has an area of 72 square meters. → The length and width of Nancy's garden is double that of Sherrie's garden, but the area did not double. → The length is doubled and the width is doubled. 2 times 2 is 4, so the area will be 4 times as large. → Right, the area quadrupled! I can put the area of Sherrie's garden inside Nancy's garden 4 times. → The length and width of the neighbor's garden tripled, and 3 times 3 is 9. The area of the neighbor's garden is 9 times that of Sherrie's.

Create a table to show the relationship among the areas and perimeters of the three gardens.

	Sherrie	Nancy	Neighbor
Perimeter	12 m	24 m	36 m
Area	8 sq m	32 sq m	72 sq m

Lesson 2: Solve multiplicative comparison word problems by applying the area and perimeter formulas.

©2015 Great Minds. eureka-math.org
G4-M3-TE-B2-1.3.1-01.2016

37

Problem Set (10 minutes)

Students should do their personal best to complete the Problem Set within the allotted 10 minutes. For some classes, it may be appropriate to modify the assignment by specifying which problems they work on first. Some problems do not specify a method for solving. Students should solve these problems using the RDW approach used for Application Problems.

Student Debrief (10 minutes)

Lesson Objective: Solve multiplicative comparison word problems by applying the area and perimeter formulas.

The Student Debrief is intended to invite reflection and active processing of the total lesson experience.

Invite students to review their solutions for the Problem Set. They should check work by comparing answers with a partner before going over answers as a class. Look for misconceptions or misunderstandings that can be addressed in the Debrief. Guide students in a conversation to debrief the Problem Set and process the lesson.

Any combination of the questions below may be used to lead the discussion.

- Discuss the relationship between the area of an original rectangle and the area of a different rectangle whose width is 3 times as long as it was to start with.

- Discuss the relationship between the perimeters of the sandboxes in Problem 4.

- For Problem 4(e), why isn't the area twice as much if the length and width are twice as much?

- What conclusion can you make about the areas of two rectangles when the widths are the same but the length of one is twice as much as the length of the other?

- What conclusion can you make about the areas of two rectangles when the length and width of one rectangle are each twice as much as the length and width of the other rectangle?

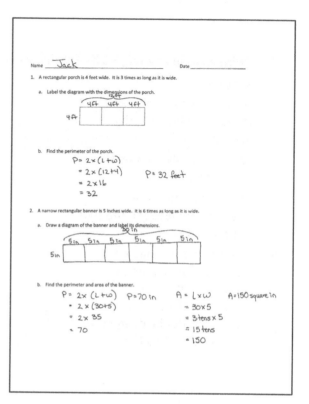

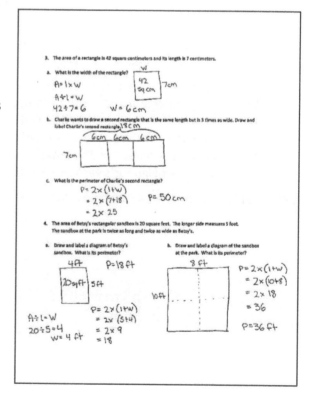

Lesson 2: Solve multiplicative comparison word problems by applying the area and perimeter formulas.

EUREKA MATH™

- What significant math vocabulary did we use today to communicate precisely?
- How did the Application Problem connect to today's lesson?

Exit Ticket (3 minutes)

After the Student Debrief, instruct students to complete the Exit Ticket. A review of their work will help with assessing students' understanding of the concepts that were presented in today's lesson and planning more effectively for future lessons. The questions may be read aloud to the students.

c. What is the relationship between the two perimeters?

Betsy's = 18 ft

Park's = 36 ft

The perimeter of the Park's sandbox is double the perimeter of Betsy's sandbox.

d. Find the area of the park's sandbox using the formula, $A = l \times w$.

$A = l \times w$

$A = 10 \times 8$

$= 80$

$A = 80 \, sq \, ft$

e. The sandbox at the park has an area that is how many times that of Betsy's sandbox?

Area of Betsy's   Area of Park's
   20 sq ft   80 sq ft

The sandbox at the park has an area that is 4 times that of Betsy's sandbox.

f. Compare how the perimeter changed with how the area changed between the two sandboxes. Explain what you notice using words, pictures, or numbers.

The perimeter of the park's sandbox is double the perimeter of Betsy's sandbox. The area is four times the area of Betsy's sandbox. When the length and width are doubled, the perimeter doubles, but the area quadruples.

Lesson 2: Solve multiplicative comparison word problems by applying the area and perimeter formulas.

©2015 Great Minds. eureka-math.org
G4-M3-TE-B2-1.3.1-01.2016

Name _____   Date _____

1. A rectangular porch is 4 feet wide. It is 3 times as long as it is wide.

    a. Label the diagram with the dimensions of the porch.

    b. Find the perimeter of the porch.

2. A narrow rectangular banner is 5 inches wide. It is 6 times as long as it is wide.

    a. Draw a diagram of the banner, and label its dimensions.

    b. Find the perimeter and area of the banner.

Lesson 2:   Solve multiplicative comparison word problems by applying the area
               and perimeter formulas.

EUREKA
MATH™

3. The area of a rectangle is 42 square centimeters. Its length is 7 centimeters.

   a. What is the width of the rectangle?

   b. Charlie wants to draw a second rectangle that is the same length but is 3 times as wide. Draw and label Charlie's second rectangle.

   c. What is the perimeter of Charlie's second rectangle?

EUREKA MATH

Lesson 2: Solve multiplicative comparison word problems by applying the area and perimeter formulas.

©2015 Great Minds. eureka-math.org
G4-M3-TE-B2-1.3.1-01.2016

41

4. The area of Betsy's rectangular sandbox is 20 square feet. The longer side measures 5 feet. The sandbox at the park is twice as long and twice as wide as Betsy's.

a. Draw and label a diagram of Betsy's sandbox. What is its perimeter?

b. Draw and label a diagram of the sandbox at the park. What is its perimeter?

c. What is the relationship between the two perimeters?

d. Find the area of the park's sandbox using the formula $A = l \times w$.

Lesson 2: Solve multiplicative comparison word problems by applying the area and perimeter formulas.

EUREKA
MATH™

e. The sandbox at the park has an area that is how many times that of Betsy's sandbox?

f. Compare how the perimeter changed with how the area changed between the two sandboxes. Explain what you notice using words, pictures, or numbers.

Lesson 2:   Solve multiplicative comparison word problems by applying the area
                 and perimeter formulas.

©2015 Great Minds. eureka-math.org
G4-M3-TE-B2-1.3.1-01.2016

43

Name _____   Date _____

1. A table is 2 feet wide. It is 6 times as long as it is wide.

   a. Label the diagram with the dimensions of the table.

   b. Find the perimeter of the table.

2. A blanket is 4 feet wide. It is 3 times as long as it is wide.

   a. Draw a diagram of the blanket, and label its dimensions.

   b. Find the perimeter and area of the blanket.

Lesson 2:   Solve multiplicative comparison word problems by applying the area
and perimeter formulas.

EUREKA
MATH™

Name _____   Date _____

1. A rectangular pool is 7 feet wide. It is 3 times as long as it is wide.

    a. Label the diagram with the dimensions of the pool.

    b. Find the perimeter of the pool.

2. A poster is 3 inches long. It is 4 times as wide as it is long.

    a. Draw a diagram of the poster, and label its dimensions.

    b. Find the perimeter and area of the poster.

Lesson 2:   Solve multiplicative comparison word problems by applying the area
and perimeter formulas.

©2015 Great Minds. eureka-math.org
G4-M3-TE-B2-1.3.1-01.2016

3. The area of a rectangle is 36 square centimeters, and its length is 9 centimeters.

   a. What is the width of the rectangle?

   b. Elsa wants to draw a second rectangle that is the same length but is 3 times as wide. Draw and label Elsa's second rectangle.

   c. What is the perimeter of Elsa's second rectangle?

Lesson 2:   Solve multiplicative comparison word problems by applying the area and perimeter formulas.

©2015 Great Minds. eureka-math.org
G4-M3-TE-B2-1.3.1-01.2016

EUREKA
MATH™

4. The area of Nathan's bedroom rug is 15 square feet. The longer side measures 5 feet. His living room rug is twice as long and twice as wide as the bedroom rug.

   a. Draw and label a diagram of Nathan's bedroom rug. What is its perimeter?

   b. Draw and label a diagram of Nathan's living room rug. What is its perimeter?

   c. What is the relationship between the two perimeters?

   d. Find the area of the living room rug using the formula $A = l \times w$.

Lesson 2: Solve multiplicative comparison word problems by applying the area and perimeter formulas.

©2015 Great Minds. eureka-math.org
G4-M3-TE-B2-1.3.1-01.2016

47

e. The living room rug has an area that is how many times that of the bedroom rug?

f. Compare how the perimeter changed with how the area changed between the two rugs. Explain what you notice using words, pictures, or numbers.

©2015 Great Minds. eureka-math.org
G4-M3-TE-B2-1.3.1-01.2016

EUREKA
MATH™

Lesson 3

Objective: Demonstrate understanding of area and perimeter formulas by solving multi-step real-world problems.

Suggested Lesson Structure

■ Fluency Practice   (12 minutes)
　 Concept Development (38 minutes)
■ Student Debrief   (10 minutes)
　 Total Time   **(60 minutes)**

Fluency Practice (12 minutes)

- Sprint: Squares and Unknown Factors **4.OA.4**   (8 minutes)
- Find the Area and Perimeter **4.MD.3**   (4 minutes)

Sprint: Squares and Unknown Factors (8 minutes)

Materials: (S) Squares and Unknown Factors Sprint

Note: This Sprint reviews skills that help students as they solve area problems.

Find the Area and Perimeter (4 minutes)

Materials: (S) Personal white board

Note: This activity reviews content from Lessons 1 and 2.

Repeat the process from Lesson 2 for the following possible sequence:

- Rectangles with dimensions of 5 cm × 2 cm, 7 cm × 2 cm, and 4 cm × 7 cm.
- Squares with lengths of 4 cm and 6 m.
- Rectangles with the following properties: area of 8 square cm, length 2 cm, width *x*; area of 15 square cm, length 5 cm, width *x*; and area of 42 square cm, width 6 cm, length *x*.

Lesson 3:   Demonstrate understanding of area and perimeter formulas by solving
              multi-step real-world problems.

49

©2015 Great Minds. eureka-math.org
G4-M3-TE-B2-1.3.1-01.2016

Concept Development (38 minutes)

Materials: (S) Problem Set

Note: For this lesson, the Problem Set comprises word problems from the Concept Development and should therefore be used during the lesson itself.

Students may work in pairs to solve Problems 1–4 below using the RDW approach to problem solving.

1. Model the problem.

Have two pairs of students who can be successful with modeling the problem work at the board while the others work independently or in pairs at their seats. Review the following questions before beginning the first problem.

- Can you draw something?
- What can you draw?
- What conclusions can you make from your drawing?

As students work, circulate. Reiterate the questions above.

After two minutes, have the two pairs of students share *only* their labeled diagrams.

For about one minute, have the demonstrating students receive and respond to feedback and questions from their peers. Depending on the problem and student work seen while circulating, supplement this component of the process as necessary with direct instruction or clarification.

2. Calculate to solve and write a statement.

Give everyone two minutes to finish work on that question, sharing his work and thinking with a peer. Students should then write their equations and statements of the answer.

3. Assess the solution.

Give students one or two minutes to assess the solutions presented by their peers on the board, comparing the solutions to their own work. Highlight alternative methods to reach the correct solution.

NOTES ON MULTIPLE MEANS OF ENGAGEMENT:

To maximize productivity, choose to make team goals for sustained effort, perseverance, and cooperation. Motivate improvement by providing specific feedback after each problem. Resist feedback that is comparative or competitive. Showcase students who incorporated feedback into their subsequent work.

NOTES ON MULTIPLE MEANS OF ENGAGEMENT:

After the discussion of relationships of perimeter in Lesson 2, challenge students to quickly predict the perimeter of the screen in the auditorium. Have students offer several examples of the multiplicative pattern.

EUREKA MATH™

Problem 1

The rectangular projection screen in the school auditorium is 5 times as long and 5 times as wide as the rectangular screen in the library. The screen in the library is 4 feet long with a perimeter of 14 feet. What is the perimeter of the screen in the auditorium?

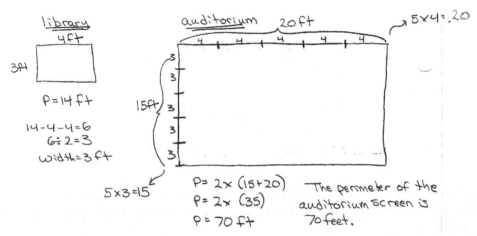

The structure of this problem and what it demands of students is similar to that found within the first and second lessons of this module. Elicit from students why both the length and the width were multiplied by 5 to find the dimensions of the larger screen. Students use the dimensions to find the perimeter of the larger screen. Look for students to use formulas for perimeter other than 2 × (*l* + *w*) for this problem, such as the formula 2*l* + 2*w*.

Problem 2

The width of David's rectangular tent is 5 feet. The length is twice the width. David's rectangular air mattress measures 3 feet by 6 feet. If David puts the air mattress in the tent, how many square feet of floor space will be available for the rest of his things?

The new complexity here is that students are finding an area within an area and determining the difference between the two. Have students draw and label the larger area first and then draw and label the area of the air mattress inside as shown above. Elicit from students how the remaining area can be found using subtraction.

Lesson 3:   Demonstrate understanding of area and perimeter formulas by solving multi-step real-world problems.

51

©2015 Great Minds. eureka-math.org
G4-M3-TE-B2-1.3.1-01.2016

Problem 3

Jackson's rectangular bedroom has an area of 90 square feet. The area of his bedroom is 9 times that of his rectangular closet. If the closet is 2 feet wide, what is its length?

90 square ft ÷ 9 = 10 square ft

$\overset{2}{ft}$ | 10 square ft |

5 ft

10 square ft ÷ 2 ft = 5 ft

The length of the closet
is 5 feet.

This multi-step problem requires students to work backwards, taking the area of Jackson's room and dividing by 9 to find the area of his closet. Students use their learning from the first and second lessons of this module to help solve this problem.

Problem 4

The length of a rectangular deck is 4 times its width. If the deck's perimeter is 30 feet, what is the deck's area?

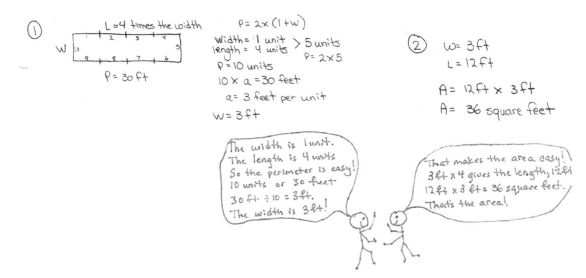

Students need to use what they know about multiplicative comparison and perimeter to find the dimensions of the deck. Students find this rectangle has 10 equal-size lengths around its perimeter. Teachers can support students who are struggling by using square tiles to model the rectangular deck. Emphasize finding the number of units around the perimeter of the rectangle. Once the width is determined, students are able to solve for the area of the deck. If students have solved using square tiles, encourage them to follow up by drawing a picture of the square tile representation. This allows students to bridge the gap between the concrete and pictorial stages.

Lesson 3:   Demonstrate understanding of area and perimeter formulas by solving
multi-step real-world problems.

EUREKA
MATH

Problem Set

Please note that the Problem Set for Lesson 3 comprises this lesson's problems, as stated in the introduction of the lesson.

Student Debrief (10 minutes)

Lesson Objective: Demonstrate understanding of area and perimeter formulas by solving multi-step real-world problems.

The Student Debrief is intended to invite reflection and active processing of the total lesson experience.

Invite students to review their solutions for the Problem Set. They should check work by comparing answers with a partner before going over answers as a class. Look for misconceptions or misunderstandings that can be addressed in the Debrief. Guide students in a conversation to debrief the Problem Set and process the lesson.

Any combination of the questions below may be used to lead the discussion.

- What simplifying strategies did you use to multiply to find the perimeter in Problem 1?
- Can David fit another air mattress of the same size in his tent? (Guide students to see that while there is sufficient area remaining, the dimensions of the air mattress and remaining area of the tent would prevent it from fitting.)
- How was solving Problem 3 different from other problems we have solved using multiplicative comparison?
- Explain how you used the figure you drew for Problem 4 to find a solution.
- When do we use *twice as much*, *2 times as many*, or *3 times as many*? When have you heard that language being used?

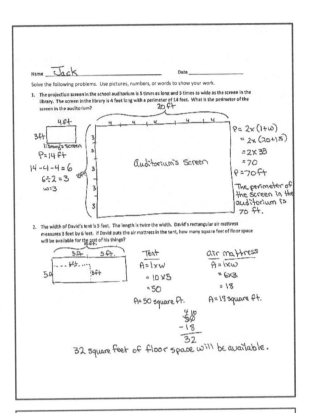

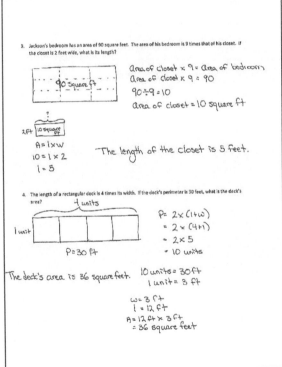

Lesson 3:   Demonstrate understanding of area and perimeter formulas by solving
multi-step real-world problems.

53

©2015 Great Minds. eureka-math.org
G4-M3-TE-B2-1.3.1-01.2016

Exit Ticket (3 minutes)

After the Student Debrief, instruct students to complete the Exit Ticket. A review of their work will help with assessing students' understanding of the concepts that were presented in today's lesson and planning more effectively for future lessons. The questions may be read aloud to the students.

Lesson 3: Demonstrate understanding of area and perimeter formulas by solving multi-step real-world problems.

©2015 Great Minds. eureka-math.org
G4-M3-TE-B2-1.3.1-01.2016

EUREKA
MATH™

A

Number Correct: _____

Squares and Unknown Factors

1.	$2 \times 2 =$	
2.	$2 \times \underline{\hspace{1cm}} = 4$	
3.	$3 \times 3 =$	
4.	$3 \times \underline{\hspace{1cm}} = 9$	
5.	$5 \times 5 =$	
6.	$5 \times \underline{\hspace{1cm}} = 25$	
7.	$1 \times \underline{\hspace{1cm}} = 1$	
8.	$1 \times 1 =$	
9.	$4 \times \underline{\hspace{1cm}} = 16$	
10.	$4 \times 4 =$	
11.	$7 \times \underline{\hspace{1cm}} = 49$	
12.	$7 \times 7 =$	
13.	$8 \times 8 =$	
14.	$8 \times \underline{\hspace{1cm}} = 64$	
15.	$10 \times 10 =$	
16.	$10 \times \underline{\hspace{1cm}} = 100$	
17.	$9 \times \underline{\hspace{1cm}} = 81$	
18.	$9 \times 9 =$	
19.	$2 \times \underline{\hspace{1cm}} = 10$	
20.	$2 \times \underline{\hspace{1cm}} = 18$	
21.	$2 \times 2 =$	
22.	$3 \times \underline{\hspace{1cm}} = 12$	

23.	$3 \times \underline{\hspace{1cm}} = 21$	
24.	$3 \times 3 =$	
25.	$4 \times \underline{\hspace{1cm}} = 20$	
26.	$4 \times \underline{\hspace{1cm}} = 32$	
27.	$4 \times 4 =$	
28.	$5 \times \underline{\hspace{1cm}} = 20$	
29.	$5 \times \underline{\hspace{1cm}} = 40$	
30.	$5 \times 5 =$	
31.	$6 \times \underline{\hspace{1cm}} = 18$	
32.	$6 \times \underline{\hspace{1cm}} = 54$	
33.	$6 \times 6 =$	
34.	$7 \times \underline{\hspace{1cm}} = 28$	
35.	$7 \times \underline{\hspace{1cm}} = 56$	
36.	$7 \times 7 =$	
37.	$8 \times \underline{\hspace{1cm}} = 24$	
38.	$8 \times \underline{\hspace{1cm}} = 72$	
39.	$8 \times 8 =$	
40.	$9 \times \underline{\hspace{1cm}} = 36$	
41.	$9 \times \underline{\hspace{1cm}} = 63$	
42.	$9 \times 9 =$	
43.	$9 \times \underline{\hspace{1cm}} = 54$	
44.	$10 \times 10 =$	

EUREKA MATH™

Lesson 3: Demonstrate understanding of area and perimeter formulas by solving multi-step real-world problems.

B

Squares and Unknown Factors

1.	$5 \times 5 =$	
2.	$5 \times \underline{\hspace{2em}} = 25$	
3.	$2 \times 2 =$	
4.	$2 \times \underline{\hspace{2em}} = 4$	
5.	$3 \times 3 =$	
6.	$3 \times \underline{\hspace{2em}} = 9$	
7.	$1 \times 1 =$	
8.	$1 \times \underline{\hspace{2em}} = 1$	
9.	$4 \times \underline{\hspace{2em}} = 16$	
10.	$4 \times 4 =$	
11.	$6 \times \underline{\hspace{2em}} = 36$	
12.	$6 \times 6 =$	
13.	$9 \times 9 =$	
14.	$9 \times \underline{\hspace{2em}} = 81$	
15.	$10 \times 10 =$	
16.	$10 \times \underline{\hspace{2em}} = 100$	
17.	$7 \times \underline{\hspace{2em}} = 49$	
18.	$7 \times 7 =$	
19.	$2 \times \underline{\hspace{2em}} = 8$	
20.	$2 \times \underline{\hspace{2em}} = 16$	
21.	$2 \times 2 =$	
22.	$3 \times \underline{\hspace{2em}} = 15$	

23.	$3 \times \underline{\hspace{2em}} = 24$	
24.	$3 \times 3 =$	
25.	$4 \times \underline{\hspace{2em}} = 12$	
26.	$4 \times \underline{\hspace{2em}} = 28$	
27.	$4 \times 4 =$	
28.	$5 \times \underline{\hspace{2em}} = 10$	
29.	$5 \times \underline{\hspace{2em}} = 35$	
30.	$5 \times 5 =$	
31.	$6 \times \underline{\hspace{2em}} = 24$	
32.	$6 \times \underline{\hspace{2em}} = 48$	
33.	$6 \times 6 =$	
34.	$7 \times \underline{\hspace{2em}} = 21$	
35.	$7 \times \underline{\hspace{2em}} = 63$	
36.	$7 \times 7 =$	
37.	$8 \times \underline{\hspace{2em}} = 32$	
38.	$8 \times \underline{\hspace{2em}} = 56$	
39.	$8 \times 8 =$	
40.	$9 \times \underline{\hspace{2em}} = 27$	
41.	$9 \times \underline{\hspace{2em}} = 72$	
42.	$9 \times 9 =$	
43.	$9 \times \underline{\hspace{2em}} = 63$	
44.	$10 \times 10 =$	

Lesson 3:   Demonstrate understanding of area and perimeter formulas by solving
multi-step real-world problems.

EUREKA
MATH™

Name _____   Date _____

Solve the following problems. Use pictures, numbers, or words to show your work.

1. The rectangular projection screen in the school auditorium is 5 times as long and 5 times as wide as the rectangular screen in the library. The screen in the library is 4 feet long with a perimeter of 14 feet. What is the perimeter of the screen in the auditorium?

2. The width of David's rectangular tent is 5 feet. The length is twice the width. David's rectangular air mattress measures 3 feet by 6 feet. If David puts the air mattress in the tent, how many square feet of floor space will be available for the rest of his things?

Lesson 3:   Demonstrate understanding of area and perimeter formulas by solving
multi-step real-world problems.

©2015 Great Minds. eureka-math.org
G4-M3-TE-B2-1.3.1-01.2016

57

3. Jackson's rectangular bedroom has an area of 90 square feet. The area of his bedroom is 9 times that of his rectangular closet. If the closet is 2 feet wide, what is its length?

4. The length of a rectangular deck is 4 times its width. If the deck's perimeter is 30 feet, what is the deck's area?

Lesson 3:   Demonstrate understanding of area and perimeter formulas by solving multi-step real-world problems.

©2015 Great Minds. eureka-math.org
G4-M3-TE-B2-1.3.1-01.2016

Name _____   Date _____

Solve the following problem. Use pictures, numbers, or words to show your work.

A rectangular poster is 3 times as long as it is wide. A rectangular banner is 5 times as long as it is wide. Both the banner and the poster have perimeters of 24 inches. What are the lengths and widths of the poster and the banner?

Lesson 3:   Demonstrate understanding of area and perimeter formulas by solving multi-step real-world problems.

©2015 Great Minds. eureka-math.org
G4-M3-TE-B2-1.3.1-01.2016

59

Name _____   Date _____

Solve the following problems. Use pictures, numbers, or words to show your work.

1. Katie cut out a rectangular piece of wrapping paper that was 2 times as long and 3 times as wide as the box that she was wrapping. The box was 5 inches long and 4 inches wide. What is the perimeter of the wrapping paper that Katie cut?

2. Alexis has a rectangular piece of red paper that is 4 centimeters wide. Its length is twice its width. She glues a rectangular piece of blue paper on top of the red piece measuring 3 centimeters by 7 centimeters. How many square centimeters of red paper will be visible on top?

Lesson 3:   Demonstrate understanding of area and perimeter formulas by solving multi-step real-world problems.

©2015 Great Minds. eureka-math.org
G4-M3-TE-B2-1.3.1-01.2016

3. Brinn's rectangular kitchen has an area of 81 square feet. The kitchen is 9 times as many square feet as Brinn's pantry. If the rectangular pantry is 3 feet wide, what is the length of the pantry?

4. The length of Marshall's rectangular poster is 2 times its width. If the perimeter is 24 inches, what is the area of the poster?

Lesson 3:   Demonstrate understanding of area and perimeter formulas by solving
             multi-step real-world problems.

©2015 Great Minds. eureka-math.org
G4-M3-TE-B2-1.3.1-01.2016

61

Mathematics Curriculum

4 GRADE

Topic B
Multiplication by 10, 100, and 1,000

4.NBT.5, 4.OA.1, 4.OA.2, 4.NBT.1

Focus Standard:	4.NBT.5	Multiply a whole number of up to four digits by a one-digit whole number, and multiply two two-digit numbers, using strategies based on place value and the properties of operations. Illustrate and explain the calculation by using equations, rectangular arrays, and/or area models.
Instructional Days:	3	
Coherence -Links from:	G3–M1	Properties of Multiplication and Division and Problem Solving with Units of 2–5 and 10
-Links to:	G5–M1	Place Value and Decimal Fractions

In Topic B, students examine multiplication patterns when multiplying by 10, 100, and 1,000. Reasoning between arrays and written numerical work allows students to see the role of place value units in multiplication (as pictured below). Students also practice the language of units to prepare them for multiplication of a single-digit factor by a factor with up to four digits. Teachers also continue using the phrase "____ is ____ times as much as ____" (e.g., 120 is 3 times as much as 40). This carries forward multiplicative comparison from Topic A, in the context of area, to Topic B, in the context of both calculations and word problems.

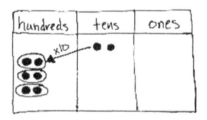

In preparation for two-digit by two-digit multiplication, students practice the new complexity of multiplying two two-digit multiples of 10. For example, students have multiplied 20 by 10 on the place value chart and know that it shifts the value one place to the left, $10 \times 20 = 200$. To multiply 20 by 30, the associative property allows for simply tripling the product, $3 \times (10 \times 20)$, or multiplying the units, 3 tens × 2 tens = 6 hundreds (alternatively, $(3 \times 10) \times (2 \times 10) = (3 \times 2) \times (10 \times 10)$).

EUREKA MATH™

Introducing this early in the module allows students to practice this multiplication during fluency activities so that by the time it is embedded within the two-digit by two-digit multiplication in Topic H, both understanding and procedural fluency have been developed.

In Lesson 4, students interpret and represent patterns when multiplying by 10, 100, and 1,000 in arrays and numerically. Next, in Lesson 5, students draw disks to multiply single-digit numbers by multiples of 10, 100, and 1,000. Finally, in Lesson 6, students use disks to multiply two-digit multiples of 10 by two-digit multiples of 10 (**4.NBT.5**) with the area model.

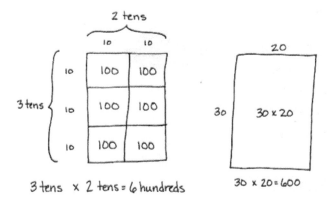

A Teaching Sequence Toward Mastery of Multiplication by 10, 100, and 1,000

Objective 1: Interpret and represent patterns when multiplying by 10, 100, and 1,000 in arrays and numerically.
(Lesson 4)

Objective 2: Multiply multiples of 10, 100, and 1,000 by single digits, recognizing patterns.
(Lesson 5)

Objective 3: Multiply two-digit multiples of 10 by two-digit multiples of 10 with the area model.
(Lesson 6)

Lesson 4

Objective: Interpret and represent patterns when multiplying by 10, 100, and 1,000 in arrays and numerically.

Suggested Lesson Structure

■ Fluency Practice   (12 minutes)
▨ Application Problem   (4 minutes)
▢ Concept Development   (34 minutes)
■ Student Debrief   (10 minutes)

Total Time   **(60 minutes)**

Fluency Practice (12 minutes)

- Rename the Unit **4.NBT.1**   (3 minutes)
- Group Count by Multiples of 10 and 100 **4.NBT.1** (5 minutes)
- Find the Area and Perimeter **4.MD.3**   (4 minutes)

Rename the Unit (3 minutes)

Materials: (S) Personal white board

Note: Renaming units helps prepare students for the next fluency activity and for this lesson's content.

Repeat the process from Lesson 2 using the following suggested sequence: 8 tens, 9 tens, 11 tens, 14 tens, 14 hundreds, 14 thousands, 18 tens, 28 tens, 28 hundreds, and 28 thousands.

Group Count by Multiples of 10 and 100 (5 minutes)

Note: Changing units helps prepare students to recognize patterns of place value in multiplication.

 T: Count by threes to 30.
 S: 3, 6, 9, 12, 15, 18, 21, 24, 27, 30.
 T: Now, count by 3 tens. When I raise my hand, stop counting.
 S: 3 tens, 6 tens, 9 tens.
 T: (Raise hand.) Say the number.
 S: 90.

EUREKA
MATH™

T: Continue.

S: 12 tens, 15 tens.

T: (Raise hand.) Say the number.

S: 150.

Repeat the process for 21 tens, 27 tens, and 30 tens.

Repeat the process, counting by 4 hundreds, stopping to convert at 12 hundreds, 20 hundreds, 32 hundreds, and 40 hundreds.

Repeat the process, counting by 6 hundreds, stopping to convert at 18 hundreds, 30 hundreds, 48 hundreds, and 60 hundreds.

Find the Area and Perimeter (4 minutes)

Materials: (S) Personal white board

Note: This activity reviews content from Lessons 1 and 2.

Repeat the process from Lesson 2 for the following possible suggestions:

- Rectangles with dimensions of 9 cm × 2 cm, 7 cm × 5 cm, and 3 cm × 8 cm.
- Squares with lengths of 7 cm and 8 m.
- Rectangles with the following properties: area of 10 square cm, length 2 cm, and width *x*; area of 35 square cm, length 5 cm, and width *x*; and area of 54 square m, width of 6 m, and length *x*.

Application Problem (4 minutes)

Samantha received an allowance of $3 every week. By babysitting, she earned an additional $30 every week. How much money did Samantha have in four weeks, combining her allowance and her babysitting?

Note: The multiplication of two-digit multiples of 10 by single-digit numbers is a Grade 3 standard (**3.NBT.3**). The second step of this problem relates to today's Concept Development. Students may solve it one way here and may find a simplifying strategy to solve after the lesson has been completed.

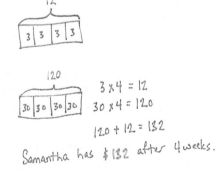

$$3 \times 4 = 12$$
$$30 \times 4 = 120$$
$$120 + 12 = 132$$

Samantha has $132 after 4 weeks.

Lesson 4:   Interpret and represent patterns when multiplying by 10, 100, and 1,000 in arrays and numerically.

©2015 Great Minds. eureka-math.org
G4-M3-TE-B2-1.3.1-01.2016

65

Concept Development (34 minutes)

Materials: (T) Thousands place value chart (Template)
(S) Personal white board, thousands place value chart (Template)

Problem 1: Draw place value disks to represent products when multiplying by a one-digit number.

T: (Draw 3 ones on the place value chart.) How many do you see?

S: 3 ones.

T: How many groups of 3 ones do you see?

S: Just 1.

T: (Write *3 ones × 1*.) Suppose I wanted to multiply 3 ones by ten instead. (Underneath, write *3 ones × 10*.) How would I do that?

S: We can just move each disk over to the tens place and get 3 tens.

T: (Draw an arrow indicating that the disks shift one place to the left, label it *× 10* and write *3 ones × 10 = 3 tens*.) What if I wanted to multiply that by 10?

S: Do the same thing. Move them one more place into the hundreds and get 3 hundreds.

T: (Repeat the procedure on the place value chart, but now write *3 ones × 10 × 10 = 3 hundreds*.) Look at my equation. I started with 3 ones. What did I multiply 3 ones by to get 3 hundreds? Turn and talk.

S: We multiplied by 10 and then multiplied by 10 again. → We multiplied by 10 × 10, but that's really 100. → I can group the 10 × 10, so this is really 3 × (10 × 10). That's just 3 × 100.

T: Work with your partner. How can you solve 3 × 1,000?

S: I showed 3 times 1,000 by showing 3 ones × 10 to get 3 tens. Then, I did times 10 again to get 3 hundreds and times 10 again to show 3 thousands. → I drew an arrow representing *times 1,000* from 3 ones to the thousands column.

T: What is 3 × 10 × 10 × 10 or 3 × 1,000?

S: 3,000.

Repeat with 4 × 10, 4 × 100, and 4 × 1,000.

NOTES ON MULTIPLE MEANS OF REPRESENTATION:

Noting patterns of ten in the place value chart is familiar to students after Modules 1 and 2. However, there may be a need to adjust the display of information by using base ten blocks to convey the magnification of the size or amount, by writing numerals instead of disks, or by writing 10 inside of each ten disk.

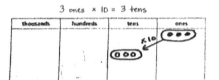

3 ones × 10 = 3 tens

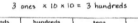

3 ones × 10 × 10 = 3 hundreds

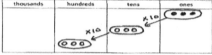

3 × 100 = 300

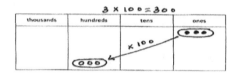

3 ones × 10 × 10 × 10 = 3 thousands

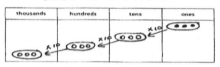

3 × 1000 = 3000

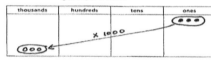

66

Lesson 4:   Interpret and represent patterns when multiplying by 10, 100, and 1,000 in arrays and numerically.

©2015 Great Minds. eureka-math.org
G4-M3-TE-B2-1.3.1-01.2016

EUREKA MATH

Problem 2: Draw place value disks to represent products when multiplying by a two-digit number.

Display 15 × 10 on the board.

T: Draw place value disks to represent 15, and then show 15 × 10. Explain what you did.

S: I drew an arrow to the next column. → I drew an arrow to show *times 10* for the 1 ten and also for the 5 ones.

T: Right. We need to show *times 10* for each of our units.

T: What is 1 ten × 10?

S: 1 hundred.

T: What is 5 ones × 10?

S: 5 tens.

T: 15 × 10 equals?

S: 150.

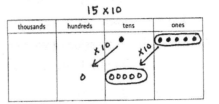

Display 22 × 100 on the board.

T: With your partner, represent 22 × 100 using place value disks. What did you draw?

S: I drew 2 tens and 2 ones and showed times 10. Then, I did times 10 again. → I drew 2 tens and 2 ones and showed times 100 by moving two place values to the left.

T: How can we express your solution strategies as multiplication sentences?

S: 22 × 10 × 10. → 22 × 100.

T: What is 22 × 100?

S: 2,200.

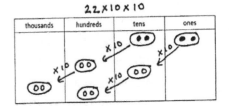

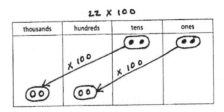

Problem 3: Decomposing multiples of 10 before multiplying.

Display 4 × 20 on the board.

T: Just like 3 × 100 can be expressed as 3 × 10 × 10, there are different ways to show 4 × 20 to help us multiply. What is another way that I could express 4 × 20?

S: 4 × 2 tens. → 4 × 2 × 10. → 8 × 10.

T: Discuss with your partner which of these methods would be most helpful to you to solve 4 × 20.

Allow one minute to discuss.

S: 4 × 2 tens is the most helpful for me, because I know 4 × 2. → 4 × 2 × 10 is the most helpful because it is similar to 4 × 2 tens. I can do 4 × 2 first, which I know is 8. Then, I can do 8 times 10, which I know is 80.

T: When multiplying with multiples of 10, you can decompose a factor to help you solve. In this example, we expressed 4 × 20 as (4 × 2) × 10.

Display 6 × 400 on the board.

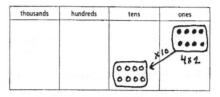

Lesson 4:   Interpret and represent patterns when multiplying by 10, 100, and
             1,000 in arrays and numerically.

©2015 Great Minds. eureka-math.org
G4-M3-TE-B2-1.3.1-01.2016

67

T: With your partner, solve 6 × 400. Use a simplifying strategy so that you are multiplying by 10, 100, or 1,000.

Allow one minute to work. Have students share their decomposition and simplifying strategies.

S: 6 × 4 hundreds. → (6 × 4) × 100. → 24 × 100.

T: Using the expression of your choice, solve for 6 × 400.

S: 6 × 400 is 24 hundreds or 2,400.

Display 4 × 500 on the board.

T: Use a simplifying strategy to solve 4 × 500.

Allow one minute to work. Have students share their decomposition and simplifying strategies.

S: 4 × 5 hundreds. → (4 × 5) × 100. → 20 × 100. → (2 × 10) × 100. → 2 × 10 × 100. → 2 × 1,000.

T: Using the expression of your choice, solve for 4 × 500.

S: 4 × 500 is 2 thousands or 20 hundreds or 2,000.

Problem Set (10 minutes)

Students should do their personal best to complete the Problem Set within the allotted 10 minutes. For some classes, it may be appropriate to modify the assignment by specifying which problems they work on first. Some problems do not specify a method for solving. Students should solve these problems using the RDW approach used for Application Problems.

Student Debrief (10 minutes)

Objective: Interpret and represent patterns when multiplying by 10, 100, and 1,000 both in arrays and numerically.

The Student Debrief is intended to invite reflection and active processing of the total lesson experience.

Invite students to review their solutions for the Problem Set. They should check work by comparing answers with a partner before going over answers as a class. Look for misconceptions or misunderstandings that can be addressed in the Debrief. Guide students in a conversation to debrief the Problem Set and process the lesson.

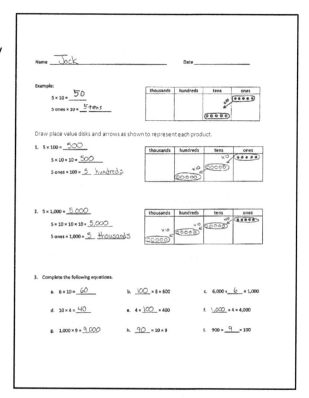

Lesson 4:   Interpret and represent patterns when multiplying by 10, 100, and 1,000 in arrays and numerically.

©2015 Great Minds. eureka-math.org
G4-M3-TE-B2-1.3.1-01.2016

EUREKA
MATH™

Any combination of the questions below may be used to lead the discussion.

- What is the difference between saying *10 more* and *10 times as many*?

- What is another expression that has the same value as 10×800 and $1,000 \times 8$?

- Think about the problems we solved during the lesson and the problems you solved in the Problem Set. When does the number of zeros in the factors not equal the number of zeros in the product?

- For Problem 4, $12 \times 10 = 120$, discuss with your partner whether or not this equation is true: $12 \times 10 = 3 \times 40$. (Problem 7 features 3×40.)

- How did the Application Problem connect to today's lesson?

Exit Ticket (3 minutes)

After the Student Debrief, instruct students to complete the Exit Ticket. A review of their work will help with assessing students' understanding of the concepts that were presented in today's lesson and planning more effectively for future lessons. The questions may be read aloud to the students.

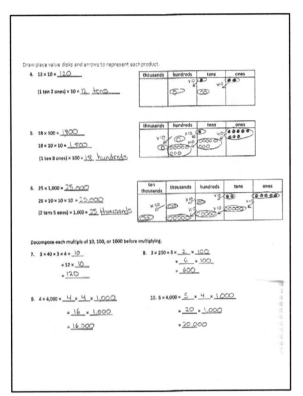

Lesson 4:   Interpret and represent patterns when multiplying by 10, 100, and 1,000 in arrays and numerically.

69

©2015 Great Minds. eureka-math.org
G4-M3-TE-B2-1.3.1-01.2016

Name _____ Date _____

Example:

$5 \times 10 =$ __50__

$5 \text{ ones} \times 10 =$ __5__ __tens__

thousands	hundreds	tens	ones

Draw **place value** disks and arrows as shown to represent each product.

1. $5 \times 100 =$ _____

   $5 \times 10 \times 10 =$ _____

   $5 \text{ ones} \times 100 =$ ____ _____

thousands	hundreds	tens	ones

2. $5 \times 1,000 =$ _____

   $5 \times 10 \times 10 \times 10 =$ _____

   $5 \text{ ones} \times 1,000 =$ ____ _____

thousands	hundreds	tens	ones

3. Fill in the blanks in the following equations.

   a. $6 \times 10 =$ _____

   b. _____ $\times 6 = 600$

   c. $6,000 =$ _____ $\times 1,000$

   d. $10 \times 4 =$ _____

   e. $4 \times$ _____ $= 400$

   f. _____ $\times 4 = 4,000$

   g. $1,000 \times 9 =$ _____

   h. _____ $= 10 \times 9$

   i. $900 =$ _____ $\times 100$

Lesson 4:   Interpret and represent patterns when multiplying by 10, 100, and 1,000 in arrays and numerically.

©2015 Great Minds. eureka-math.org
G4-M3-TE-B2-1.3.1-01.2016

EUREKA MATH

Draw place value disks and arrows to represent each product.

4. 12 × 10 = _____

    (1 ten 2 ones) × 10 = _____

thousands	hundreds	tens	ones

5. 18 × 100 = _____

    18 × 10 × 10 = _____

    (1 ten 8 ones) × 100 = _____

thousands	hundreds	tens	ones

6. 25 × 1,000 = _____

    25 × 10 × 10 × 10 = _____

    (2 tens 5 ones) × 1,000 =

    _____

ten thousands	thousands	hundreds	tens	ones

Decompose each multiple of 10, 100, or 1,000 before multiplying.

7. 3 × 40 = 3 × 4 × _____

    = 12 × _____

    = _____

8. 3 × 200 = 3 × _____ × _____

    = _____ × _____

    = _____

9. 4 × 4,000 = _____ × _____ × _____

    = _____ × _____

    = _____

10. 5 × 4,000 = _____ × _____ × _____

    = _____ × _____

    = _____

Lesson 4:   Interpret and represent patterns when multiplying by 10, 100, and
1,000 in arrays and numerically.

71

©2015 Great Minds. eureka-math.org
G4-M3-TE-B2-1.3.1-01.2016

Name _____ Date _____

Fill in the blanks in the following equations.

a. 5 × 10 = _____

b. _____ × 5 = 500

c. 5,000 = _____ × 1000

d. 10 × 2 = _____

e. _____ × 20 = 2,000

f. 2,000 = 10 × _____

g. 100 × 18 = _____

h. _____ = 10 × 32

i. 4,800 = _____ × 100

j. 60 × 4 = _____

k. 5 × 600 = _____

l. 8,000 × 5 = _____

Lesson 4: Interpret and represent patterns when multiplying by 10, 100, and 1,000 in arrays and numerically.

EUREKA MATH™

Name _____   Date _____

Example:

$5 \times 10 =$ ___50___

5 ones $\times 10 =$ ___5 tens___

thousands	hundreds	tens	ones

Draw place value disks and arrows as shown to represent each product.

1. $7 \times 100 =$ _____

    $7 \times 10 \times 10 =$ _____

    7 ones $\times 100 =$ _____

thousands	hundreds	tens	ones

2. $7 \times 1{,}000 =$ _____

    $7 \times 10 \times 10 \times 10 =$ _____

    7 ones $\times 1{,}000 =$ _____

    _____

thousands	hundreds	tens	ones

3. Fill in the blanks in the following equations.

    a. $8 \times 10 =$ _____

    b. _____ $\times 8 = 800$

    c. $8{,}000 =$ _____ $\times 1{,}000$

    d. $10 \times 3 =$ _____

    e. $3 \times$ _____ $= 3{,}000$

    f. _____ $\times 3 = 300$

    g. $1{,}000 \times 4 =$ _____

    h. _____ $= 10 \times 4$

    i. $400 =$ _____ $\times 100$

EUREKA MATH™

Lesson 4: Interpret and represent patterns when multiplying by 10, 100, and 1,000 in arrays and numerically.

73

Draw place value disks and arrows to represent each product.

4. 15 × 10 = _____

   (1 ten 5 ones) × 10 = _____

thousands	hundreds	tens	ones

5. 17 × 100 = _____

   17 × 10 × 10 = _____

   (1 ten 7 ones) × 100 = _____

thousands	hundreds	tens	ones

6. 36 × 1,000 = _____

   36 × 10 × 10 × 10 = _____

   (3 tens 6 ones) × 1,000 = _____

ten thousands	thousands	hundreds	tens	ones

Decompose each multiple of 10, 100, or 1000 before multiplying.

7. 2 × 80 = 2 × 8 × _____

   = 16 × _____

   = _____

8. 2 × 400 = 2 × _____ × _____

   = _____ × _____

   = _____

9. 5 × 5,000 = _____ × _____ × _____

   = _____ × _____

   = _____

10. 7 × 6,000 = _____ × _____ × _____

    = _____ × _____

    = _____

Lesson 4: Interpret and represent patterns when multiplying by 10, 100, and 1,000 in arrays and numerically.

EUREKA MATH™

thousands	hundreds	tens	ones

thousands place value chart

Lesson 4: Interpret and represent patterns when multiplying by 10, 100, and
1,000 in arrays and numerically.

©2015 Great Minds. eureka-math.org
G4-M3-TE-B2-1.3.1-01.2016

75

Lesson 5

Objective: Multiply multiples of 10, 100, and 1,000 by single digits, recognizing patterns.

Suggested Lesson Structure

■ Fluency Practice   (8 minutes)

☐ Concept Development   (42 minutes)

■ Student Debrief   (10 minutes)

Total Time   **(60 minutes)**

Fluency Practice (8 minutes)

▪ Group Count by Multiples of 10 and 100 **4.NBT.1**   (4 minutes)

▪ Multiply Units **4.NBT.1**   (4 minutes)

Group Count by Multiples of 10 and 100 (4 minutes)

Note: Changing units helps to prepare students to recognize patterns of place value in multiplication.

Repeat the process from Lesson 4 using the following suggested sequence:

- Sevens, stopping to convert at 14 tens, 35 tens, 63 tens, and 70 tens.
- Eights, stopping to convert at 24 hundreds, 40 hundreds, 64 hundreds, and 80 hundreds.
- Nines, stopping to convert at 27 hundreds, 45 hundreds, 63 hundreds, and 90 hundreds.

Multiply Units (4 minutes)

Materials: (S) Personal white board

Note: This fluency activity gives students practice reviewing content from Lesson 4.

T: (Write $3 \times 2 =$ ____.) Say the multiplication sentence in unit form.

S: 3 ones $\times$ 2 = 6 ones.

T: On your personal white boards, write the answer in standard form.

S: (Write 6.)

T: (Write $30 \times 2 =$ ____.) Say the multiplication sentence in unit form.

S: 3 tens $\times$ 2 = 6 tens.

T: Write the answer in standard form.

S: (Write 60.)

Repeat for the following possible sequence: 3 hundreds $\times$ 2, 3 thousands $\times$ 2, 5 ones $\times$ 3, 5 tens $\times$ 3, 5 thousands $\times$ 3, 5 thousands $\times$ 4, 5 tens $\times$ 4, 5 ones $\times$ 8, 5 hundreds $\times$ 8, and 9 tens $\times$ 7.

Lesson 5:   Multiply multiples of 10, 100, and 1,000 by single digits, recognizing
patterns.

©2015 Great Minds. eureka-math.org
G4-M3-TE-B2-1.3.1-01.2016

Concept Development (42 minutes)

Materials: (T) Thousands place value chart (Lesson 4 Template)
(S) Personal white board, thousands place value chart
(Lesson 4 Template)

Problem 1: Use place value disks to represent multiplication patterns.

Write the following on the board:

2 ones × 4   2 tens × 4   2 hundreds × 4   2 thousands × 4

	2 ones × 4		
thousands	hundreds	tens	ones

	2 tens × 4		
thousands	hundreds	tens	ones

	2 hundreds × 4		
thousands	hundreds	tens	ones

T: Show 2 ones × 4 on your place value chart. Circle each group of 2 ones.

T: Show 2 tens × 4 on your place value chart. Circle each group of 2 tens.

T: 2 ones × 4 is…?

S: 8 ones.

T: 2 tens × 4 is…?

S: 8 tens. → 80.

T: With your partner, represent 2 hundreds × 4. Circle each group of 2 hundreds.

T: (Allow about one minute.) What did you notice about multiplying 2 hundreds × 4 compared to 2 tens × 4?

S: There was the same number of place value disks. → It was almost the same, except I used disks that represented 1 hundred instead of 10. → The value of the disks is in the hundreds, so my answer is larger.

T: 2 hundreds × 4 is …?

S: 8 hundreds. → 800.

T: What do you think would happen if we multiplied 2 thousands × 4?

S: It would look the same again! But, instead of disks representing 100, we would use disks representing 1,000. → The answer would be 8 thousands because we multiplied 2 times 4 in the thousands column.

Repeat with 30 × 3, 300 × 3, and 3,000 × 3.

Problem 2: Numerically represent single-digit numbers times a multiple of 10.

Display 8 × 2, 8 × 20, 8 × 200, and 8 × 2,000 horizontally on the board.

T: With your partner, solve these multiplication problems in unit form.

Allow students two minutes to work in pairs.

**NOTES ON
MULTIPLE MEANS
OF ACTION AND
EXPRESSION:**

Learners differ in their physical abilities. Provide alternatives to drawing place value disks, such as placing cubes or concrete disks or indicating their selection. In addition, use color to highlight the movement of the array from the ones, to the tens, to the hundreds place.

EUREKA MATH™

Lesson 5:   Multiply multiples of 10, 100, and 1,000 by single digits, recognizing patterns.

©2015 Great Minds. eureka-math.org
G4-M3-TE-B2-1.3.1-01.2016

77

T: What patterns do you notice?

S: All of the problems have 8 as a factor. → The units are in order of the place value chart, smallest to largest. → The unit we multiply is the same unit we get in our answer, like 8 × 2 tens equals 16 tens and 8 × 2 hundreds is 16 hundreds.

T: What happens if we change the unit from 8 × 2 hundreds to 8 hundreds × 2? Does the answer change?

S: Nothing happens. → The answer stays the same even though the unit changed. → 8 × 2 hundreds can be written as 8 × (2 × 100), and 8 hundreds × 2 can be written as (8 × 100) × 2. Both statements are equivalent.

8×2 ones $= 16$ ones
8×2 tens $= 16$ tens
8×2 hundreds $= 16$ hundreds
8×2 thousands $= 16$ thousands

8 × 2 hundreds

thousands	hundreds	tens	ones
	⊙⊙ ⊙⊙		
	⊙⊙ ⊙⊙		
	⊙⊙ ⊙⊙		
	⊙⊙ ⊙⊙		

Repeat with 5 × 2, 5 × 20, 5 × 200, and 5 × 2,000 horizontally on the board. As students begin to recognize the pattern of zeros as they multiply by multiples of 10, note the complexity in the additional zero when multiplying 5 times 2.

8 hundreds × 2

thousands	hundreds	tens	ones
	▫▫▫▫		
	▫▫▫▫		

Problem 3: Solve a word problem by finding the sum of two different products of a single-digit number by a two- and three-digit multiple of 10.

1.   Francisco played a video game and earned 60 points for every coin he collected. He collected 7 coins. How many points did he earn for the coins that he collected?

2.   Francisco also earned 200 points for every level he completed in the game. He completed 7 levels. How many points did he earn for the levels that he completed?

3.   What was the total number of points that Francisco earned?

Introduce each step of the problem separately, instructing students to follow the RDW process. Students should ask themselves what they know and draw a tape diagram as needed before solving. Encourage students to show how they decompose each multiplication problem and promote simplifying strategies for the addition.

NOTES ON MULTIPLE MEANS OF ACTION AND EXPRESSION:

Teach English language learners and others to track information from the word problem as notes or as a model as they read sentence by sentence.

$= 7 \times 60$
$= 7 \times 6 \times 10$
$= 42 \times 10$
$= 420$

Francisco earned 420 points for the coins he collected.

$= 7 \times 200$
$= 7 \times 2 \times 100$
$= 14 \times 100$
$= 1,400$

Francisco earned 1,400 points for the levels he completed.

$$\begin{array}{r} 1,400 \\ +\ 420 \\ \hline 1,820 \end{array}$$

Francisco earned a total of 1,820 points.

EUREKA MATH™

Problem 4: Solve a word problem involving *1,000 times as many.*

At a concert, there were 5,000 people in the audience. That was 1,000 times the number of performers. How many performers were at the concert?

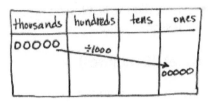

> **MP.4**
>
> T: Write an equation to solve for how many performers were at the concert. Solve using a method of your choice.
>
> S: I know 1,000 times the number of performers is 5,000, so to solve the equation of $p \times 1{,}000 = 5{,}000$, I know that there were 5 performers. → There are 1,000 times as many people in the audience, so I can divide 5,000 by 1,000 to find 5 performers.

Problem Set (10 minutes)

Students should do their personal best to complete the Problem Set within the allotted 10 minutes. For some classes, it may be appropriate to modify the assignment by specifying which problems they work on first. Some problems do not specify a method for solving. Students should solve these problems using the RDW approach used for Application Problems.

Student Debrief (10 minutes)

Lesson Objective: Multiply multiples of 10, 100, and 1,000 by single digits, recognizing patterns.

The Student Debrief is intended to invite reflection and active processing of the total lesson experience.

Invite students to review their solutions for the Problem Set. They should check work by comparing answers with a partner before going over answers as a class. Look for misconceptions or misunderstandings that can be addressed in the Debrief. Guide students in a conversation to debrief the Problem Set and process the lesson.

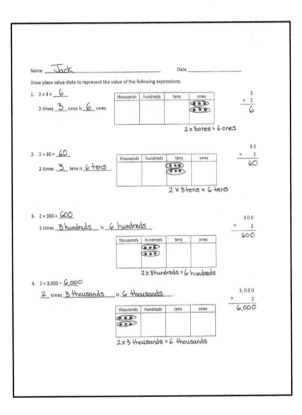

Any combination of the questions below may be used to lead the discussion.

- What pattern did you notice while solving Problems 1, 2, and 3?
- Sometimes, we decompose using addition, such as saying 30 = 10 + 10 + 10, and sometimes we decompose using multiplication, such as saying 30 = 3 × 10. What are some possible decompositions of 24 using addition? Multiplication?
- What did you notice about 5 × 2, 5 × 20, 5 × 200, and 5 × 2,000? (Note: Try to elicit that there is a "hidden" or "extra" zero because 5 × 2 ones is 1 ten, 5 × 2 tens is 10 tens, etc.)

©2015 Great Minds. eureka-math.org
G4-M3-TE-B2-1.3.1-01.2016

- Explain to your partner how you solved for the Problems 5(i)–(l). Explain to your partner the value and importance of the number zero in the factor and the product.

- What significant math vocabulary did we use today to communicate precisely?

- How did the last lesson prepare you for this lesson?

Exit Ticket (3 minutes)

After the Student Debrief, instruct students to complete the Exit Ticket. A review of their work will help with assessing students' understanding of the concepts that were presented in today's lesson and planning more effectively for future lessons. The questions may be read aloud to the students.

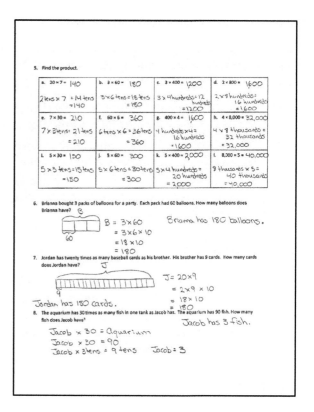

Lesson 5:   Multiply multiples of 10, 100, and 1,000 by single digits, recognizing patterns.

©2015 Great Minds. eureka-math.org
G4-M3-TE-B2-1.3.1-01.2016

EUREKA MATH™

Name _____ Date _____

Draw place value disks to represent the value of the following expressions.

1. 2 × 3 = _____

    2 times _____ ones is _____ ones.

thousands	hundreds	tens	ones

$$\begin{array}{r} 3 \\ \times\ 2 \\ \hline \end{array}$$

2. 2 × 30 = _____

    2 times _____ tens is _____ .

thousands	hundreds	tens	ones

$$\begin{array}{r} 30 \\ \times\ 2 \\ \hline \end{array}$$

3. 2 × 300 = _____

    2 times _____ is _____.

thousands	hundreds	tens	ones

$$\begin{array}{r} 300 \\ \times\ 2 \\ \hline \end{array}$$

4. 2 × 3,000 = _____

    ____ times _____ is _____ .

thousands	hundreds	tens	ones

$$\begin{array}{r} 3,000 \\ \times\ 2 \\ \hline \end{array}$$

Lesson 5:   Multiply multiples of 10, 100, and 1,000 by single digits, recognizing patterns.

5. Find the product.

a. 20 × 7	b. 3 × 60	c. 3 × 400	d. 2 × 800
e. 7 × 30	f. 60 × 6	g. 400 × 4	h. 4 × 8,000
i. 5 × 30	j. 5 × 60	k. 5 × 400	l. 8,000 × 5

6. Brianna buys 3 packs of balloons for a party. Each pack has 60 balloons. How many balloons does Brianna have?

Lesson 5: Multiply multiples of 10, 100, and 1,000 by single digits, recognizing patterns.

EUREKA
MATH™

7. Jordan has twenty times as many baseball cards as his brother. His brother has 9 cards. How many cards does Jordan have?

8. The aquarium has 30 times as many fish in one tank as Jacob has. The aquarium has 90 fish. How many fish does Jacob have?

Lesson 5:   Multiply multiples of 10, 100, and 1,000 by single digits, recognizing patterns.

©2015 Great Minds. eureka-math.org
G4-M3-TE-B2-1.3.1-01.2016

83

Name _____   Date _____

Draw place value disks to represent the value of the following expressions.

1. 4 × 200 = _____

    4 times _____ is _____.

thousands	hundreds	tens	ones

    $$\begin{array}{r} 2\,0\,0 \\ \times 4 \\ \hline \end{array}$$

2. 4 × 2,000 = _____

    _____ times _____ is _____.

thousands	hundreds	tens	ones

    $$\begin{array}{r} 2{,}0\,0\,0 \\ \times 4 \\ \hline \end{array}$$

3. Find the product.

a. 30 × 3	b. 8 × 20	c. 6 × 400	d. 2 × 900
e. 8 × 80	f. 30 × 4	g. 500 × 6	h. 8 × 5,000

4. Bonnie worked for 7 hours each day for 30 days. How many hours did she work altogether?

Lesson 5:   Multiply multiples of 10, 100, and 1,000 by single digits, recognizing patterns.

©2015 Great Minds. eureka-math.org
G4-M3-TE-B2-1.3.1-01.2016

EUREKA MATH™

Name _____ Date _____

Draw place value disks to represent the value of the following expressions.

1. 5 × 2 = _____

    5 times _____ ones is _____ ones.

thousands	hundreds	tens	ones

$$\begin{array}{r} 2 \\ \times\ 5 \\ \hline \end{array}$$

2. 5 × 20 = _____

    5 times _____ tens is _____.

thousands	hundreds	tens	ones

$$\begin{array}{r} 20 \\ \times\ \ 5 \\ \hline \end{array}$$

3. 5 × 200 = _____

    5 times _____ is _____.

thousands	hundreds	tens	ones

$$\begin{array}{r} 200 \\ \times\ \ \ 5 \\ \hline \end{array}$$

4. 5 × 2,000 = _____

    ____ times _____ is _____.

thousands	hundreds	tens	ones

$$\begin{array}{r} 2,000 \\ \times\ \ \ \ 5 \\ \hline \end{array}$$

EUREKA
MATH™

Lesson 5:   Multiply multiples of 10, 100, and 1,000 by single digits, recognizing
            patterns.

85

©2015 Great Minds. eureka-math.org
G4-M3-TE-B2-1.3.1-01.2016

5. Find the product.

a. 20 × 9	b. 6 × 70	c. 7 × 700	d. 3 × 900
e. 9 × 90	f. 40 × 7	g. 600 × 6	h. 8 × 6,000
i. 5 × 70	j. 5 × 80	k. 5 × 200	l. 6,000 × 5

6. At the school cafeteria, each student who orders lunch gets 6 chicken nuggets. The cafeteria staff prepares enough for 300 kids. How many chicken nuggets does the cafeteria staff prepare altogether?

Lesson 5:   Multiply multiples of 10, 100, and 1,000 by single digits, recognizing patterns.

©2015 Great Minds. eureka-math.org
G4-M3-TE-B2-1.3.1-01.2016

EUREKA
MATH

7. Jaelynn has 30 times as many stickers as her brother. Her brother has 8 stickers. How many stickers does Jaelynn have?

8. The flower shop has 40 times as many flowers in one cooler as Julia has in her bouquet. The cooler has 120 flowers. How many flowers are in Julia's bouquet?

Lesson 5: Multiply multiples of 10, 100, and 1,000 by single digits, recognizing patterns.

©2015 Great Minds. eureka-math.org
G4-M3-TE-B2-1.3.1-01.2016

87

Lesson 6

Objective: Multiply two-digit multiples of 10 by two-digit multiples of 10 with the area model.

Suggested Lesson Structure

■ Fluency Practice   (12 minutes)
■ Application Problem   (5 minutes)
  Concept Development   (33 minutes)
■ Student Debrief   (10 minutes)
  Total Time   **(60 minutes)**

Fluency Practice (12 minutes)

- Multiply by Different Units **4.NBT.1**   (4 minutes)
- Take Out the 10, 100, or 1,000 **4.NBT.1**   (2 minutes)
- Multiply by Multiples of 10, 100, and 1,000 **4.NBT.1**   (6 minutes)

Multiply by Different Units (4 minutes)

Note: This activity reviews concepts practiced in Lesson 5.

    T: (Write 3 × 2 = ____.) Say the multiplication sentence in unit form.
    S: 3 ones × 2 = 6 ones.

Repeat for the following possible sequence: 30 × 2, 300 × 2, 3,000 × 2, 3,000 × 3, 30 × 3, 300 × 5, 70 × 5, 400 × 8, 40 × 5, and 800 × 5.

Take Out the 10, 100, or 1,000 (2 minutes)

Note: This activity helps prepare students to multiply by multiples of 10, 100, or 1,000.

    T: I'll say a number. I want you to restate the number as a multiplication sentence, taking out the 10, 100, or 1,000. Ready. 20.
    S: 2 × 10.
    T: 200.
    S: 2 × 100.
    T: 2,000.
    S: 2 × 1,000.

Repeat the process for the following possible sequence: 5,000, 30, 700, 8,000, and 90.

Lesson 6:   Multiply two-digit multiples of 10 by two-digit multiples of 10 with the
                          area model.

©2015 Great Minds. eureka-math.org
G4-M3-TE-B2-1.3.1-01.2016

Multiply by Multiples of 10, 100, and 1,000 (6 minutes)

Materials: (S) Personal white board

Note: This activity reviews concepts practiced in Lesson 5.

  T: (Write 5 × 300.) Say the multiplication expression.
  S: 5 × 300.
  T: Rewrite the multiplication sentence, taking out the 100, and solve.
  S: (Write 5 × 3 × 100 = 1,500.)

Repeat the process for the following possible sequence: 70 × 3, 8 × 4,000, 6 × 200, and 50 × 8.

Application Problem (5 minutes)

There are 400 children at Park Elementary School. Park High School has 4 times as many students.

  a.   How many students in all attend both schools?
  b.   Lane High School has 5 times as many students as Park Elementary. How many more students attend
       Lane High School than Park High School?

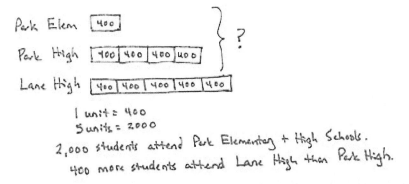

NOTES ON MULTIPLE MEANS OF ENGAGEMENT:

Differentiate the difficulty of the Application Problem by adjusting the numbers. Extend for students working above grade level with these open-ended questions:

- How many students would you predict attend the middle school? Explain your reasoning.

- If these were estimates of the number of students, what might be the actual numbers?

Note: These problems are a review of work from Lesson 5.

Lesson 6:   Multiply two-digit multiples of 10 by two-digit multiples of 10 with the area model.

©2015 Great Minds. eureka-math.org
G4-M3-TE-B2-1.3.1-01.2016

89

Concept Development (33 minutes)

Materials: (T) Thousands place value chart (Lesson 4 Template) (S) Personal white board, thousands place value chart (Lesson 4 Template)

Problem 1: Use the place value chart to multiply a two-digit multiple of 10 by a two-digit multiple of 10.

Display 30 × 20 on the board.

T: Here we are multiplying a two-digit number by another two-digit number. What are some other ways we could express 30 × 20?

S: 3 tens × 2 tens.

    10 × 20 × 3.

    10 × 30 × 2.

    2 × 30 × 10.

    3 × 20 × 10.

T: Let's use 10 × 20 × 3 in a place value chart to help us solve 30 × 20. (Project place value chart as shown to the right.)

T: What is 2 tens times 10?

S: 2 tens times 10 is 2 hundreds.

T: So, the value of 10 × 20 is …?

S: 200.

T: And, then 200 × 3?

S: Triple that group. → 200 times 3. → 3 times 2 hundreds. → 3 groups of 2 hundred.

T: 10 × 20 × 3 is …?

S: 600.

T: With your partner, represent one of the following on your place value chart:

        10 × 30 × 2 as 10 groups of 30 times 2.

        2 × 30 × 10 as 2 groups of 30 times 10.

        3 × 20 × 10 as 3 groups of 20 times 10.

Allow students two minutes to work.

T: Did you get the same answer?

S: Yes, we got 6 hundreds again.

T: When we multiply a two-digit number by another two-digit number, there are many equivalent ways to express it as a product. Decomposing our multiplication problem into more units can help us solve.

> **NOTES ON MULTIPLE MEANS OF REPRESENTATION:**
>
> For students developing oral language skills, alternate between choral response and written response. Encourage students to explain their math thinking in the language of their choice. Allow added response time for English language learners to gather their thoughts.

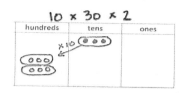

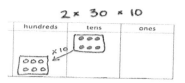

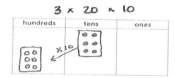

Lesson 6: Multiply two-digit multiples of 10 by two-digit multiples of 10 with the area model.

©2015 Great Minds. eureka-math.org
G4-M3-TE-B2-1.3.1-01.2016

EUREKA MATH™

Problem 2: Create an area model to represent the multiplication of a two-digit multiple of 10 by a two-digit multiple of 10.

T: (Display 40 × 20.) Let's model 40 × 20 as an area. Tell your partner what 40 × 20 is.

S: 4 tens times 20. That's 80 tens, or 800.

T: (Record student statement.) What is 20 in unit form?

S: 2 tens.

T: So, then, what is 4 tens times 2 tens?

S: I know 4 times 2 is 8. I don't know what to do with the units. → I know 4 times 2 is 8. That leaves both tens. 10 tens. It's like saying 4 times 2 times 10 tens!

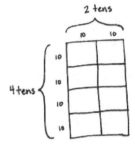

4 tens × 2 tens = 8 hundreds

T: Let's prove how we can multiply the units. Draw a 40 by 20 rectangle on your personal white board. Partition the horizontal side into 2 tens and the vertical side into 4 tens. Label each side. What is the area of one square? (Point to a 10 by 10 square.)

S: 10 × 10 = 100.

T: Say a multiplication sentence for how many of the squares there are.

S: 4 × 2 = 8.

T: Tell your partner how this rectangle shows 4 tens times 2 tens equals 8 hundreds.

S: Each square is 10 by 10. That makes 100. There are 8 hundreds.

Problem 3: Use an area model to represent the multiplication of a two-digit multiple of 10 by a two-digit multiple of 10.

Display 50 × 40 horizontally on the board.

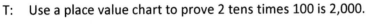

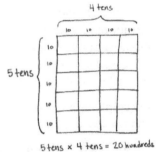

5 tens × 4 tens = 20 hundreds

T: Name 50 × 40 in unit form.

S: 5 tens × 4 tens.

T: With your partner, draw a rectangle to represent 5 tens times 4 tens.

S: I can draw the vertical side as 5 tens and the horizontal side as 4 tens. 10 times 10 is 100. 5 times 4 is 20. 20 is the same as 2 tens. 2 tens times 100 is 2,000.

T: Use a place value chart to prove 2 tens times 100 is 2,000.

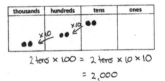

2 tens × 100 = 2 tens × 10 × 10
= 2,000

Students draw a place value chart.

T: What is 50 × 40?

S: 2,000.

T: What conclusion can be made about multiplying a unit of 10 times a unit of 10?

S: 10 times 10 is always 100. So, I can decompose any unit of 10, multiply how many units of 10 there are, and it will be that many hundreds. 7 tens times 8 tens is 56 of some unit. I just have to find the unit. Ten times ten is 100. So, it's 56 hundreds or 5,600.

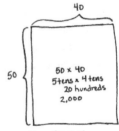

Repeat with 60 × 30.

EUREKA
MATH™

Lesson 6:   Multiply two-digit multiples of 10 by two-digit multiples of 10 with the area model.

91

©2015 Great Minds. eureka-math.org
G4-M3-TE-B2-1.3.1-01.2016

Problem Set (10 minutes)

Students should do their personal best to complete the Problem Set within the allotted 10 minutes. For some classes, it may be appropriate to modify the assignment by specifying which problems they work on first. Some problems do not specify a method for solving. Students should solve these problems using the RDW approach used for Application Problems.

Student Debrief (10 minutes)

Lesson Objective: Multiply two-digit multiples of 10 by two-digit multiples of 10 with the area model.

The Student Debrief is intended to invite reflection and active processing of the total lesson experience.

Invite students to review their solutions for the Problem Set. They should check work by comparing answers with a partner before going over answers as a class. Look for misconceptions or misunderstandings that can be addressed in the Debrief. Guide students in a conversation to debrief the Problem Set and process the lesson.

Any combination of the questions below may be used to lead the discussion.

- What patterns did you notice while solving Problem 1?

- Explain to your partner how to solve the problem 80 × 50 from Problem 10. What does the answer have to do with thousands when the units in 80 and 50 are 8 tens and 5 tens?

- To solve 4 × 10 × 2 × 10, you can multiply 4 × 2 to get 8, then multiply 10 × 10 to get 100, then multiply the 8 times 100. Is it always possible to rearrange numbers like this when multiplying?

- Talk to your partner about how you solved Problem 2. Can you come up with a different way to solve this problem?

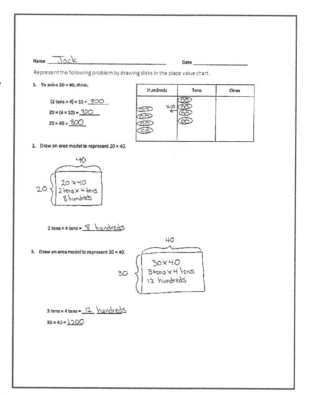

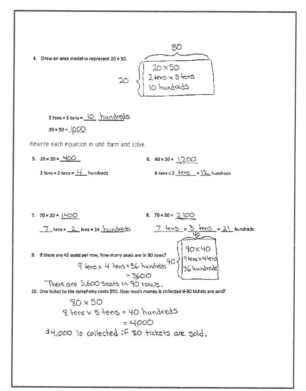

Lesson 6:   Multiply two-digit multiples of 10 by two-digit multiples of 10 with the area model.

©2015 Great Minds. eureka-math.org
G4-M3-TE-B2-1.3.1-01.2016

Exit Ticket (3 minutes)

After the Student Debrief, instruct students to complete the Exit Ticket. A review of their work will help with assessing students' understanding of the concepts that were presented in today's lesson and planning more effectively for future lessons. The questions may be read aloud to the students.

Lesson 6:   Multiply two-digit multiples of 10 by two-digit multiples of 10 with the area model.

93

Name _____   Date _____

Represent the following problem by drawing disks in the place value chart.

1. To solve 20 × 40, think

    (2 tens × 4) × 10 = _____

    20 × (4 × 10) = _____

    20 × 40 = _____

hundreds	tens	ones

2. Draw an area model to represent 20 × 40.

    2 tens × 4 tens = _____ _____

3. Draw an area model to represent 30 × 40.

    3 tens × 4 tens = _____ _____

    30 × 40 = _____

Lesson 6:   Multiply two-digit multiples of 10 by two-digit multiples of 10 with the area model.

©2015 Great Minds. eureka-math.org
G4-M3-TE-B2-1.3.1-01.2016

4. Draw an area model to represent 20 × 50.

2 tens × 5 tens = _____ _____

20 × 50 = _____

Rewrite each equation in unit form and solve.

5. 20 × 20 = _____

2 tens × 2 tens = _____ hundreds

6. 60 × 20 = _____

6 tens × 2 _____ = _____ hundreds

7. 70 × 20 = _____

_____ tens × _____ tens = 14 _____

8. 70 × 30 = _____

_____ _____ × _____ _____ = _____ hundreds

Lesson 6:   Multiply two-digit multiples of 10 by two-digit multiples of 10 with the area model.

95

©2015 Great Minds. eureka-math.org
G4-M3-TE-B2-1.3.1-01.2016

9. If there are 40 seats per row, how many seats are in 90 rows?

10. One ticket to the symphony costs $50. How much money is collected if 80 tickets are sold?

Multiply two-digit multiples of 10 by two-digit multiples of 10 with the
              area model.

EUREKA
MATH™

Name _____   Date _____

Represent the following problem by drawing disks in the place value chart.

1. To solve 20 × 30, think

hundreds	tens	ones

      (2 tens × 3) × 10 = _____

      20 × (3 × 10) = _____

      20 × 30 = _____

2. Draw an area model to represent 20 × 30.

      2 tens × 3 tens = _____ _____

3. Every night, Eloise reads 40 pages. How many total pages does she read at night during the 30 days of November?

Lesson 6:   Multiply two-digit multiples of 10 by two-digit multiples of 10 with the area model.

97

©2015 Great Minds. eureka-math.org
G4-M3-TE-B2-1.3.1-01.2016

Name _____ Date _____

Represent the following problem by drawing disks in the place value chart.

1. To solve 30 × 60, think

   (3 tens × 6) × 10 = _____

   30 × (6 × 10) = _____

   30 × 60 = _____

hundreds	tens	ones

2. Draw an area model to represent 30 × 60.

   3 tens × 6 tens = _____ _____

3. Draw an area model to represent 20 × 20.

   2 tens × 2 tens = _____ _____

   20 × 20 = _____

Lesson 6:   Multiply two-digit multiples of 10 by two-digit multiples of 10 with the area model.

©2015 Great Minds. eureka-math.org
G4-M3-TE-B2-1.3.1-01.2016

EUREKA MATH™

4.   Draw an area model to represent 40 × 60.

   4 tens × 6 tens = _____ _____

   40 × 60 = _____

Rewrite each equation in unit form and solve.

5.   50 × 20 = _____

   5 tens × 2 tens = _____ hundreds

6.   30 × 50 = _____

   3 tens × 5 _____ = _____ hundreds

7.   60 × 20 = _____

   _____ tens × _____ tens = 12 _____

8.   40 × 70 = _____

   ____ _____ × ____ _____ = _____ hundreds

          Lesson 6:   Multiply two-digit multiples of 10 by two-digit multiples of 10 with the
                             area model.

                 ©2015 Great Minds. eureka-math.org
                 G4-M3-TE-B2-1.3.1-01.2016

99

9. There are 60 seconds in a minute and 60 minutes in an hour. How many seconds are in one hour?

10. To print a comic book, 50 pieces of paper are needed. How many pieces of paper are needed to print 40 comic books?

Lesson 6: Multiply two-digit multiples of 10 by two-digit multiples of 10 with the area model.

©2015 Great Minds. eureka-math.org
G4-M3-TE-B2-1.3.1-01.2016

Topic C

Multiplication of up to Four Digits by Single-Digit Numbers

4.NBT.5, 4.OA.2, 4.NBT.1

Focus Standard:	4.NBT.5	Multiply a whole number of up to four digits by a one-digit whole number, and multiply two two-digit numbers, using strategies based on place value and the properties of operations. Illustrate and explain the calculation by using equations, rectangular arrays, and/or area models.
Instructional Days:	5	
Coherence -Links from:	G3–M1	Properties of Multiplication and Division and Problem Solving with Units of 2–5 and 10
	G3–M3	Multiplication and Division with Units of 0, 1, 6–9, and Multiples of 10
-Links to:	G5–M2	Multi-Digit Whole Number and Decimal Fraction Operations

Building on their work in Topic B, students begin in Topic C decomposing numbers into base ten units in order to find products of single-digit by multi-digit numbers. Students practice multiplying by using models before being introduced to the standard algorithm. Throughout the topic, students practice multiplication in the context of word problems, including multiplicative comparison problems.

In Lessons 7 and 8, students use place value disks to represent the multiplication of two-, three-, and four-digit numbers by a one-digit whole number.

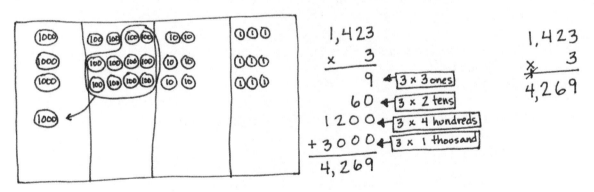

Lessons 9 and 10 move students to the abstract level as they multiply three- and four-digit numbers by one-digit numbers using the standard algorithm.

Finally, in Lesson 11, partial products, the standard algorithm, and the area model are compared and connected via the distributive property (**4.NBT.5**).

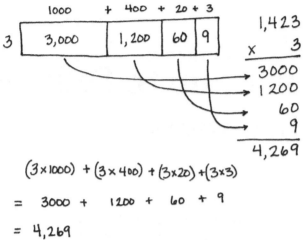

$$(3 \times 1000) + (3 \times 400) + (3 \times 20) + (3 \times 3)$$

$$= 3000 + 1200 + 60 + 9$$

$$= 4,269$$

These calculations are then contextualized within multiplicative comparison word problems.

Jackson's younger brother, Sam, ran 1,423 meters. Jackson ran 3 times as far as Sam. How far did Jackson run?

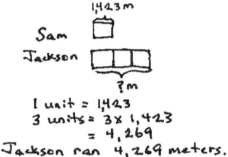

A Teaching Sequence Toward Mastery of Multiplication of Up to Four Digits by Single-Digit Numbers

Objective 1: Use place value disks to represent two-digit by one-digit multiplication.
(Lesson 7)

Objective 2: Extend the use of place value disks to represent three- and four-digit by one-digit multiplication.
(Lesson 8)

Objective 3: Multiply three- and four-digit numbers by one-digit numbers applying the standard algorithm.
(Lessons 9–10)

Objective 4: Connect the area model and the partial products method to the standard algorithm.
(Lesson 11)

EUREKA MATH™

Lesson 7

Objective: Use place value disks to represent two-digit by one-digit multiplication.

Suggested Lesson Structure

■ Fluency Practice   (12 minutes)
▨ Application Problem   (10 minutes)
▨ Concept Development   (28 minutes)
■ Student Debrief   (10 minutes)

Total Time   **(60 minutes)**

Fluency Practice (12 minutes)

- Sprint: Multiply Multiples of 10, 100, and 1,000 **4.NBT.1**   (9 minutes)
- Multiply Mentally **4.NBT.4**   (3 minutes)

Sprint: Multiply Multiples of 10, 100, and 1,000 (9 minutes)

Materials: (S) Multiply Multiples of 10, 100, and 1,000 Sprint

Note: This Sprint reinforces concepts taught and reviewed in Lessons 1–6.

Multiply Mentally (3 minutes)

Note: Reviewing these mental multiplication strategies provides a foundation for students to succeed during the Concept Development.

T: (Write $3 \times 2 = $ ____.) Say the multiplication sentence.
S: $3 \times 2 = 6$.
T: (Write $3 \times 2 = 6$. Below it, write $40 \times 2 = $ ____.) Say the multiplication sentence.
S: $40 \times 2 = 80$.
T: (Write $40 \times 2 = 80$. Below it, write $43 \times 2 = $ ____.) Say the multiplication sentence.
S: $43 \times 2 = 86$.

Repeat process for the following possible sequence: 32×3, 21×4, and 24×4, directing students to follow the format demonstrated for them.

©2015 Great Minds. eureka-math.org
G4-M3-TE-B2-1.3.1-01.2016

Application Problem (10 minutes)

The basketball team is selling T-shirts for $9 each. On Monday, they sold 4 T-shirts. On Tuesday, they sold 5 times as many T-shirts as on Monday. How much money did the team earn altogether on Monday and Tuesday?

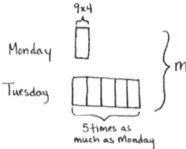

Note: This is a multi-step word problem reviewing multiplying by multiples of 10 from Lesson 5, including multiplicative comparison.

NOTES ON MULTIPLE MEANS OF ENGAGEMENT:

Extend the Application Problem for students above grade level with open-ended questions, such as the following:

- What might be an explanation for the large difference in T-shirt sales between Monday and Tuesday?

- Based on your thoughts, what might be a strategy for generating the most money from T-shirt sales?

- Given the increase in T-shirts sold, should the team increase or decrease the price of the shirt? Explain your reasoning.

Concept Development (28 minutes)

Materials: (T) Ten thousands place value chart (Template)
(S) Personal white board, ten thousands place value chart (Template)

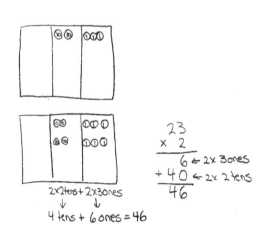

Problem 1: Represent 2 × 23 with disks. Write a matching equation, and record the partial products vertically.

- T: Use your place value chart and draw disks to represent 23.

- T: Draw disks on your place value chart to show 1 more group of 23. What is the total value in the ones?

- S: 2 × 3 ones = 6 ones = 6.

- T: Write 2 × 3 ones under the ones column. Let's record 2 × 23 vertically.

- T: We record the total number for the ones below, just like in addition. (Record the 6 ones as shown above.)

- T: Let's look at the tens. What is the total value in the tens?

Lesson 7:   Use place value disks to represent two-digit by one-digit multiplication.

EUREKA MATH™

S: 2 × 2 tens = 4 tens = 40.

T: Write 2 × 2 tens under the tens column. Let's represent our answer in the problem. We write 40 to represent the value of the tens.

T: What is the total value represented by the disks?

S: The total value is 46 because 4 tens + 6 ones = 46.

T: Notice that when we add the values we wrote below the line that they add to 46, the product!

Repeat with 3 × 23.

Problem 2: Model and solve 4 × 54.

T: Draw disks to represent 54 on your place value chart. What is 54 in unit form?

S: 5 tens 4 ones.

T: Draw three more groups of 54 on your chart, and then write the expression 4 × 54 vertically on your personal white board.

T: What is the value of the ones now?

S: 4 × 4 ones = 16 ones.

T: Record the value of the ones. What is the value of the tens?

S: 4 × 5 tens = 20 tens.

T: Record the value of the tens.

T: Add up the **partial products** you recorded. What is the sum?

S: 216.

T: Let's look at our place value chart to confirm.

T: Can we change to make larger units?

MP.4 S: Yes, we can change 10 ones for 1 ten and 10 tens for 1 hundred twice.

T: Show me.

S: (Change 10 smaller units for 1 larger.)

T: What value is represented on the place value chart?

S: 2 hundreds, 1 ten, and 6 ones. That's 216.

Repeat with 5 × 42.

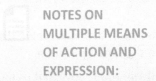

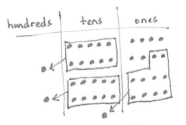

NOTES ON MULTIPLE MEANS OF ACTION AND EXPRESSION:

Some learners may have difficulty drawing, tracking, and organizing place value disks to represent 4 × 54. A similar demonstration of renaming in the tens and ones place can be shown through 3 × 34. Alternatively, students can model numerals (i.e., writing 4 instead of 4 ones disks).

Lesson 7:   Use place value disks to represent two-digit by one-digit multiplication.

105

Problem Set (10 minutes)

Students should do their personal best to complete the Problem Set within the allotted 10 minutes. For some classes, it may be appropriate to modify the assignment by specifying which problems they work on first. Some problems do not specify a method for solving. Students should solve these problems using the RDW approach used for Application Problems.

Student Debrief (10 minutes)

Lesson Objective: Use place value disks to represent two-digit by one-digit multiplication.

The Student Debrief is intended to invite reflection and active processing of the total lesson experience.

Invite students to review their solutions for the Problem Set. They should check work by comparing answers with a partner before going over answers as a class. Look for misconceptions or misunderstandings that can be addressed in the Debrief. Guide students in a conversation to debrief the Problem Set and process the lesson.

Any combination of the questions below may be used to lead the discussion.

- What pattern do you notice in the answers to Problems 1(a), 1(b), 1(c), and 1(d)?
- Describe the renaming you had to do when solving Problem 2(a). How is it different from the renaming you had to do when solving Problem 2(b)?
- Why did some of the problems require you to use a hundreds column in the place value chart, but others did not?
- When you start solving one of these problems, is there a way to tell if you are going to need to change 10 tens to 1 hundred or 10 ones to 1 ten?
- How did the Application Problem connect to today's lesson?
  - If we found the total number of T-shirts sold first (24) and then multiplied to find the total amount of money, what would our multiplication problem have been? (24 × 9.)
  - What do the **partial products** for 24 × 9 represent in the context of the word problem?

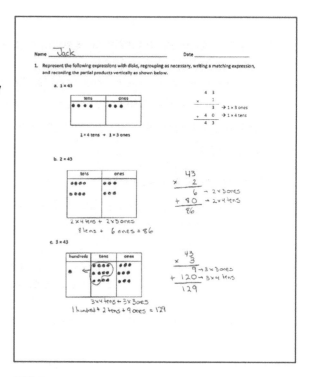

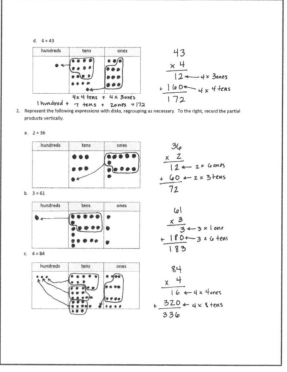

Lesson 7:   Use place value disks to represent two-digit by one-digit multiplication.

EUREKA MATH™

- Talk to your partner about which method you prefer. Do you prefer writing the partial products or using a place value chart with disks? Is one of these methods easier for you to understand? Does one of them help you solve the problem faster?

Exit Ticket (3 minutes)

After the Student Debrief, instruct students to complete the Exit Ticket. A review of their work will help with assessing students' understanding of the concepts that were presented in today's lesson and planning more effectively for future lessons. The questions may be read aloud to the students.

Lesson 7:   Use place value disks to represent two-digit by one-digit multiplication.

107

©2015 Great Minds. eureka-math.org
G4-M3-TE-B2-1.3.1-01.2016

A

Multiply Multiples of 10, 100, and 1,000

1.	3 × 2 =	
2.	30 × 2 =	
3.	300 × 2 =	
4.	3,000 × 2 =	
5.	2 × 3,000 =	
6.	2 × 4 =	
7.	2 × 40 =	
8.	2 × 400 =	
9.	2 × 4,000 =	
10.	3 × 3 =	
11.	30 × 3 =	
12.	300 × 3 =	
13.	3,000 × 3 =	
14.	4,000 × 3 =	
15.	400 × 3 =	
16.	40 × 3 =	
17.	5 × 3 =	
18.	500 × 3 =	
19.	7 × 2 =	
20.	70 × 2 =	
21.	4 × 4 =	
22.	4,000 × 4 =	

23.	7 × 5 =	
24.	700 × 5 =	
25.	8 × 3 =	
26.	80 × 3 =	
27.	9 × 4 =	
28.	9,000 × 4 =	
29.	7 × 6 =	
30.	7 × 600 =	
31.	8 × 9 =	
32.	8 × 90 =	
33.	6 × 9 =	
34.	6 × 9,000 =	
35.	900 × 9 =	
36.	8,000 × 8 =	
37.	7 × 70 =	
38.	6 × 600 =	
39.	800 × 7 =	
40.	7 × 9,000 =	
41.	200 × 5 =	
42.	5 × 60 =	
43.	4,000 × 5 =	
44.	800 × 5 =	

Lesson 7:   Use place value disks to represent two-digit by one-digit multiplication.

B

Number Correct: _____

Improvement: _____

Multiply Multiples of 10, 100, and 1,000

1.	4 × 2 =	
2.	40 × 2 =	
3.	400 × 2 =	
4.	4,000 × 2 =	
5.	2 × 4,000 =	
6.	3 × 3 =	
7.	3 × 30 =	
8.	3 × 300 =	
9.	3 × 3,000 =	
10.	2 × 3 =	
11.	20 × 3 =	
12.	200 × 3 =	
13.	2,000 × 3 =	
14.	3,000 × 4 =	
15.	300 × 4 =	
16.	30 × 4 =	
17.	3 × 5 =	
18.	30 × 5 =	
19.	6 × 2 =	
20.	60 × 2 =	
21.	4 × 4 =	
22.	400 × 4 =	

23.	9 × 5 =	
24.	900 × 5 =	
25.	8 × 4 =	
26.	80 × 4 =	
27.	9 × 3 =	
28.	9,000 × 3 =	
29.	6 × 7 =	
30.	6 × 700 =	
31.	8 × 7 =	
32.	8 × 70 =	
33.	9 × 6 =	
34.	9 × 6,000 =	
35.	800 × 8 =	
36.	9,000 × 9 =	
37.	7 × 700 =	
38.	6 × 60 =	
39.	700 × 8 =	
40.	9 × 7,000 =	
41.	20 × 5 =	
42.	5 × 600 =	
43.	400 × 5 =	
44.	8,000 × 5 =	

EUREKA MATH

Lesson 7:   Use place value disks to represent two-digit by one-digit multiplication.

109

Name _____ Date _____

1. Represent the following expressions with disks, regrouping as necessary, writing a matching expression, and recording the partial products vertically as shown below.

a. 1 × 43

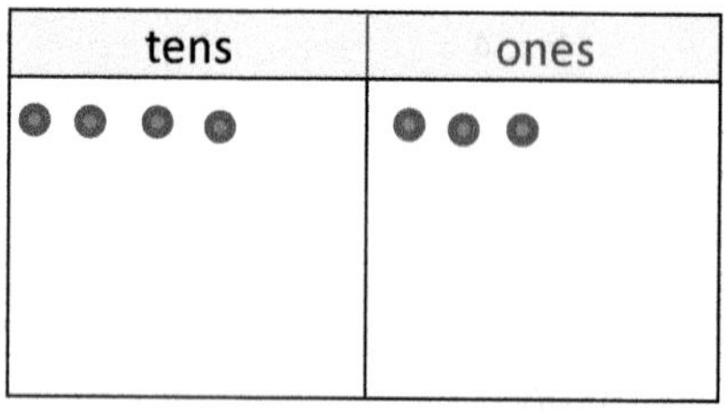

tens	ones
● ● ● ●	● ● ●

$$
\begin{array}{r}
4\ 3 \\
\times \quad 1 \\
\hline
3 \\
+\ 4\ 0 \\
\hline
4\ 3
\end{array}
$$

→ 1 × 3 ones

→ 1 × 4 tens

b. 2 × 43

tens	ones

c. 3 × 43

hundreds	tens	ones

Lesson 7:   Use place value disks to represent two-digit by one-digit multiplication.

©2015 Great Minds. eureka-math.org
G4-M3-TE-B2-1.3.1-01.2016

EUREKA
MATH™

d. 4 × 43

hundreds	tens	ones

2. Represent the following expressions with disks, regrouping as necessary. To the right, record the partial products vertically.

a. 2 × 36

hundreds	tens	ones

b. 3 × 61

hundreds	tens	ones

c. 4 × 84

hundreds	tens	ones

Lesson 7: Use place value disks to represent two-digit by one-digit multiplication.

111

Name _____   Date _____

Represent the following expressions with disks, regrouping as necessary. To the right, record the partial products vertically.

1. 6 × 41

hundreds	tens	ones

2. 7 × 31

hundreds	tens	ones

Lesson 7:   Use place value disks to represent two-digit by one-digit multiplication.

EUREKA
MATH™

Name _____   Date _____

1. Represent the following expressions with disks, regrouping as necessary, writing a matching expression, and recording the partial products vertically.

    a. 3 × 24

tens	ones

    b. 3 × 42

hundreds	tens	ones

    c. 4 × 34

hundreds	tens	ones

EUREKA MATH™

Lesson 7:   Use place value disks to represent two-digit by one-digit multiplication.

113

©2015 Great Minds. eureka-math.org
G4-M3-TE-B2-1.3.1-01.2016

2. Represent the following expressions with disks, regrouping as necessary. To the right, record the partial products vertically.

   a. 4 × 27

hundreds	tens	ones

   b. 5 × 42

hundreds	tens	ones

3. Cindy says she found a shortcut for doing multiplication problems. When she multiplies 3 × 24, she says, "3 × 4 is 12 ones, or 1 ten and 2 ones. Then, there's just 2 tens left in 24, so add it up, and you get 3 tens and 2 ones." Do you think Cindy's shortcut works? Explain your thinking in words, and justify your response using a model or partial products.

Lesson 7:   Use place value disks to represent two-digit by one-digit multiplication.

ten thousands	thousands	hundreds	tens	ones

ten thousands place value chart

Lesson 8

Objective: Extend the use of place value disks to represent three- and four-digit by one-digit multiplication.

Suggested Lesson Structure

■ Fluency Practice   (12 minutes)
▨ Application Problem   (8 minutes)
▢ Concept Development   (30 minutes)
■ Student Debrief   (10 minutes)

    Total Time   **(60 minutes)**

Fluency Practice (12 minutes)

- Expanded Form **2.NBT.3**   (3 minutes)
- Multiply Mentally **4.NBT.4**   (3 minutes)
- Multiply Using Disks **4.NBT.5**   (6 minutes)

Expanded Form (3 minutes)

Materials: (S) Personal white board

Note: Reviewing standard form versus expanded form prepares students to decompose multi-digit multiplication sentences into a series of multiplication sentences.

    T: (Write 200 + 30 + 4.) Say the addition sentence with the answer in standard form.

    S: 200 + 30 + 4 = 234.

Repeat the process for the following possible sequence: 3,000 + 500 + 60 + 8 and 400 + 7 + 90.

    T: (Write 572.) Say the number.

    S: 572.

    T: On your personal white board, write 572 in expanded form.

    S: (Write 572 = 500 + 70 + 2.)

Repeat the process using the following possible sequence: 8,463 and 9,075.

EUREKA
MATH™

Multiply Mentally (3 minutes)

Note: Reviewing these mental multiplication strategies provides a foundation for students to succeed during the Concept Development.

Repeat the process from Lesson 7 using the following possible sequence: 34 × 2, 31 × 3, 22 × 4, and 24 × 3.

Multiply Using Disks (6 minutes)

Materials: (S) Personal white board

Note: This fluency activity reviews Lesson 7's content.

T: (Write 1 × 32.) On your personal white board, draw place value disks to show this multiplication sentence.

S: (Draw 3 tens disks and 2 ones disks.)

T: (Write 1 × ____ tens + 1 × ____ ones.) Fill in the blanks, and write the problem vertically.

S: (Write 1 × 3 tens + 1 × 2 ones, and write the problem vertically.)

Repeat the process using the following possible sequence: 2 × 32, 3 × 32, 4 × 32, 2 × 28, and 3 × 51.

Application Problem (8 minutes)

Andre buys a stamp to mail a letter. The stamp costs 46 cents. Andre also mails a package. The postage to mail the package costs 5 times as much as the cost of the stamp. How much does it cost to mail the package and letter?

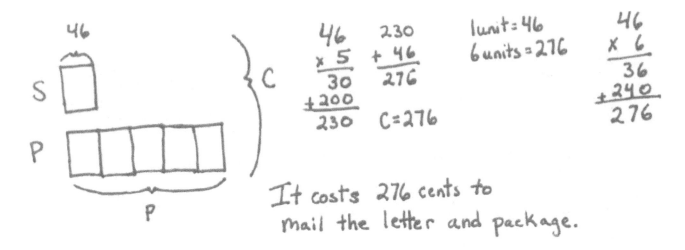

Note: This problem is a review of Lesson 7 and incorporates multiplicative comparison. Students who examine the tape diagram find a more rapid solution is to multiply to find 6 units of 46 cents.

Lesson 8:   Extend the use of place value disks to represent three- and four-digit
by one-digit multiplication.

©2015 Great Minds. eureka-math.org
G4-M3-TE-B2-1.3.1-01.2016

117

Concept Development (30 minutes)

Materials: (T) Ten thousands place value chart (Lesson 7 Template) (S) Personal white board, ten thousands place value chart (Lesson 7 Template)

Note: Today's lesson is an extension of Lesson 7. Students solve three- and four-digit by one-digit multiplication using the same method as they used in Lesson 7. Students should be given more autonomy to work on the problems in partnerships or individually. A connection regarding the process should be made so that students understand that although the numbers are larger, the process is the same.

Problem 1: Represent 2 × 324 with disks. Write a matching equation, and record the partial products vertically.

T: Use your place value chart to represent 2 times 324.

T: What is the value in the ones?

S: 2 times 4 ones is 8 ones or 8.

T: The tens?

S: 2 times 2 tens is 4 tens or 40.

T: The hundreds?

S: 2 times 3 hundreds is 6 hundreds or 600.

T: Beneath your place value chart, as we did in yesterday's lesson, write an expression that shows the total value expressed in the chart.

S: (Write 2 × 3 hundreds + 2 × 2 tens + 2 × 4 ones.)

T: Write 2 times 324 vertically on your personal white board. Record the partial products for the ones, tens, and hundreds.

T: What is the value of the disks represented on the chart?

S: 648.

T: Add the values that you wrote in the problem. What is their sum?

S: 648. It's another way to represent the answer!

T: Work with a partner to solve 3 × 231.

Monitor and provide assistance as students work in pairs to solve.

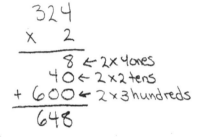

**NOTES ON
MULTIPLE MEANS
OF REPRESENTATION:**

Clarify math language such as *expression, value, vertically, partial products, equation,* and *sum* for English language learners. Offer explanations in students' first language if possible. Link vocabulary to words they may be more familiar with, for example, *sum* has a similar meaning to *total.* Make sure to distinguish *some* from *sum.*

Lesson 8: Extend the use of place value disks to represent three- and four-digit by one-digit multiplication.

**EUREKA
MATH**™

Problem 2: Model and solve 4 × 605 on the place value chart.

T: Draw disks to represent 4 times 605 on your place value chart. Write 4 × 605 vertically on your board.

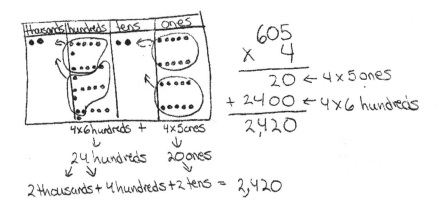

T: Tell your partner the value of the digit in each place.

S: The value of the ones is 4 times 5 ones equals 20 ones. The value of the tens is 4 times 0 tens equals 0 tens. The value of the hundreds is 4 times 6 hundreds equals 24 hundreds.

T: Do we need to regroup?

S: Yes. We can change 10 ones for 1 ten twice and 10 hundreds for 1 thousand twice.

T: Show me. (Students regroup.)

T: What value is represented on the place value chart?

S: 2 thousands, 4 hundreds, 2 tens, and 0 ones. That's 2,420.

T: Add the numbers that we wrote in the problem. What is the sum?

S: 2,420.

Repeat with 5 × 464.

> **NOTES ON MULTIPLE MEANS OF REPRESENTATION:**
>
> Challenged by representing 605 as place value disks 4 times, students may begin to seek more efficient ways of modeling multiplication of large numbers. Review the advantages of tracking regrouping, yet encourage innovation and discovery of a quicker method as introduced in Problem 3.

Problem 3: Solve 3 × 851 using a partial products drawing on the place value chart.

T: Write the problem 3 × 851 vertically. This time, rather than recording 3 groups of 851 to begin, let's record the partial products as we multiply each unit.

T: 3 times 1 one is…?

S: 3 ones.

T: Record that in your place value chart at the top of the ones place.

T: 3 times 5 tens?

S: 15 tens.

Lesson 8:   Extend the use of place value disks to represent three- and four-digit by one-digit multiplication.

119

©2015 Great Minds. eureka-math.org
G4-M3-TE-B2-1.3.1-01.2016

T: Record that in your place value chart as 1 hundred 5 tens a bit lower than the ones so you can see the separate partial product.

T: 3 times 8 hundreds?

S: 24 hundreds.

T: Record that in your place value chart as…?

S: 2 thousands 4 hundreds.

T: Where?

S: A bit lower than the 1 hundred 5 tens.

T: Just as we record the partial products numerically, we draw them. This does not show the connection to addition well, but it does show the partial products well. Can you see the three partial products?

S: Yes.

T: Just looking at the place value chart for now, what are the products from least to greatest in unit form?

S: 3 ones, 1 hundred 5 tens, and 2 thousands 4 hundreds.

T: What is the total product recorded both in your vertical problem and in your place value chart?

S: 2,553.

Repeat with 3 × 763.

Problem 4: Solve 4 × 6,379 using a partial products drawing on the place value chart.

T: Write the equation 4 × 6,379. Let's record the partial products as we multiply each unit.

T: 4 times 9 ones is…?

S: 36 ones or 3 tens 6 ones.

T: Record that in your place value chart at the top.

T: 4 times 7 tens?

S: 28 tens.

T: Record that in your place value chart as 2 hundreds 8 tens a bit lower than the 3 tens 6 ones so you can see the separate partial product.

T: 4 times 3 hundreds?

S: 12 hundreds.

T: Record that in your place value chart as…?

S: 1 thousand 2 hundreds.

T: Where?

S: A bit lower than the 2 hundreds 8 tens.

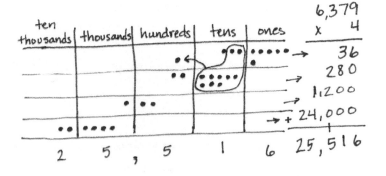

EUREKA
MATH™

©2015 Great Minds. eureka-math.org
G4-M3-TE-B2-1.3.1-01.2016

T: 4 times 6 thousands?

S: 24 thousands. → 2 ten thousands 4 thousands.

T: Where?

S: A bit lower than the 1 thousand 2 hundreds.

T: Can you see the four partial products?

S: Yes.

T: Find the total of the partial products both in your problem and in your place value chart. Notice that you will need to regroup when you find the total of the partial products. What is the total?

S: 25,516.

T: Work with a partner to solve 3 × 2,567.

Give students time to work through the problem and provide guidance as needed.

Problem Set (10 minutes)

Students should do their personal best to complete the Problem Set within the allotted 10 minutes. For some classes, it may be appropriate to modify the assignment by specifying which problems they work on first. Some problems do not specify a method for solving. Students should solve these problems using the RDW approach used for Application Problems.

Student Debrief (10 minutes)

Lesson Objective: Extend the use of place value disks to represent three- and four-digit by one-digit multiplication.

The Student Debrief is intended to invite reflection and active processing of the total lesson experience.

Invite students to review their solutions for the Problem Set. They should check work by comparing answers with a partner before going over answers as a class. Look for misconceptions or misunderstandings that can be addressed in the Debrief. Guide students in a conversation to debrief the Problem Set and process the lesson.

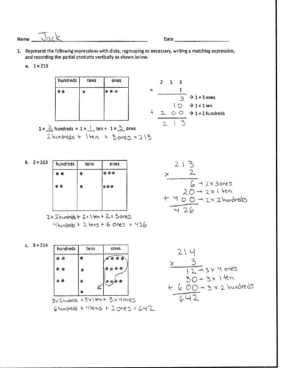

Any combination of the questions below may be used to lead the discussion.

- What pattern did you notice in the answers to Problem 1(a) and (b)?
- If you needed an estimate for Problem 1(c), how could you round one of the numbers? How close would your estimate be to the exact answer?
- Explain to your partner how to solve Problem 2(c). How did you make sure you didn't make any mistakes when there were so many steps to this problem?

EUREKA MATH™

Lesson 8:   Extend the use of place value disks to represent three- and four-digit by one-digit multiplication.

121

©2015 Great Minds. eureka-math.org
G4-M3-TE-B2-1.3.1-01.2016

- How did the Application Problem connect to today's lesson?

- Compare the two methods of drawing the multiplication on the place value chart.

- Can you think of a word problem that could be modeled by Problem 2(d)?

Exit Ticket (3 minutes)

After the Student Debrief, instruct students to complete the Exit Ticket. A review of their work will help with assessing students' understanding of the concepts that were presented in today's lesson and planning more effectively for future lessons. The questions may be read aloud to the students.

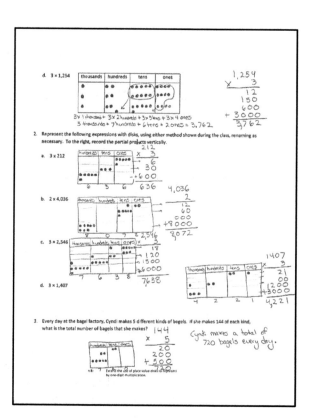

122   **Lesson 8:**   Extend the use of place value disks to represent three- and four-digit
                                  by one-digit multiplication.

©2015 Great Minds. eureka-math.org
G4-M3-TE-B2-1.3.1-01.2016

EUREKA
MATH™

Name _____ Date _____

1. Represent the following expressions with disks, regrouping as necessary, writing a matching expression, and recording the partial products vertically as shown below.

   a. 1 × 213

hundreds	tens	ones

```
      2   1   3
  ×           1
  _____
                  → 1 × 3 ones
                  → 1 × 1 ten
                  → 1 × 2 hundreds
  +
  _____
```

   1 × ___ hundreds + 1 × ___ ten + 1 × ___ ones

   b. 2 × 213

hundreds	tens	ones

   c. 3 × 214

hundreds	tens	ones

Lesson 8:   Extend the use of place value disks to represent three- and four-digit by one-digit multiplication.

123

d. 3 × 1,254

thousands	hundreds	tens	ones

2. Represent the following expressions with disks, using either method shown during class, regrouping as necessary. To the right, record the partial products vertically.

   a. 3 × 212

   b. 2 × 4,036

Extend the use of place value disks to represent three- and four-digit by one-digit multiplication.

EUREKA
MATH™

c. $3 \times 2,546$

d. $3 \times 1,407$

3. Every day at the bagel factory, Cyndi makes 5 different kinds of bagels. If she makes 144 of each kind, what is the total number of bagels that she makes?

Lesson 8:   Extend the use of place value disks to represent three- and four-digit by one-digit multiplication.

©2015 Great Minds. eureka-math.org
G4-M3-TE-B2-1.3.1-01.2016

125

Name _____   Date _____

Represent the following expressions with disks, regrouping as necessary. To the right, record the partial products vertically.

1. 4×513

2. $3 \times 1,054$

Lesson 8:   Extend the use of place value disks to represent three- and four-digit by one-digit multiplication.

©2015 Great Minds. eureka-math.org
G4-M3-TE-B2-1.3.1-01.2016

EUREKA
MATH™

Name _____   Date _____

1. Represent the following expressions with disks, regrouping as necessary, writing a matching expression, and recording the partial products vertically as shown below.

    a. 2 × 424

hundreds	tens	ones
● ● ● ●	● ●	● ● ● ●

    ```
          4   2   4
      ×           2
      _____      → 2 × ___ ones
                               → 2 × ___ _____
      +                        → ___ × ___ _____
    ```

    2 × ___ _____ + 2 × ___ _____ + 2 × ___ ones

    b. 3 × 424

hundreds	tens	ones

    c. 4 × 1,424

Lesson 8:   Extend the use of place value disks to represent three- and four-digit   **127**
                  by one-digit multiplication.

©2015 Great Minds. eureka-math.org
G4-M3-TE-B2-1.3.1-01.2016

2. Represent the following expressions with disks, using either method shown in class, regrouping as necessary. To the right, record the partial products vertically.

   a. 2 × 617

   b. 5 × 642

   c. 3 × 3,034

Lesson 8: Extend the use of place value disks to represent three- and four-digit by one-digit multiplication.

©2015 Great Minds. eureka-math.org
G4-M3-TE-B2-1.3.1-01.2016

EUREKA MATH™

3. Every day, Penelope jogs three laps around the playground to keep in shape. The playground is rectangular with a width of 163 m and a length of 320 m.

    a. Find the total amount of meters in one lap.

    b. Determine how many meters Penelope jogs in three laps.

Lesson 8:   Extend the use of place value disks to represent three- and four-digit
by one-digit multiplication.

©2015 Great Minds. eureka-math.org
G4-M3-TE-B2-1.3.1-01.2016

129

Lesson 9

Objective: Multiply three- and four-digit numbers by one-digit numbers applying the standard algorithm.

Suggested Lesson Structure

■ Fluency Practice   (12 minutes)
■ Application Problem   (4 minutes)
■ Concept Development   (34 minutes)
■ Student Debrief   (10 minutes)

   Total Time   **(60 minutes)**

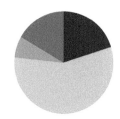

Fluency Practice (12 minutes)

- Expanded Form **2.NBT.3**   (3 minutes)
- Multiply Mentally **4.NBT.4**   (3 minutes)
- Multiply Using Disks **4.NBT.5**   (6 minutes)

Expanded Form (3 minutes)

Materials: (S) Personal white board

Note: Reviewing standard form versus expanded form prepares students to decompose multi-digit multiplication sentences into a series of multiplication sentences.

Repeat the process from Lesson 8 for the following possible sequence: 300 + 40 + 3; 4,000 + 600 + 70 + 9; 500 + 8 + 20; 275; 4,638; and 9,705.

Multiply Mentally (3 minutes)

Note: Reviewing these mental multiplication strategies provides a foundation for students to succeed during the Concept Development.

Repeat the process from Lesson 7, expanding to three-digits, for the following possible sequence: 432 × 2, 312 × 3, 212 × 4, and 124 × 3.

Multiply Using Disks (6 minutes)

Materials: (S) Personal white board

Note: This fluency activity reviews Lesson 8's Concept Development. Repeat the process from Lesson 8, expanding to three- and four-digit numbers, for the following possible sequence: 1 × 312, 2 × 312, 3 × 312, 2 × 2,154, 4 × 212, and 3 × 1,504.

Application Problem (4 minutes)

Calculate the total amount of milk in three cartons if each carton contains 236 mL of milk.

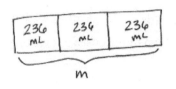

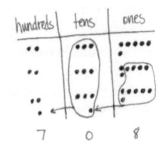

There are 708mL in 3 cartons of milk.

Note: This problem is a review of Lesson 8, practicing three-digit by one-digit multiplication.

Concept Development (34 minutes)

Materials: (T) Ten thousands place value chart (Lesson 7 Template) (S) Personal white board, ten thousands place value chart (Lesson 7 Template)

Problem 1: Represent and solve 6 × 162 in the place value chart. Relate the process to solving using the standard algorithm.

> T: Represent 6 × 162 on your place value chart using the repeated addition way. Work with a partner to solve. Was it necessary to regroup?
>
> S: Yes. On my place value chart, I had 6 hundreds, 36 tens, and 12 ones. I regrouped 10 ones for 1 ten and 30 tens for 3 hundreds. My answer is 9 hundreds, 7 tens, and 2 ones.
>
> T: Write the expression 6 × 162 again vertically on your personal white boards. Let's find a faster way to express your answer. Use the place value chart to help.

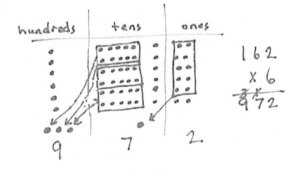

> T: Tell me what happened in the ones column of your place value chart.
>
> S: I multiplied 6 times 2 ones to get 12 ones. We regrouped 10 ones for 1 ten and were left with 2 ones.
>
> T: Record the number of regrouped tens on the line under the tens column. Record the number of ones in the ones place.
>
> T: Tell me what happened in the tens column of your place value chart.
>
> S: I multiplied 6 times 6 tens and got 36 tens. We exchanged 30 tens for 3 hundreds and were left with 6 tens. → But, we have the 1 ten regrouped from the ones, so 36 tens plus the 1 ten makes 37 tens. So, we have 3 hundreds and 7 tens after we regroup.

Lesson 9:   Multiply three- and four-digit numbers by one-digit numbers applying the standard algorithm.

131

T: Record the number of hundreds on the line in the hundreds column. Record the number of tens in the tens place. What about the 1 that was written on the line in the tens place, do I need it anymore?

S: No, we counted it already.

T: Right, so if we're done with it, let's get rid of it. Cross it out.

T: Now, let's look at the hundreds. What was the value of the hundreds?

S: We had 6 times 1 hundred equals 6 hundreds. 6 hundreds plus the 3 hundreds we regrouped equals 9 hundreds.

T: Since there's no need to regroup, write the number of hundreds in the hundreds place. Have we already counted the 3 hundreds we regrouped?

S: Yes!

T: Cross it out. What's the product?

S: 972. That's the same number we got with the place value chart!

Problem 2: Solve 5 × 237 using the partial products algorithm. Then solve using the standard algorithm, and relate the two methods to each other.

T: Write the expression 5 × 237 vertically on your board. Draw and solve using partial products.

Students work individually or in pairs to draw and solve using partial products.

T: Now, let's solve using the standard algorithm. Starting in the ones column, what do we do?

S: We multiply 5 times 7 ones and get 35 ones.

T: Tell your partner how you record 35 ones as partial products.

S: 35 ones is 3 tens 5 ones, so we record 3 tens in the tens column and 5 ones in the ones column on the same line.

T: Let's record 3 tens 5 ones using the standard algorithm. (Record 3 tens on the line and 5 ones in the ones column.) Tell your partner what you notice about this recording.

S: The 3 tens is on the line in the tens like in addition and the 5 ones is in the ones place, so it still shows 35 ones. → We add partial products together, so the 3 tens on the line means it will get added to the product.

T: Working in the tens column, what do we do next?

S: We multiply 5 times 3 tens and get 15 tens.

T: 15 tens was recorded on the second line in the partial products method. For the standard algorithm, add 3 tens to 15 tens.

S: 18 tens.

T: Say 18 tens as hundreds and tens.

S: 1 hundred 8 tens.

T: Record 1 hundred on the line in the hundreds column and 8 tens in the tens column. Cross out 3 tens because it was added.

T: What do we do next?

$$
\begin{array}{r}
237 \\
\times\ 5 \\
\hline
35 \\
150 \\
+\ 1000 \\
\hline
1{,}185
\end{array}
\qquad
\begin{array}{r}
2\,3\,7 \\
\times\ 5 \\
\hline
1\,1\,8\,5
\end{array}
$$

©2015 Great Minds. eureka-math.org
G4-M3-TE-B2-1.3.1-01.2016

S: Next, we multiply 5 times 2 hundreds and get 10 hundreds. → But, in the standard algorithm we have to add the 1 hundred that is on the line to make 11 hundreds.

T: Remember to cross off the 1 since we have already included it in our answer. Because there are no more numbers to multiply, we can just record 11 hundreds directly in the product, which is…?

S: 1,185.

T: Look back at the work that you did when you solved using partial products. What was the product?

S: 1,185. It's the same thing. We came up with the same product even though our methods were different.

T: What are the advantages to the standard algorithm?

S: We record our answer on one line. → We are doing all of the calculations in a few steps.

Repeat using 6 × 716.

Problem 3: Multiply three- and four-digit numbers by one-digit numbers applying the standard algorithm.

Write or project the following:

Shane measured 457 mL of water in a beaker. Olga measured 3 times as much water. How much water did they measure altogether?

T: Draw a tape diagram and discuss with a partner how you would solve this problem.

S: We would multiply 4 times 457 to solve this problem. If Olga measured 3 times as much water as Shane, we multiply by four to find the total.

T: Solve using the standard algorithm. What do we multiply first?

S: Four times 7 ones equals 28 ones.

T: Show me how to record 28 ones.

S: I write the 2 on the line under the tens place. I write the 8 in the ones.

T: What do we multiply next?

S: Four times 5 tens is 20 tens plus 2 tens that were changed from the ones. I have 22 tens. I cross off the 2 because I just included it in the total for the tens. I write 22 tens in my answer. The 2 is written in the hundreds place on the line to show that we regrouped to the hundreds, and the 2 is written in the tens.

T: What do we multiply next?

S: Four times 4 hundreds equals 16 hundreds. Then, I add 2 hundreds to get 18 hundreds. I cross off the 2 because I included it in the total hundreds. Because there are no more numbers to multiply, I record 18 hundreds directly in my product. The product is 1,828.

> **NOTES ON MULTIPLE MEANS OF ENGAGEMENT:**
>
> Have students use and compare the two methods: partial products and the standard algorithm. Encourage learners to analyze their proficiency and efficiency using each method. Guide students to ask, "What mistakes do I make? When? Which method is easier for me? When? Why?"

Lesson 9: Multiply three- and four-digit numbers by one-digit numbers applying the standard algorithm.

©2015 Great Minds. eureka-math.org
G4-M3-TE-B2-1.3.1-01.2016

133

Problem Set (10 minutes)

Students should do their personal best to complete the Problem Set within the allotted 10 minutes. For some classes, it may be appropriate to modify the assignment by specifying which problems they work on first. Some problems do not specify a method for solving. Students solve these problems using the RDW approach used for Application Problems.

Student Debrief (10 minutes)

Lesson Objective: Multiply three- and four-digit numbers by one-digit numbers applying the standard algorithm.

The Student Debrief is intended to invite reflection and active processing of the total lesson experience.

Invite students to review their solutions for the Problem Set. They should check work by comparing answers with a partner before going over answers as a class. Look for misconceptions or misunderstandings that can be addressed in the Debrief. Guide students in a conversation to debrief the Problem Set and process the lesson.

Any combination of the questions below may be used to lead the discussion.

- Explain to your partner how you used partial products and the standard algorithm to solve Problems 1(a) and 1(b). Why do both methods work? How are they different?

- Look at the questions in Problem 2. Which ones would give you estimates that are very close to the actual product if you rounded the larger number to the hundreds place?

- Do you think that you would get a different answer for Problem 4 if the question instead asked you to find 457 times as much as 9? Why or why not?

- Explain to your partner how you solved Problem 7. How did you keep track of what each of the numbers meant?

- How could you use a tape diagram to represent the work you did on the Application Problem?

- What significant vocabulary did we use today?

NOTES ON MULTIPLE MEANS OF REPRESENTATION:

Many learners, in addition to English language learners, will appreciate a review of *standard algorithm* and *partial products* as new math language. Point out, if beneficial, smaller words embedded in these compound words, such as *part* in *partial*. Students may benefit from recording these new terms with clarifying examples in their own math dictionaries.

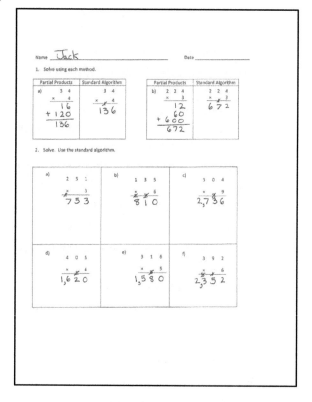

Lesson 9:   Multiply three- and four-digit numbers by one-digit numbers applying the standard algorithm.

Exit Ticket (3 minutes)

After the Student Debrief, instruct students to complete the Exit Ticket. A review of their work will help you assess the students' understanding of the concepts that were presented in the lesson today and plan more effectively for future lessons. The questions may be read aloud to the students.

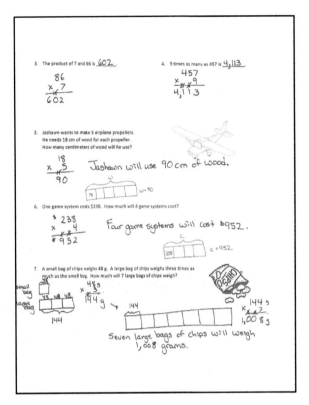

Lesson 9:   Multiply three- and four-digit numbers by one-digit numbers applying the standard algorithm.

©2015 Great Minds. eureka-math.org
G4-M3-TE-B2-1.3.1-01.2016

135

Name _____   Date _____

1. Solve using each method.

Partial Products	Standard Algorithm

a.   3   4
    ×   4
	3 4
	   × 4

Partial Products	Standard Algorithm

b.   2   2   4
     ×   3
	2 2 4
	    × 3

2. Solve. Use the standard algorithm.

a.   2   5   1
     ×   3
	b. 1 3 5
	     × 6
		c. 3 0 4
		     × 9

d.   4   0   5
     ×   4
	e. 3 1 6
	     × 5
		f. 3 9 2
		     × 6

Lesson 9:   Multiply three- and four-digit numbers by one-digit numbers applying the standard algorithm.

©2015 Great Minds. eureka-math.org
 G4-M3-TE-B2-1.3.1-01.2016

EUREKA MATH™

3.   The product of 7 and 86 is _____.

4.   9 times as many as 457 is _____.

5.   Jashawn wants to make 5 airplane propellers.
     He needs 18 centimeters of wood for each propeller.
     How many centimeters of wood will he use?

Lesson 9:   Multiply three- and four-digit numbers by one-digit numbers
                    applying the standard algorithm.

©2015 Great Minds. eureka-math.org
G4-M3-TE-B2-1.3.1-01.2016

137

6. One game system costs $238. How much will 4 game systems cost?

7. A small bag of chips weighs 48 grams. A large bag of chips weighs three times as much as the small bag. How much will 7 large bags of chips weigh?

Lesson 9:   Multiply three- and four-digit numbers by one-digit numbers applying the standard algorithm.

©2015 Great Minds. eureka-math.org
G4-M3-TE-B2-1.3.1-01.2016

EUREKA
MATH

Name _____   Date _____

1. Solve using the standard algorithm.

a.	b.
6 0 8 × 9	5 7 4 × 7

2. Morgan is 23 years old. Her grandfather is 4 times as old. How old is her grandfather?

Lesson 9:   Multiply three- and four-digit numbers by one-digit numbers applying the standard algorithm.

©2015 Great Minds. eureka-math.org
G4-M3-TE-B2-1.3.1-01.2016

139

Name _____ Date _____

1. Solve using each method.

Partial Products	Standard Algorithm

a.   4 6
 	
    ×   2
	4 6
	
	    × 2

Partial Products	Standard Algorithm

b.   3 1 5
 	
    ×   4
	3 1 5
	
	    × 4

2. Solve using the standard algorithm.

a.
 	
      2 3 2
   ×   4
	b.
	
	      1 4 2
	   × 6
		c.
		
		      3 1 4
		   × 7

d.
 	
      4 4 0
   ×   3
	e.
	
	      5 0 7
	   × 8
		f.
		
		      3 8 4
		   × 9

Lesson 9:   Multiply three- and four-digit numbers by one-digit numbers
              applying the standard algorithm.

EUREKA
MATH™

3. What is the product of 8 and 54?

4. Isabel earned 350 points while she was playing Blasting Robot. Isabel's mom earned 3 times as many points as Isabel. How many points did Isabel's mom earn?

5. To get enough money to go on a field trip, every student in a club has to raise $53 by selling chocolate bars. There are 9 students in the club. How much money does the club need to raise to go on the field trip?

EUREKA
MATH™

Lesson 9:   Multiply three- and four-digit numbers by one-digit numbers
                   applying the standard algorithm.

©2015 Great Minds. eureka-math.org
G4-M3-TE-B2-1.3.1-01.2016

141

6. Mr. Meyers wants to order 4 tablets for his classroom. Each tablet costs $329. How much will all four tablets cost?

7. Amaya read 64 pages last week. Amaya's older brother, Rogelio, read twice as many pages in the same amount of time. Their big sister, Elianna, is in high school and read 4 times as many pages as Rogelio did. How many pages did Elianna read last week?

Lesson 10

Objective: Multiply three- and four-digit numbers by one-digit numbers applying the standard algorithm.

Suggested Lesson Structure

■ Fluency Practice   (12 minutes)
▨ Application Problem   (5 minutes)
▢ Concept Development   (33 minutes)
▨ Student Debrief   (10 minutes)
Total Time   **(60 minutes)**

Fluency Practice (12 minutes)

- Represent Expanded Form **2.NBT.3**   (3 minutes)
- Multiply Mentally **4.NBT.4**   (3 minutes)
- Multiply Using Partial Products **4.NBT.4** (6 minutes)

Represent Expanded Form (3 minutes)

Materials: (S) Place value disks

Note: This activity incorporates expanded form fluency from Lessons 8 and 9 while reviewing how to use place value disks.

    T: (Write 532.) Say the number in expanded form.

    S: 532 equals 500 plus 30 plus 2.

    T: Say it in unit form.

    S: 532 equals 5 hundreds 3 tens 2 ones.

    T: Use your disks to show 5 hundreds 3 tens 2 ones.

Repeat the process for the following possible sequence: 415, 204, 3,241, and 2,053.

> **NOTES ON MULTIPLE MEANS OF ENGAGEMENT:**
>
> Extend Represent Expanded Form by challenging students above grade level to do one of the following:
>
> - Use your disks to show 1,000/100/10 less/more than 3,241.
> - Use your disks to show another number that would be rounded to the same ten/hundred as 2,053.

Multiply Mentally (3 minutes)

Note: Reviewing these mental multiplication strategies provides a foundation for students to succeed during the Concept Development.

Repeat the process from Lesson 7 for the following possible sequence: 342 × 2, 132 × 3, 221 × 4, and 213 × 4.

Lesson 10:   Multiply three- and four-digit numbers by one-digit numbers applying the standard algorithm.

143

Multiply Using Partial Products (6 minutes)

Materials: (S) Personal white board

Note: This activity serves as a review of the Concept Development in Lessons 7 and 8.

$$\begin{array}{r} 322 \\ \times\ 7 \\ \hline 14 \\ 140 \\ +\ 2100 \\ \hline 2254 \end{array}$$

    T: (Write 322 × 7.) Say the multiplication expression.

    S: 322 × 7.

    T: Say it as a three-product addition expression in unit form.

    S: (3 hundreds × 7) + (2 tens x 7) + (2 ones × 7).

    T: Write 322 × 7 vertically, and solve using the partial product strategy.

Repeat the process for the following possible sequence: 7 thousands 1 hundred 3 tens 5 ones × 5 and 3 × 7,413.

Application Problem (5 minutes)

The principal wants to buy 8 pencils for every student at her school. If there are 859 students, how many pencils does the principal need to buy?

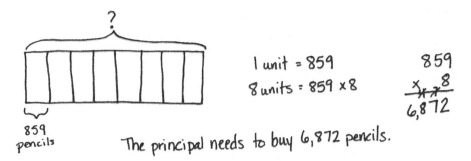

Note: This problem is a review of Lesson 9. Students may solve using the algorithm or partial products. Both are place value strategies.

Concept Development (33 minutes)

Materials: (S) Personal white board

Problem 1: Solve 5 × 2,374 using partial products, and then connect to the algorithm.

Display 5 × 2,374 vertically on the board.

    T: With your partner, solve 5 × 2,374 using the partial products method.

Allow two minutes to solve.

    T: Now, let's solve using the algorithm. Say a multiplication sentence for the ones column.

    Multiply three- and four-digit numbers by one-digit numbers applying the standard algorithm.

EUREKA MATH™

S: 4 ones times 5 is 20 ones or 2 tens.

T: Tell your partner how to record 20 ones or 2 tens.

S: I am going to record 2 tens on the line in the tens column and the 0 in the ones column.

T: Do you have 20 ones recorded in your answer from the partial products?

S: Yes!

T: What is multiplied in the tens column?

S: 7 tens times 5 is 35 tens. → I notice when I look back at the partial products, I also have 35 tens or 3 hundreds 5 tens.

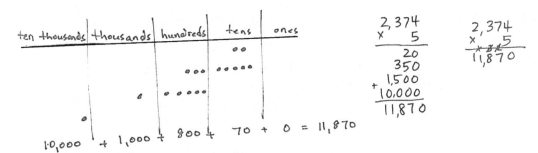

T: Tell your partner what to do with 3 hundreds 5 tens and the 2 tens we recorded on the line.

S: We have to add the 2 tens to get 37 tens or 3 hundreds 7 tens. → Why do the partial products only show 350 though?

MP.4

T: Discuss with your partner why the algorithm shows 37 tens, but the partial product shows 35 tens.

S: In the partial products method, we add the 2 tens to 35 tens later after multiplying each place value separately. In the algorithm, you add as you go.

T: Let's record 3 hundreds 7 tens or 37 tens. Cross off the 2 tens on the line because they've been added in.

T: What is our multiplication sentence for the hundreds column?

S: 3 hundreds times 5 is 15 hundreds or 1 thousand 5 hundreds. → I noticed the 1,500 in the partial products strategy came next. The algorithm is multiplying in the same order starting with the ones column and moving left. → We add the 3 hundreds that were changed from tens. Now we have 18 hundreds. I cross out the 3 on the line because I've added it.

T: Right. Last, we have the thousands column.

S: 2 thousands times 5 plus 1 thousand is 11 thousands.

T: Notice that our answer is the same when we used the algorithm and the partial products strategy.

Repeat using 9 × 3,082.

**NOTES ON
MULTIPLE MEANS
OF REPRESENTATION:**

Learners and mathematicians differ in the strategies they use to solve a problem. Whether we use the standard algorithm or partial products strategy, our product is the same. Cultivate a classroom culture of acceptance of multiple methods to solve. Encourage students to share and innovate efficient strategies for this and other math topics.

Lesson 10: Multiply three- and four-digit numbers by one-digit numbers applying the standard algorithm.

©2015 Great Minds. eureka-math.org
G4-M3-TE-B2-1.3.1-01.2016

145

Problem 2: Solve 6 × 3,817 using the algorithm.

Display 6 × 3,817 vertically on the board.

> T: With your partner, solve 6 × 3,817 using the algorithm.

Allow students two minutes to solve. Listen for use of unit language to multiply, such as 6 times 7 ones is 42 ones.

Repeat with 3 × 7,109.

Problem 3: Solve a word problem that requires four-digit by one-digit multiplication using the algorithm.

There are 5,280 feet in a mile. If Bryan ran 4 miles, how many feet did he run?

> T: Discuss with your partner how you would solve this problem.
>
> T: On your own, use the algorithm to solve for how many feet Bryan ran.
>
> S: 5,280 × 4 is 21,120. Bryan ran 21,120 feet.

Problem Set (10 minutes)

Students should do their personal best to complete the Problem Set within the allotted 10 minutes. For some classes, it may be appropriate to modify the assignment by specifying which problems they work on first. Some problems do not specify a method for solving. Students should solve these problems using the RDW approach used for Application Problems.

Student Debrief (10 minutes)

Lesson Objective: Multiply three- and four-digit numbers by one-digit numbers applying the standard algorithm.

The Student Debrief is intended to invite reflection and active processing of the total lesson experience.

Invite students to review their solutions for the Problem Set. They should check work by comparing answers with a partner before going over answers as a class. Look for misconceptions or misunderstandings that can be addressed in the Debrief. Guide students in a conversation to debrief the Problem Set and process the lesson.

Any combination of the questions below may be used to lead the discussion.

- What pattern did you notice while solving Problems 1(a) and (b)?

- What happens to the product if one factor is doubled? Halved?

- What other patterns did you notice while working on Problem 1?

Lesson 10:   Multiply three- and four-digit numbers by one-digit numbers
              applying the standard algorithm.

EUREKA
MATH™

- Problem 3 only gave one factor. How did you find the other factor?

- If one of your classmates was absent for the past week, how would you explain how you solved Problem 4? Describe any visuals you could use to help you with your explanation.

- How did Lesson 9 help you to understand today's lesson?

Exit Ticket (3 minutes)

After the Student Debrief, instruct students to complete the Exit Ticket. A review of their work will help you assess the students' understanding of the concepts that were presented in the lesson today and plan more effectively for future lessons. The questions may be read aloud to the students

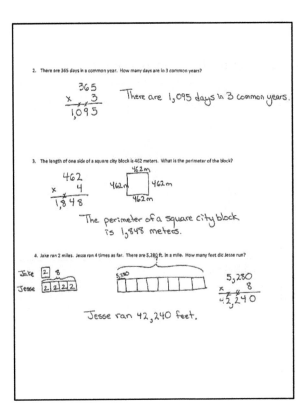

Lesson 10:   Multiply three- and four-digit numbers by one-digit numbers applying the standard algorithm.

©2015 Great Minds. eureka-math.org
G4-M3-TE-B2-1.3.1-01.2016

Name _____ Date _____

1. Solve using the standard algorithm.

a. 3 × 42	b. 6 × 42
c. 6 × 431	d. 3 × 431
e. 3 × 6,212	f. 3 × 3,106
g. 4 × 4,309	h. 4 × 8,618

Lesson 10:   Multiply three- and four-digit numbers by one-digit numbers applying the standard algorithm.

©2015 Great Minds. eureka-math.org
G4-M3-TE-B2-1.3.1-01.2016

EUREKA
MATH™

2. There are 365 days in a common year. How many days are in 3 common years?

3. The length of one side of a square city block is 462 meters. What is the perimeter of the block?

4. Jake ran 2 miles. Jesse ran 4 times as far. There are 5,280 feet in a mile. How many feet did Jesse run?

EUREKA
MATH™

Lesson 10:   Multiply three- and four-digit numbers by one-digit numbers
applying the standard algorithm.

149

©2015 Great Minds. eureka-math.org
G4-M3-TE-B2-1.3.1-01.2016

Name _____   Date _____

1. Solve using the standard algorithm.

a. $2,348 \times 6$	b. $1,679 \times 7$

2. A farmer planted 4 rows of sunflowers. There were 1,205 plants in each row. How many sunflowers did he plant?

Lesson 10:   Multiply three- and four-digit numbers by one-digit numbers applying the standard algorithm.

©2015 Great Minds. eureka-math.org
G4-M3-TE-B2-1.3.1-01.2016

EUREKA
MATH

Name _____ Date _____

1. Solve using the standard algorithm.

a. 3 × 41	b. 9 × 41
c. 7 × 143	d. 7 × 286
e. 4 × 2,048	f. 4 × 4,096
g. 8 × 4,096	h. 4 × 8,192

Lesson 10: Multiply three- and four-digit numbers by one-digit numbers applying the standard algorithm.

©2015 Great Minds. eureka-math.org
G4-M3-TE-B2-1.3.1-01.2016

2. Robert's family brings six gallons of water for the players on the football team. If one gallon of water contains 128 fluid ounces, how many fluid ounces are in six gallons?

3. It takes 687 Earth days for the planet Mars to revolve around the sun once. How many Earth days does it take Mars to revolve around the sun four times?

4. Tammy buys a 4-gigabyte memory card for her camera. Dijonea buys a memory card with twice as much storage as Tammy's. One gigabyte is 1,024 megabytes. How many megabytes of storage does Dijonea have on her memory card?

Lesson 10:   Multiply three- and four-digit numbers by one-digit numbers applying the standard algorithm.

EUREKA
MATH™

Lesson 11

Objective: Connect the area model and the partial products method to the standard algorithm.

Suggested Lesson Structure

■ Fluency Practice	(12 minutes)
■ Application Problem	(7 minutes)
☐ Concept Development	(31 minutes)
■ Student Debrief	(10 minutes)
Total Time	**(60 minutes)**

Fluency Practice (12 minutes)

- Multiply Mentally **4.NBT.4** (4 minutes)
- Multiply in Three Different Ways **4.NBT.4** (8 minutes)

Multiply Mentally (4 minutes)

Note: Reviewing these mental multiplication strategies provides a foundation for students to succeed during the Concept Development.

Repeat the process from Lesson 7, expanding to four-digits for the following possible sequence: $4,312 \times 2$, $2,032 \times 3$, $2,212 \times 4$, and $3,203 \times 4$.

Multiply in Three Different Ways (8 minutes)

Materials: (S) Place value disks

Note: This fluency activity reviews the Concept Development in Lessons 7–10.

T: (Write 43×2.) Say the multiplication expression in unit form.

S: 4 tens 3 ones × 2.

T: Show the multiplication expression using partial products.

S: (Write $(40 \times 2) + (3 \times 2)$.)

T: Show the multiplication expression using place value disks.

S: (Show multiplication expression using place value disks.)

T: Write the multiplication expression using the standard algorithm.

T: (Students do so.)

Repeat the process using the following possible sequence: 54×2 and 63×3.

Lesson 11:   Connect the area model and the partial products method to the standard algorithm.

153

©2015 Great Minds. eureka-math.org
G4-M3-TE-B2-1.3.1-01.2016

Application Problem (7 minutes)

```
        30              4
┌─────────────────┐  ┌──┐
│                 │  │  │
8│                 │  │  │
│                 │  │  │
└─────────────────┘  └──┘
```

Write an equation for the area of each rectangle. Then, find the sum of the two areas.

Extension: Find a faster method for finding the area of the combined rectangles.

$A = 8 \times 30$ $A = 8 \times 4$ $A = 8 \times (30+4)$
$A = 240$ $A = 32$ $A = 8 \times 34$

$\begin{array}{r} 240 \\ +32 \\ \hline 272 \end{array}$ The area of the combined rectangles is 272.

$\begin{array}{r} 34 \\ \times8 \\ \hline 272 \end{array}$

Note: This problem is designed to bridge learning from Topic A, in which students solved for the area, to this lesson, where they learn to model multiplication problems using the area model. The placement of the small rectangle to the right of the larger rectangle is intentional for showing the tens and ones of the area model. It is recommended that this problem be presented immediately prior to the Concept Development.

NOTES ON
MULTIPLE MEANS
OF ACTION AND
EXPRESSION:

Scaffold student use of the area model to solve with the following options:

- Provide a blank area model template for students to slip into their personal white boards.

- Review expanded form with place value cards or place value disks.

- Simplify the multiplication. For example, use 4 as a factor rather than 8.

Concept Development (31 minutes)

Materials: (S) Personal white board

Problem 1: Multiply a three-digit number by a one-digit number using the area model.

- T: Draw a rectangle with a width of 8 and a length of 200.
- S: (Draw.)
- T: Tell your neighbor how to find the area.
- S: Multiply 8 times 200. That equals 1,600.
- T: Write the area inside your rectangle.
- T: Think back to the Application Problem (above). We had two rectangles also with the width of 8. Let's combine all three rectangles: this one and the two from the Application Problem. (Draw them.) With your partner, discuss how to find the area of all three rectangles put together.

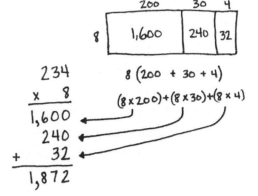

$\begin{array}{r} 234 \\ \times8 \\ \hline 1{,}600 \\ 240 \\ +32 \\ \hline 1{,}872 \end{array}$

$8\,(200 + 30 + 4)$

$(8\times200)+(8\times30)+(8\times4)$

154   Lesson 11:   Connect the area model and the partial products method to the
standard algorithm.

©2015 Great Minds. eureka-math.org
G4-M3-TE-B2-1.3.1-01.2016

EUREKA
MATH™

S: In the Application Problem, I multiplied 8 times 4 and 8 times 30. So, then I can also multiply 8 times 200 and add all the sums together.

T: Record that as one continuous addition problem with your partner.

Guide students to record (8 × 200) + (8 × 30) + (8 × 4).

T: You are saying to multiply each section of the lengths by 8? (Record 8 (200 + 30 + 4) on the board.)

S: Yes.

T: Solve to find the area of the entire rectangle. Let's begin with the largest rectangle.

T: 8 times 200?

S: 1,600. (Record 1,600 as a partial product in the area model and in the written method.)

T: 8 times 30?

S: 240. (Record 240 as a partial product in the area model and in the written method.)

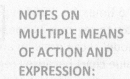

T: Show your partner where to record 8 times 4. Tell your partner the multiplication sentence represented by the area model.

S: 8 times 234 equals 1,872.

T: Compare the partial products to the rectangular area model.

S: The area inside each smaller rectangle is the same as each of the partial products.

T: We recorded the partial products starting with the largest unit, the hundreds. Does the order of partial products change the final product? Work with your partner to solve 8 times 234 using partial products, beginning with the smallest unit, the ones.

S: The answer is the same. I can multiply in any order using partial products. → The order of addends does not matter. That's the commutative property of addition. I can record partial products using the smallest or largest unit first.

T: Yes, the rectangle, or area model, is another way to represent the partial products in multiplication.

NOTES ON
MULTIPLE MEANS
OF ACTION AND
EXPRESSION:

One advantage of the area model is its flexibility for learners. Students can represent their partial products as arrays of place value disks, in unit form, or standard form. Though not as efficient as the standard algorithm, it may be an effective scaffold for students working below grade level.

Problem 2: Multiply a three-digit number by a one-digit number, connecting the area model to the standard algorithm.

Display 316 × 4.

T: How many hundreds, tens, and ones are in 316?

S: 3 hundreds 1 ten 6 ones.

T: Draw an area model with a length of 3 hundreds 1 ten 6 ones and a width of 4.

T: Tell your partner how to solve using the area model.

Lesson 11:   Connect the area model and the partial products method to the standard algorithm.

©2015 Great Minds. eureka-math.org
G4-M3-TE-B2-1.3.1-01.2016

155

S: The rectangle is partitioned into hundreds, tens, and ones. I'll multiply 4 times 3 hundreds, 4 times 1 ten, and 4 times 6 ones and add the three products together for the answer. → That's like the break apart and distribute property we learned last year.

T: Yes, the **distributive property** allows us to break apart the large multiplication problem into three smaller ones.

T: Work with your partner to multiply.

Circulate, providing assistance, while students work.

T: 4 times 3 hundreds is…?

S: 12 hundreds.

T: 4 times 1 ten is…?

S: 4 tens.

T: 4 times 6 ones is…?

S: 24 ones.

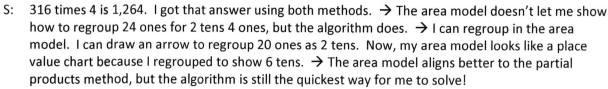

T: Solve 316 times 4 using the standard algorithm, and compare your answer to the area model.

MP.5

S: 316 times 4 is 1,264. I got that answer using both methods. → The area model doesn't let me show how to regroup 24 ones for 2 tens 4 ones, but the algorithm does. → I can regroup in the area model. I can draw an arrow to regroup 20 ones as 2 tens. Now, my area model looks like a place value chart because I regrouped to show 6 tens. → The area model aligns better to the partial products method, but the algorithm is still the quickest way for me to solve!

Repeat with 5,463 × 5, drawing the area model and comparing it to the algorithm or the partial products method.

Problem 3: Solve a word problem using the standard algorithm, area model, or partial products strategy.

A cafeteria makes 4,408 lunches each day. How many lunches are made Monday through Friday?

T: Discuss with your partner how to solve this problem.

T: What are some methods you could use to solve this?

S: An area model could help. → I like using the partial products method. → I think I can just use the algorithm.

T: You could also use the distributive property to help break apart and solve. Choose your method and solve.

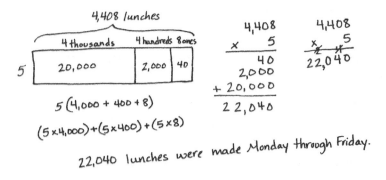

Lesson 11:   Connect the area model and the partial products method to the standard algorithm.

©2015 Great Minds. eureka-math.org
G4-M3-TE-B2-1.3.1-01.2016

EUREKA MATH™

S: 4,408 × 5 is 22,040. The cafeteria makes 22,040 lunches Monday through Friday.

When debriefing the solution, make note of how to draw an area model without a digit in the tens column.

Problem Set (10 minutes)

Students should do their personal best to complete the Problem Set within the allotted 10 minutes. For some classes, it may be appropriate to modify the assignment by specifying which problems they work on first. Some problems do not specify a method for solving. Students should solve these problems using the RDW approach used for Application Problems.

Student Debrief (10 minutes)

Lesson Objective: Connect the area model and the partial products method to the standard algorithm.

The Student Debrief is intended to invite reflection and active processing of the total lesson experience.

Invite students to review their solutions for the Problem Set. They should check work by comparing answers with a partner before going over answers as a class. Look for misconceptions or misunderstandings that can be addressed in the Debrief. Guide students in a conversation to debrief the Problem Set and process the lesson.

Any combination of the questions below may be used to lead the discussion.

- Can you solve any of the expressions in Problem 1 using a different method or strategy?
- In Problem 1, how does the area model connect to the expressions written below the area model? How could the **distributive property** be used to solve problems without drawing the area model?
- For Problems 4–6, which method(s) did you choose and why?
- How did the Application Problem introduce today's lesson?
- How is finding the area of a rectangle similar to finding the product using the area model?

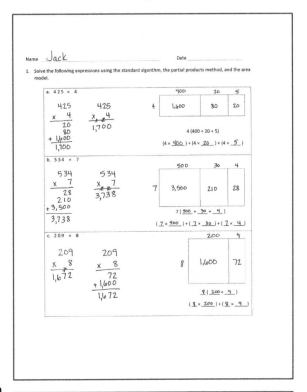

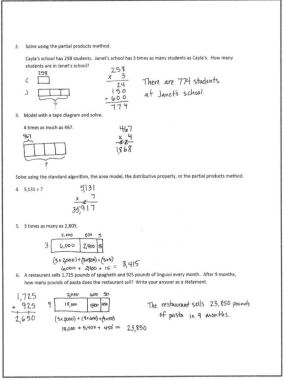

Lesson 11: Connect the area model and the partial products method to the standard algorithm.

©2015 Great Minds. eureka-math.org
G4-M3-TE-B2-1.3.1-01.2016

157

Exit Ticket (3 minutes)

After the Student Debrief, instruct students to complete the Exit Ticket. A review of their work will help with assessing students' understanding of the concepts that were presented in today's lesson and planning more effectively for future lessons. The questions may be read aloud to the students.

.

Lesson 11:   Connect the area model and the partial products method to the standard algorithm.

©2015 Great Minds. eureka-math.org
G4-M3-TE-B2-1.3.1-01.2016

Name _____   Date _____

1. Solve the following expressions using the standard algorithm, the partial products method, and the area model.

a. 4 2 5 × 4

4 (400 + 20 + 5)

(4 × _____) + (4 × _____) + (4 × _____)

b. 5 3 4 × 7

7 (____ + ____ + ____)

(__ × _____) + (__ × _____) + (__ × ____)

c. 2 0 9 × 8

__ (____ + ____)

(__ × _____) + (__ × _____)

Lesson 11:   Connect the area model and the partial products method to the standard algorithm.

159

©2015 Great Minds. eureka-math.org
G4-M3-TE-B2-1.3.1-01.2016

2. Solve using the partial products method.

Cayla's school has 258 students. Janet's school has 3 times as many students as Cayla's. How many students are in Janet's school?

3. Model with a tape diagram and solve.

4 times as much as 467

Solve using the standard algorithm, the area model, the distributive property, or the partial products method.

4. $5,131 \times 7$

Lesson 11: Connect the area model and the partial products method to the standard algorithm.

©2015 Great Minds. eureka-math.org
G4-M3-TE-B2-1.3.1-01.2016

EUREKA
MATH

5. 3 times as many as 2,805

6. A restaurant sells 1,725 pounds of spaghetti and 925 pounds of linguini every month. After 9 months, how many pounds of pasta does the restaurant sell?

Lesson 11: Connect the area model and the partial products method to the standard algorithm.

161

©2015 Great Minds. eureka-math.org
G4-M3-TE-B2-1.3.1-01.2016

Name _____ Date _____

1. Solve using the standard algorithm, the area model, the distributive property, or the partial products method.

   2,809 × 4

2. The monthly school newspaper is 9 pages long. Mrs. Smith needs to print 675 copies. What will be the total number of pages printed?

162   Lesson 11:   Connect the area model and the partial products method to the
                          standard algorithm.

                ©2015 Great Minds. eureka-math.org
                G4-M3-TE-B2-1.3.1-01.2016

Name _____ Date _____

1. Solve the following expressions using the standard algorithm, the partial products method, and the area model.

---

a. 3 0 2 × 8

8 (300 + 2)

(8 × _____) + (8 × _____)

---

b. 2 1 6 × 5

5 (____ + ____ + ____)

(__ × _____) + (__ × _____) + (__ × _____)

---

c. 5 9 3 × 9

__ (____ + ____ + ____)

(__ × _____) + (__ × _____) + (__ × _____)

EUREKA
MATH™

Lesson 11:   Connect the area model and the partial products method to the standard algorithm.

163

©2015 Great Minds. eureka-math.org
G4-M3-TE-B2-1.3.1-01.2016

2. Solve using the partial products method.

   On Monday, 475 people visited the museum. On Saturday, there were 4 times as many visitors as there were on Monday. How many people visited the museum on Saturday?

3. Model with a tape diagram and solve.

   6 times as much as 384

Solve using the standard algorithm, the area model, the distributive property, or the partial products method.

4. $6,253 \times 3$

EUREKA MATH

5. 7 times as many as 3,073

6. A cafeteria makes 2,516 pounds of white rice and 608 pounds of brown rice every month. After 6 months, how many pounds of rice does the cafeteria make?

Lesson 11:   Connect the area model and the partial products method to the standard algorithm.

©2015 Great Minds. eureka-math.org
G4-M3-TE-B2-1.3.1-01.2016

165

Mathematics Curriculum

4
GRADE

Topic D

Multiplication Word Problems

4.OA.1, 4.OA.2, 4.OA.3, 4.NBT.5

Focus Standards:	4.OA.1	Interpret a multiplication equation as a comparison, e.g., interpret 35 = 5 × 7 as a statement that 35 is 5 times as many as 7 and 7 times as many as 5. Represent verbal statements of multiplicative comparisons as multiplication equations.
	4.OA.2	Multiply or divide to solve word problems involving multiplicative comparison, e.g., by using drawings and equations with a symbol for the unknown number to represent the problem, distinguishing multiplicative comparison from additive comparison. (See CCLS Glossary, Table 2.)
	4.OA.3	Solve multistep word problems posed with whole numbers and having whole-number answers using the four operations, including problems in which remainders must be interpreted. Represent these problems using equations with a letter standing for the unknown quantity. Assess the reasonableness of answers using mental computation and estimation strategies including rounding.
	4.NBT.5	Multiply a whole number of up to four digits by a one-digit whole number, and multiply two two-digit numbers, using strategies based on place value and the properties of operations. Illustrate and explain the calculation by using equations, rectangular arrays, and/or area models.
Instructional Days:	2	
Coherence -Links from:	G3–M1	Properties of Multiplication and Division and Solving Problems with Units of 2–5 and 10
-Links to:	G3–M3	Multiplication and Division with Units of 0, 1, 6–9, and Multiples of 10
	G5–M2	Multi-Digit Whole Number and Decimal Fraction Operations

Topic D gives students the opportunity to apply their new multiplication skills (**4.NBT.5**). In Lesson 12, students extend their work with multiplicative comparison from Topic A to solve real-world problems (**4.OA.2**). As shown on the next page, students use a combination of addition, subtraction, and multiplication to solve multi-step problems in Lesson 13 (**4.OA.3**).

EUREKA
MATH™

Problem 4: In one month, Charlie read 814 pages. In the same month his mom read 4 times as many pages as Charlie, and that was 143 pages more than Charlie's dad read. What was the total number of pages read by Charlie and his parents?

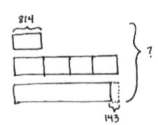

Solution A:

$$\begin{array}{r} 814 \\ \times\ 4 \\ \hline 3256 \end{array}$$

$$\begin{array}{r} 3256 \\ -\ 143 \\ \hline 3113 \end{array}$$

$$\begin{array}{r} 3256 \\ 3113 \\ +\ 814 \\ \hline 7{,}183 \end{array}$$

Charlie and his parents read 7,183 pages in one month.

Solution B:

$$\begin{array}{r} 814 \\ \times\ 9 \\ \hline 7326 \end{array}$$

$$\begin{array}{r} 7326 \\ -\ 143 \\ \hline 7{,}183 \end{array}$$

A Teaching Sequence Toward Mastery of Multiplication Word Problems

Objective 1: Solve two-step word problems, including multiplicative comparison. (Lesson 12)

Objective 2: Use multiplication, addition, or subtraction to solve multi-step word problems. (Lesson 13)

Topic D: Multiplication Word Problems

167

©2015 Great Minds. eureka-math.org
G4-M3-TE-B2-1.3.1-01.2016

Lesson 12

Objective: Solve two-step word problems, including multiplicative comparison.

Suggested Lesson Structure

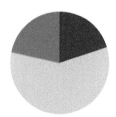

■ Fluency Practice   (12 minutes)
  Concept Development   (35 minutes)
■ Student Debrief   (13 minutes)
  Total Time   **(60 minutes)**

Fluency Practice (12 minutes)

- Multiply Mentally 4.NBT.5   (4 minutes)
- Multiply in Three Different Ways 4.NBT.5   (8 minutes)

Multiply Mentally (4 minutes)

Note: Reviewing these mental multiplication strategies provides a foundation for students to succeed during the Concept Development.

Repeat the process from Lesson 7 with the following possible sequence: $3{,}421 \times 2$, $2{,}302 \times 3$, $2{,}112 \times 4$, and $2{,}023 \times 4$.

Multiply in Three Different Ways (8 minutes)

Materials: (S) Place value disks

Note: This fluency activity reviews the concepts learned in Topic C.

Repeat the fluency activity from Lesson 11, expanding to three- and four-digit numbers for the following possible sequence: 245×2, 301×5, and $5{,}241 \times 2$.

EUREKA
MATH™

Concept Development (35 minutes)

Materials: (S) Problem Set

Note: For this lesson, the Problem Set comprises word problems from the Concept Development and is therefore to be used during the lesson itself.

Students may work in pairs to solve Problems 1–4 below using the RDW approach to problem solving.

1. Model the problem.

Have two pairs of students who can be successful with modeling the problem work at the board while the others work independently or in pairs at their seats. Review the following questions before beginning the first problem.

- Can you draw something?
- What can you draw?
- What conclusions can you make from your drawing?

NOTES ON
MULTIPLE MEANS
OF ENGAGEMENT:

Give everyone a fair chance to be successful by providing appropriate scaffolds. Demonstrating students may use translators, interpreters, or sentence frames to present and respond to feedback. Models shared may include concrete manipulatives. If the pace of the lesson is a consideration, prepare presenters beforehand. The first problem may be most approachable for students working below grade level.

As students work, circulate. Reiterate the questions above.

After two minutes, have the two pairs of students share *only* their labeled diagrams.

For about one minute, have the demonstrating students receive and respond to feedback and questions from their peers.

2. Calculate to solve and write a statement.

Give everyone two minutes to finish work on that question, sharing the work and thinking with a peer. All should then write their equations and statements of the answer.

3. Assess the solution.

Give students one to two minutes to assess the solutions presented by their peers on the board, comparing the solutions to their own work. Highlight alternative methods to reach the correct solution.

Lesson 12:   Solve two-step word problems, including multiplicative comparison.

169

Problem 1

The table shows the cost of party favors. Each party guest receives a bag with 1 balloon, 1 lollipop, and 1 bracelet. What is the total cost for 9 guests?

Item	Cost
1 balloon	26¢
1 lollipop	14¢
1 bracelet	33¢

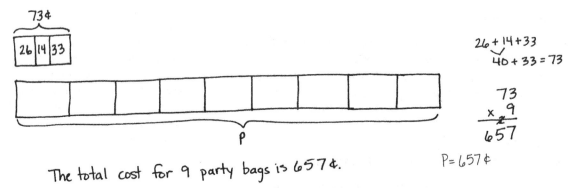

This two-step problem requires students to determine the cost of party favors for one guest and then use that information to determine the total cost of party favors for 9 guests. Although RDW is reviewed prior to beginning work on this problem, because of its simplicity, many students might elect to begin solving immediately. Some students may choose to multiply each item by 9 before adding those amounts. Based on their prior experience with money, some students may represent the total amount of 657 cents as $6.57, but they are not required to do so.

Problem 2

The Turner family uses 548 liters of water per day. The Hill family uses 3 times as much water per day. How much water does the Hill family use per week?

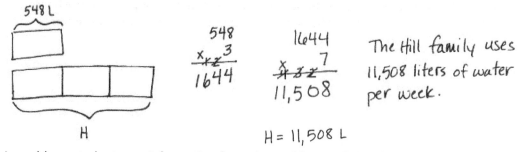

In solving this problem, students use information from the problem and their knowledge of language denoting multiplicative comparison to determine their answer. They must also remember that there are 7 days in a week in order to complete the computation necessary to finish the problem. Models chosen for this problem may include tape diagrams as shown.

Problem 3

Jayden has 347 marbles. Elvis has 4 times as many as Jayden. Presley has 799 fewer than Elvis. How many marbles does Presley have?

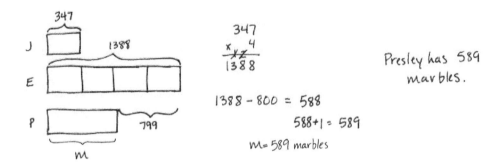

This two-step problem affords students another opportunity to model with tape diagrams. They are required to apply what they have learned about multiplying multi-digit numbers by single digits, as well as practice their subtraction with multiple regrouping skills from Module 1. Encourage students to also practice mental math, such as when subtracting 799 from 1,388. As illustrated above, note that the diagram may or may not accurately show the relationship between 799 and the unit size, 347. Nevertheless, discuss how one might use mental math to estimate how long Presley's bar should be.

Problem 4

a. Write an equation that would allow someone to find the value of R.

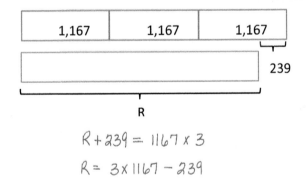

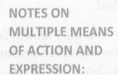

Student equations may include one or both of the equations above. They must include the use of the R for the unknown quantity and show that R is equal to 239 less than three times 1,167.

b.   Write your own word problem to correspond to the tape diagram, and then solve.

Patti's sandals weigh 1,167 grams. She bought 3 pairs, all different colors! All 3 pairs of sandals together weigh 239 grams more than her winter boots. What is the weight of Patti's winter boots?

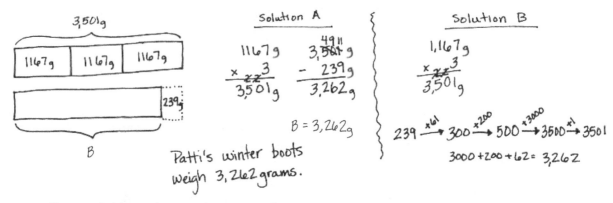

Responses will vary. Guide students with a context for creating a problem, such as the number of students who attend two schools or the weights of objects.

Problem Set

Please note that the Problem Set for Lesson 12 comprises the problems from the Concept Development, as stated in the introduction of the lesson.

Student Debrief (13 minutes)

Lesson Objective: Solve two-step word problems, including multiplicative comparison.

The Student Debrief is intended to invite reflection and active processing of the total lesson experience.

Invite students to review their solutions for the Problem Set. They should check work by comparing answers with a partner before going over answers as a class. Look for misconceptions or misunderstandings that can be addressed in the Debrief. Guide students in a conversation to debrief the problems and process the lesson.

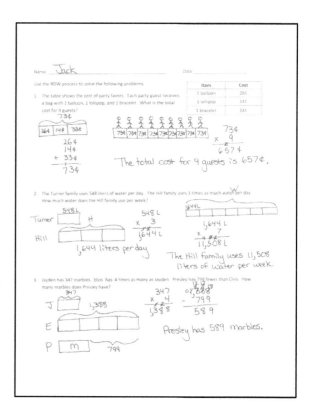

EUREKA
MATH™

Any combination of the questions below may be used to lead the discussion.

- How was Problem 1 similar to the other problems we did today? How was it different?

- How was setting up Problem 2 similar to setting up Problem 3? At what point did the two problems become quite different?

- What piece of information did you need to know to solve Problem 2 that was not given to you in the problem?

- Share the word problem you created for Problem 4(b) with your partner. Solve your partner's problem. Explain the strategy you used to solve it.

Exit Ticket (3 minutes)

After the Student Debrief, instruct students to complete the Exit Ticket. A review of their work will help with assessing students' understanding of the concepts that were presented in today's lesson and planning more effectively for future lessons. The questions may be read aloud to the students.

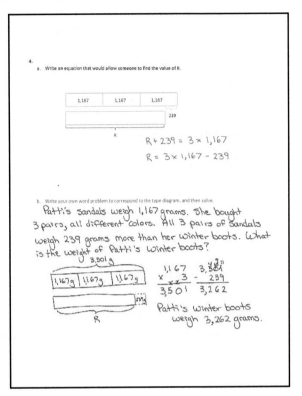

Lesson 12: Solve two-step word problems, including multiplicative comparison.

173

EUREKA
MATH™

Name _____   Date _____

Use the RDW process to solve the following problems.

Item	Cost
1 balloon	26¢
1 lollipop	14¢
1 bracelet	33¢

1. The table shows the cost of party favors. Each party guest receives a bag with 1 balloon, 1 lollipop, and 1 bracelet. What is the total cost for 9 guests?

2. The Turner family uses 548 liters of water per day. The Hill family uses 3 times as much water per day. How much water does the Hill family use per week?

3. Jayden has 347 marbles. Elvis has 4 times as many as Jayden. Presley has 799 fewer than Elvis. How many marbles does Presley have?

Lesson 12:   Solve two-step word problems, including multiplicative comparison.

©2015 Great Minds. eureka-math.org
G4-M3-TE-B2-1.3.1-01.2016

4. a.   Write an equation that would allow someone to find the value of R.

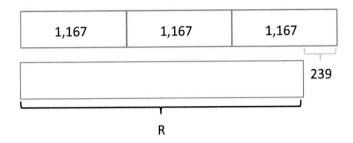

b.   Write your own word problem to correspond to the tape diagram, and then solve.

Name _____   Date _____

Use the RDW process to solve the following problem.

Jennifer has 256 beads. Stella has 3 times as many beads as Jennifer. Tiah has 104 more beads than Stella. How many beads does Tiah have?

Lesson 12:   Solve two-step word problems, including multiplicative comparison.

©2015 Great Minds. eureka-math.org
G4-M3-TE-B2-1.3.1-01.2016

Name _____ Date _____

Use the RDW process to solve the following problems.

1. The table shows the number of stickers of various types in Chrissy's new sticker book. Chrissy's six friends each own the same sticker book. How many stickers do Chrissy and her six friends have altogether?

Type of Sticker	Number of Stickers
flowers	32
smiley faces	21
hearts	39

2. The small copier makes 437 copies each day. The large copier makes 4 times as many copies each day. How many copies does the large copier make each week?

3. Jared sold 194 Boy Scout chocolate bars. Matthew sold three times as many as Jared. Gary sold 297 fewer than Matthew. How many bars did Gary sell?

Lesson 12:   Solve two-step word problems, including multiplicative comparison.

©2015 Great Minds. eureka-math.org
G4-M3-TE-B2-1.3.1-01.2016

177

4. a. Write an equation that would allow someone to find the value of M.

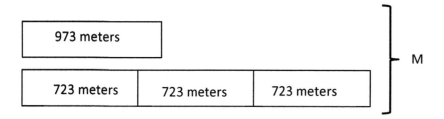

    b. Write your own word problem to correspond to the tape diagram, and then solve.

Lesson 12:   Solve two-step word problems, including multiplicative comparison.

EUREKA
MATH™

Lesson 13

Objective: Use multiplication, addition, or subtraction to solve multi-step word problems.

Suggested Lesson Structure

■ Fluency Practice   (12 minutes)
   Concept Development   (35 minutes)
■ Student Debrief   (13 minutes)
   Total Time   **(60 minutes)**

Fluency Practice (12 minutes)

- Sprint: Mental Multiplication **4.NBT.5**   (9 minutes)
- Multiply Using the Standard Algorithm **4.NBT.4**   (3 minutes)

Sprint: Mental Multiplication (9 minutes)

Materials: (S) Mental Multiplication Sprint

Note: This Sprint reinforces partial product multiplication strategies.

Multiply Using the Standard Algorithm (3 minutes)

Materials: (S) Personal white board

Note: This fluency activity reviews the Concept Development from Lessons 10 and 11.

T: (Write 773 × 2.) On your personal white board, solve the expression using the standard algorithm.

Repeat the process for the following possible sequence: 147 × 3, 1,605 × 3, and 5,741 × 5.

Concept Development (35 minutes)

Materials: (S) Problem Set

Note: For this lesson, the Problem Set comprises word problems from the Concept Development and is therefore to be used during the lesson itself.

Students may work in pairs to solve Problems 1–4 below using the RDW approach to problem solving.

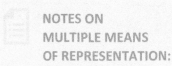

NOTES ON
MULTIPLE MEANS
OF REPRESENTATION:

Depending on English language learners' needs, it may be helpful to provide today's Problem Set in students' first language.

Lesson 13:   Use multiplication, addition, or subtraction to solve multi-step word problems.

©2015 Great Minds. eureka-math.org
G4-M3-TE-B2-1.3.1-01.2016

179

1. Model the problem.

Have two pairs of students who can be successful with modeling the problem work at the board while the others work independently or in pairs at their seats. Review the following questions before beginning the first problem.

- Can you draw something?
- What can you draw?
- What conclusions can you make from your drawing?

As students work, circulate. Reiterate the questions above.

After two minutes, have the two pairs of students share *only* their labeled diagrams.

For about one minute, have the demonstrating students receive and respond to feedback and questions from their peers.

2. Calculate to solve and write a statement.

Give everyone two minutes to finish work on that question, sharing work and thinking with a peer. All should then write their equations and statements of the answer.

3. Assess the solution.

Give students one to two minutes to assess the solutions presented by their peers on the board, comparing the solutions to their own work. Highlight alternative methods to reach the correct solution.

NOTES ON MULTIPLE MEANS OF ENGAGEMENT:

Extend the problems for students working above grade level.

Problem 1: If Kate also deposited $36 of each paycheck into her savings, how much money does she have left to spend after buying the computer and clothes?

Problem 2: Construct a graph or chart that shows Sylvia's weight over the years.

Problem 3: Use classroom resources to find out about how many kilograms the crate of apples weighed.

Problem 1

Over the summer, Kate earned $180 each week for 7 weeks. Of that money, she spent $375 on a new computer and $137 on new clothes. How much money did she have left?

This multi-step problem requires students to apply their knowledge of multiplication of a multi-digit number by a single-digit number. While most students may apply the multiplication algorithm, they should be encouraged to use whichever strategy they are most comfortable with to complete the multiplication. The sum of $375 and $137 may be found before subtracting it from Kate's total salary, or the two amounts may be subtracted separately.

Lesson 13:   Use multiplication, addition, or subtraction to solve multi-step word problems.

©2015 Great Minds. eureka-math.org
G4-M3-TE-B2-1.3.1-01.2016

EUREKA
MATH™

Problem 2

Sylvia weighed 8 pounds when she was born. By her first birthday, her weight had tripled. By her second birthday, she had gained 12 more pounds. At that time, Sylvia's father weighed 5 times as much as she did. What was Sylvia and her dad's combined weight?

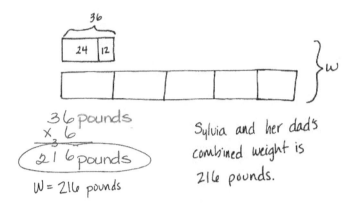

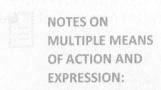

In this problem, students need to compute Sylvia's weight at two separate points in time. Some students may gravitate to calculations. Others may use tape diagrams or other models to represent the problem. Either is acceptable. Then, they may multiply Sylvia's current weight by 6 to find her and her father's combined weight.

NOTES ON MULTIPLE MEANS OF ACTION AND EXPRESSION:

Learners differ in their solution strategies, and classroom discussion is enriched with the sharing of diverse, innovative, efficient, and thoughtful solutions.

Students may choose to omit the modeling part of a multi-step problem. For example, the work to the left does not show the tripling of 8. Therefore, the sharing of student work when solving multi-step problems can be even more interesting.

It is best to be prepared to model each step of the problem since students may be overwhelmed by the simplest words when they are embedded within a multi-step problem.

Problem 3

Three boxes weighing 128 pounds each and one box weighing 254 pounds were loaded onto the back of an empty truck. A crate of apples was then loaded onto the same truck. If the total weight loaded onto the truck was 2,000 pounds, how much did the crate of apples weigh?

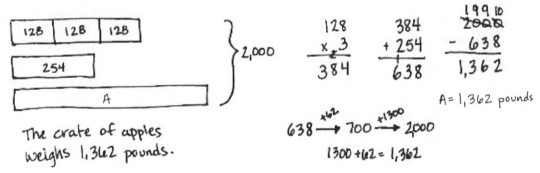

This multi-step problem may be modeled or simply solved using algorithms. Students need to recognize that 128 must be tripled before that total is added to 254. To arrive at the answer to the problem, this new sum must be subtracted from 2,000, requiring students to use a simplifying strategy or to regroup across multiple zeros (a skill they mastered in Module 1).

Lesson 13: Use multiplication, addition, or subtraction to solve multi-step word problems.

©2015 Great Minds. eureka-math.org
G4-M3-TE-B2-1.3.1-01.2016

Problem 4

In one month, Charlie read 814 pages. In the same month, his mom read 4 times as many pages as Charlie, and that was 143 pages more than Charlie's dad read. What was the total number of pages read by Charlie and his parents?

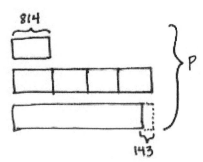

Solution A:

$$814 \times 4 = 3256$$

$$3256 - 143 = 3113$$

$$3256 + 3113 + 814 = 7{,}183$$

$$P = 7{,}183$$

Solution B:

$$814 \times 9 = 7326$$

$$7326 - 143 = 7{,}183$$

Charlie and his parents read 7,183 pages in one month.

In this multi-step problem, students may find that each calculation is dependent upon the following calculation. Encourage students to use simplifying strategies when solving, such as seeing in the model that there are 9 equal-size rectangles worth 814 pages, minus 143 pages.

Problem Set

Please note that the Problem Set for Lesson 13 comprises the problems from the Concept Development, as stated in the introduction.

Student Debrief (13 minutes)

Lesson Objective: Use multiplication, addition, or subtraction to solve multi-step word problems.

The Student Debrief is intended to invite reflection and active processing of the total lesson experience.

Invite students to review their solutions for the Problem Set. They should check work by comparing answers with a partner before going over answers as a class. Look for misconceptions or misunderstandings that can be addressed in the Debrief. Guide students in a conversation to debrief the Problem Set and process the lesson.

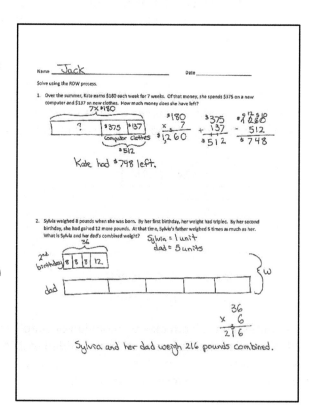

Lesson 13:   Use multiplication, addition, or subtraction to solve multi-step word problems.

©2015 Great Minds. eureka-math.org
G4-M3-TE-B2-1.3.1-01.2016

EUREKA MATH™

Any combination of the questions below may be used to lead the discussion.

- Explain to your partner how you solved Problem 1. If you used different strategies, discuss how you arrived at the same answer.

- Let's look at how two different students modeled Problem 2. How are they similar? How are they different?

- Student A, in Problem 4, why did you multiply 814 by 9 and subtract 143? From the model, I only see 5 units of 814. (Also, draw out the alternate strategies from Problem 3.)

- Student B, would you present your solution? (Student presents.) Does anyone have comments or questions for Student B?

- How did you know what to do when you saw the word *tripled* in Problem 2?

- When might it be better to use multiplication rather than addition?

- What are the advantages of knowing several methods for solving a multiplication problem?

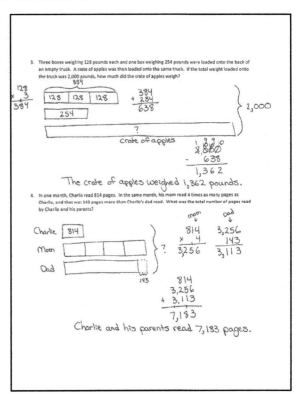

Exit Ticket (3 minutes)

After the Student Debrief, instruct students to complete the Exit Ticket. A review of their work will help with assessing students' understanding of the concepts that were presented in today's lesson and planning more effectively for future lessons. The questions may be read aloud to the students.

Lesson 13:   Use multiplication, addition, or subtraction to solve multi-step word problems.

©2015 Great Minds. eureka-math.org
G4-M3-TE-B2-1.3.1-01.2016

183

A

Number Correct: _____

Mental Multiplication

1.	1 × 4 =	
2.	10 × 4 =	
3.	11 × 4 =	
4.	1 × 2 =	
5.	20 × 2 =	
6.	21 × 2 =	
7.	2 × 3 =	
8.	30 × 3 =	
9.	32 × 3 =	
10.	3 × 5=	
11.	20 × 5 =	
12.	23 × 5 =	
13.	3 × 3 =	
14.	40 × 3 =	
15.	43 × 3 =	
16.	4 × 2 =	
17.	70 × 2 =	
18.	74 × 2 =	
19.	2 × 3 =	
20.	60 × 3 =	
21.	62 × 3 =	
22.	63 × 3 =	

23.	21 × 3 =	
24.	121 × 3 =	
25.	42 × 2 =	
26.	142 × 2 =	
27.	242 × 2 =	
28.	342 × 2 =	
29.	442 × 2 =	
30.	3 × 3 =	
31.	13 × 3 =	
32.	213 × 3 =	
33.	1,213 × 3 =	
34.	2,113 × 3 =	
35.	2,131 × 3 =	
36.	2,311 × 3 =	
37.	24 × 4 =	
38.	35 × 5 =	
39.	54 × 3 =	
40.	63 × 6 =	
41.	125 × 4 =	
42.	214 × 3 =	
43.	5,213 × 2 =	
44.	2,135 × 4 =	

Lesson 13: Use multiplication, addition, or subtraction to solve multi-step word problems.

©2015 Great Minds. eureka-math.org
G4-M3-TE-B2-1.3.1-01.2016

B

Number Correct: _____

Improvement: _____

Mental Multiplication

1.	$1 \times 6 =$		23.	$21 \times 4 =$	
2.	$10 \times 6 =$		24.	$121 \times 4 =$	
3.	$11 \times 6 =$		25.	$24 \times 2 =$	
4.	$1 \times 2 =$		26.	$124 \times 2 =$	
5.	$30 \times 2 =$		27.	$224 \times 2 =$	
6.	$31 \times 2 =$		28.	$324 \times 2 =$	
7.	$3 \times 3 =$		29.	$424 \times 2 =$	
8.	$20 \times 3 =$		30.	$3 \times 2 =$	
9.	$23 \times 3 =$		31.	$13 \times 2 =$	
10.	$5 \times 5 =$		32.	$213 \times 2 =$	
11.	$20 \times 5 =$		33.	$1,213 \times 2 =$	
12.	$25 \times 5 =$		34.	$2,113 \times 2 =$	
13.	$4 \times 4 =$		35.	$2,131 \times 2 =$	
14.	$30 \times 4 =$		36.	$2,311 \times 2 =$	
15.	$34 \times 4 =$		37.	$23 \times 4 =$	
16.	$4 \times 2 =$		38.	$53 \times 5 =$	
17.	$90 \times 2 =$		39.	$45 \times 3 =$	
18.	$94 \times 2 =$		40.	$36 \times 6 =$	
19.	$2 \times 3 =$		41.	$215 \times 3 =$	
20.	$40 \times 3 =$		42.	$125 \times 4 =$	
21.	$42 \times 3 =$		43.	$5,312 \times 2 =$	
22.	$43 \times 3 =$		44.	$1,235 \times 4 =$	

Lesson 13:   Use multiplication, addition, or subtraction to solve multi-step word problems.

©2015 Great Minds. eureka-math.org
G4-M3-TE-B2-1.3.1-01.2016

185

Name _____   Date _____

Solve using the RDW process.

1. Over the summer, Kate earned $180 each week for 7 weeks. Of that money, she spent $375 on a new computer and $137 on new clothes. How much money did she have left?

2. Sylvia weighed 8 pounds when she was born. By her first birthday, her weight had tripled. By her second birthday, she had gained 12 more pounds. At that time, Sylvia's father weighed 5 times as much as she did. What was Sylvia and her dad's combined weight?

Lesson 13:   Use multiplication, addition, or subtraction to solve multi-step word
                               problems.

©2015 Great Minds. eureka-math.org
G4-M3-TE-B2-1.3.1-01.2016

3. Three boxes weighing 128 pounds each and one box weighing 254 pounds were loaded onto the back of an empty truck. A crate of apples was then loaded onto the same truck. If the total weight loaded onto the truck was 2,000 pounds, how much did the crate of apples weigh?

4. In one month, Charlie read 814 pages. In the same month, his mom read 4 times as many pages as Charlie, and that was 143 pages more than Charlie's dad read. What was the total number of pages read by Charlie and his parents?

Lesson 13:   Use multiplication, addition, or subtraction to solve multi-step word problems.

©2015 Great Minds. eureka-math.org
G4-M3-TE-B2-1.3.1-01.2016

187

Name _____   Date _____

Solve using the RDW process.

1.   Michael earns $9 per hour. He works 28 hours each week. How much does he earn in 6 weeks?

2.   David earns $8 per hour. He works 40 hours each week. How much does he earn in 6 weeks?

3.   After 6 weeks, who earned more money? How much more money?

Lesson 13:   Use multiplication, addition, or subtraction to solve multi-step word problems.

©2015 Great Minds. eureka-math.org
G4-M3-TE-B2-1.3.1-01.2016

Name _____ Date _____

Solve using the RDW process.

1. A pair of jeans costs $89. A jean jacket costs twice as much. What is the total cost of a jean jacket and 4 pairs of jeans?

2. Sarah bought a shirt on sale for $35. The original price of the shirt was 3 times that amount. Sarah also bought a pair of shoes on sale for $28. The original price of the shoes was 5 times that amount. Together, how much money did the shirt and shoes cost before they went on sale?

Lesson 13:   Use multiplication, addition, or subtraction to solve multi-step word problems.

©2015 Great Minds. eureka-math.org
G4-M3-TE-B2-1.3.1-01.2016

189

3. All 3,000 seats in a theater are being replaced. So far, 5 sections of 136 seats and a sixth section containing 348 seats have been replaced. How many more seats do they still need to replace?

4. Computer Depot sold 762 reams of paper. Paper Palace sold 3 times as much paper as Computer Depot and 143 reams more than Office Supply Central. How many reams of paper were sold by all three stores combined?

Lesson 13: Use multiplication, addition, or subtraction to solve multi-step word problems.

©2015 Great Minds. eureka-math.org
G4-M3-TE-B2-1.3.1-01.2016

EUREKA
MATH

Name _____   Date _____

1. Draw an area model to solve the following. Find the value of the following expressions.

    a. 30×60

    b. 3×269

2. Use any place value strategy to multiply.

    a. 3×68

    b. 4×371

    c. $7 \times 1,305$

    d. $6,034 \times 5$

©2015 Great Minds. eureka-math.org
G4-M3-TE-B2-1.3.1-01.2016

Solve using a model or equation. Show your work and write your answer as a statement.

3. A movie theater has two rooms. Room A has 9 rows of seats with 18 seats in each row. Room B has three times as many seats as Room A. How many seats are there in both rooms?

4. The high school art teacher has 9 cases of crayons with 52 boxes in each case. The elementary school art teacher has 6 cases of crayons with 104 boxes in each case. How many total boxes of crayons do both teachers have? Is your answer reasonable? Explain.

EUREKA
MATH™

5. Last year, Mr. Petersen's rectangular garden had a width of 5 meters and an area of 20 square meters. This year, he wants to make the garden three times as long and two times as wide.

    a. Solve for the length of last year's garden using the area formula. Then, draw and label the measurements of this year's garden.

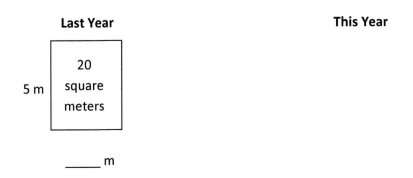

    Last Year

    5 m | 20 square meters

    _____ m

    This Year

    b. How much area for planting will Mr. Petersen have in the new garden?

c. Last year, Mr. Petersen had a fence all the way around his garden. He can reuse all of the fence he had around the garden last year, but he needs to buy more fencing to go around this year's garden. How many more meters of fencing is needed for this year's garden than last year's?

d. Last year, Mr. Petersen was able to plant 4 rows of carrots with 13 plants in each row. This year, he plans to plant twice as many rows with twice as many carrot plants in each. How many carrot plants will he plant this year? Write a multiplication equation to solve. Assess the reasonableness of your answer.

©2015 Great Minds. eureka-math.org
G4-M3-TE-B2-1.3.1-01.2016

| Mid-Module Assessment Task | Topics A–D |
| Standards Addressed | |

Use the four operations with whole numbers to solve problems.

4.OA.1 Interpret a multiplication equation as a comparison, e.g., interpret 35 = 5 × 7 as a statement that 35 is 5 times as many as 7 and 7 times as many as 5. Represent verbal statements of multiplicative comparisons as multiplication equations.

4.OA.2 Multiply or divide to solve word problems involving multiplicative comparison, e.g., by using drawings and equations with a symbol for the unknown number to represent the problem, distinguishing multiplicative comparison from additive comparison.

4.OA.3 Solve multistep word problems posed with whole numbers and having whole-number answers using the four operations, including problems in which remainders must be interpreted. Represent these problems using equations with a letter standing for the unknown quantity. Assess the reasonableness of answers using mental computation and estimation strategies including rounding.

Use place value understanding and properties of operations to perform multi-digit arithmetic.

4.NBT.5 Multiply a whole number of up to four digits by a one-digit whole number, and multiply two two-digit numbers, using strategies based on place value and the properties of operations. Illustrate and explain the calculation by using equations, rectangular arrays, and/or area models.

Solve problems involving measurement and conversion of measurements from a larger unit to a smaller unit.

4.MD.3 Apply the area and perimeter formulas for rectangles in real world and mathematical problems. *For example, find the width of a rectangular room given the area of the flooring and the length, by viewing the area formula as a multiplication equation with an unknown factor.*

Evaluating Student Learning Outcomes

A Progression Toward Mastery is provided to describe steps that illuminate the gradually increasing understandings that students develop *on their way to proficiency.* In this chart, this progress is presented from left (Step 1) to right (Step 4). The learning goal for students is to achieve Step 4 mastery. These steps are meant to help teachers and students identify and celebrate what the students CAN do now, and what they need to work on next.

A Progression Toward Mastery				
Assessment Task Item	STEP 1 Little evidence of reasoning without a correct answer. (1 Point)	STEP 2 Evidence of some reasoning without a correct answer. (2 Points)	STEP 3 Evidence of some reasoning with a correct answer or evidence of solid reasoning with an incorrect answer. (3 Points)	STEP 4 Evidence of solid reasoning with a correct answer. (4 Points)
1 4.NBT.5	The student is unable to complete both area models with correct calculations.	The student correctly solves one part using the area model.	The student correctly solves both parts but has an error in one of the area models, or the student represents both area models correctly but miscalculates for one part.	The student correctly completes all components—draws the area model for each problem with correct answers: a. 1,800 b. 807
2 4.NBT.5	The student is unable to solve more than one problem correctly.	The student correctly solves at least two of the four problems with evidence of some place value knowledge.	The student correctly solves at least three of the problems showing reasoning through a place value strategy, or the student correctly answers four problems, only showing solid reasoning for three problems.	The student correctly answers all parts, showing all work using area models, partial products, or the general method: a. 204 b. 1,484 c. 9,135 d. 30,170
3 4.OA.1 4.OA.2 4.OA.3 4.NBT.5	The student answers incorrectly with little attempt at solving the problem.	The student attempts to use an equation or model, resulting in an incorrect answer.	The student solves the problem using an equation or model but with an incorrect answer, or the student answers correctly showing only some reasoning.	The student correctly answers 648 seats in an answer statement and uses an equation or model correctly to solve.

Module 3:   Multi-Digit Multiplication and Division

A Progression Toward Mastery				
4 **4.NBT.5** **4.OA.1** **4.OA.3**	The student answers incorrectly and provides little or no evidence of reasoning through estimation.	The student answers incorrectly but shows some evidence in reasoning through estimation.	The student correctly answers *1,092 boxes* using a model or equation accurately but is unable to clearly reason using estimation, or the student provides clear reasoning and an attempt at solving but provides an incorrect answer.	The student correctly answers *1,092 boxes* in an answer statement, uses an area model or equation to solve, and validates the reasonableness of his answer through estimation.
5 **4.NBT.5** **4.OA.1** **4.OA.2** **4.OA.3** **4.MD.3**	The student shows little to no reasoning and answers more than two parts incorrectly.	The student correctly answers two of four parts, showing little reasoning in Part (d) and little evidence of place value understanding.	The student answers three of the four parts correctly, or the student answers all four parts correctly with unclear reasoning in Part (d), or the student does not show solid evidence of place value understanding in all solutions.	The student correctly answers: a. $5 \text{ m} \times 4 \text{ m} = 20$ square meters and expresses length as 4 m; draws a rectangle; labels the width as 10 meters and length as 12 meters. b. 120 square meters. c. 26 meters. d. 208 plants; shows a written equation and reasons correctly through estimation.

Name_____Jack_____ Date _____

1. Draw an area model to solve the following. Find the value of the following expressions.

a. 30×60

b. 3×269

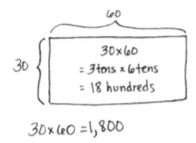

$30 \times 60 = 1,800$

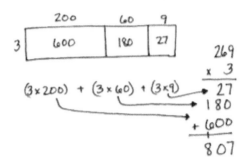

$(3 \times 200) + (3 \times 60) + (3 \times 9)$

$$\begin{array}{r} 269 \\ \times\ 3 \\ \hline 27 \\ 180 \\ +\ 600 \\ \hline 807 \end{array}$$

2. Use any place value strategy to multiply.

a. 3×68

$$\begin{array}{r} 68 \\ \times\ 3 \\ \hline 24 \\ +\ 180 \\ \hline 204 \end{array}$$

b. 4×371

$$\begin{array}{r} 371 \\ \times\ 4 \\ \hline 4 \\ 280 \\ +\ 1\,200 \\ \hline 1,484 \end{array}$$

c. $7 \times 1,305$

$$\begin{array}{r} 1305 \\ \times\ 7 \\ \hline 35 \\ 2100 \\ +\ 7000 \\ \hline 9,135 \end{array}$$

d. $6,034 \times 5$

$$\begin{array}{r} 6034 \\ \times\ 5 \\ \hline 20 \\ 150 \\ +\ 30,000 \\ \hline 30,170 \end{array}$$

EUREKA
MATH

Solve using a model or equation. Show your work and write your answer as a statement.

3. A movie theater has two rooms. Room A has 9 rows of seats with 18 seats in each row. Room B has three times as many seats as Room A. How many seats are there in both rooms?

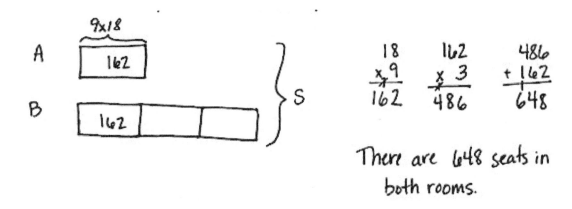

$$\begin{array}{ccc} 18 & 162 & 486 \\ \times 9 & \times 3 & +162 \\ \hline 162 & 486 & 648 \end{array}$$

There are 648 seats in both rooms.

4. The high school art teacher has 9 cases of crayons with 52 boxes in each case. The elementary school art teacher has 6 cases of crayons with 104 boxes in each case. How many total boxes of crayons do both teachers have? Is your answer reasonable? Explain.

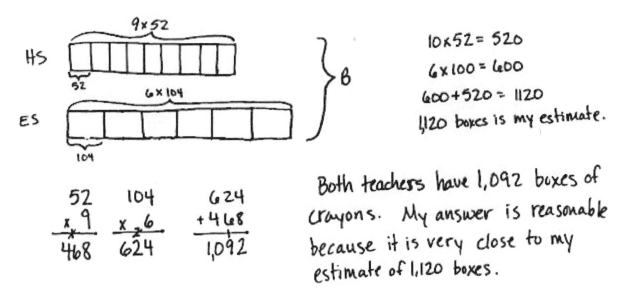

$10 \times 52 = 520$

$6 \times 100 = 600$

$600 + 520 = 1120$

1,120 boxes is my estimate.

$$\begin{array}{ccc} 52 & 104 & 624 \\ \times 9 & \times 6 & +468 \\ \hline 468 & 624 & 1,092 \end{array}$$

Both teachers have 1,092 boxes of crayons. My answer is reasonable because it is very close to my estimate of 1,120 boxes.

5. Last year, Mr. Petersen's rectangular garden had a width of 5 meters and an area of 20 square meters. This year, he wants to make the garden three times as long and two times as wide.

a. Solve for the length of last year's garden using the area formula. Then, draw and label the measurements of this year's garden.

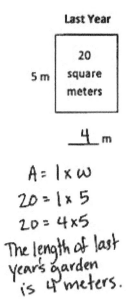

Last Year

5 m | 20 square meters

____4____ m

A = l × w
20 = l × 5
20 = 4 × 5
The length of last year's garden is 4 meters.

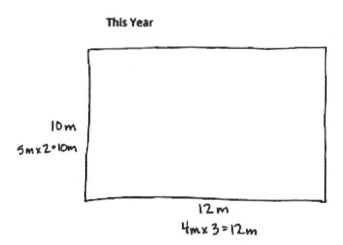

This Year

10 m
5m × 2 = 10m

12 m
4m × 3 = 12m

This year's garden has a width of 10 meters and a length of 12 meters.

b. How much area for planting will Mr. Petersen have in the new garden?

A = l × w
  = 12 × 10
  = 120

Mr. Petersen's new garden has an area of 120 square meters.

©2015 Great Minds. eureka-math.org
G4-M3-TE-B2-1.3.1-01.2016

EUREKA MATH™

c. Last year, Mr. Petersen had a fence all the way around his garden. He can reuse all of the fence he
    had around the garden last year, but he needs to buy more fencing to go around this year's garden.
    How many more meters of fencing is needed for this year's garden than last year's?

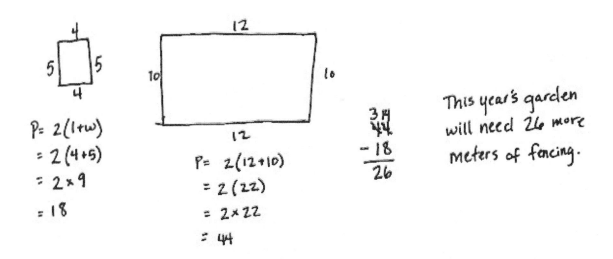

$P = 2(l + w)$
$\quad = 2(4 + 5)$
$\quad = 2 \times 9$
$\quad = 18$

$P = 2(12 + 10)$
$\quad = 2(22)$
$\quad = 2 \times 22$
$\quad = 44$

$\begin{array}{r} 3\,{}^{1}\!\!\!4 \\ 4\!\!\!/4 \\ -18 \\ \hline 26 \end{array}$

This year's garden
will need 26 more
meters of fencing.

d. Last year, Mr. Petersen was able to plant 4 rows of carrots with 13 plants in each row. This year, he
    plans to plant twice as many rows with twice as many carrot plants in each. How many carrot plants
    will he plant this year? Write a multiplication equation to solve. Assess the reasonableness of your
    answer.

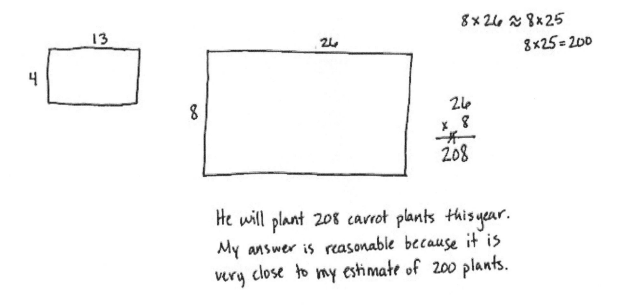

$8 \times 26 \approx 8 \times 25$
$8 \times 25 = 200$

$\begin{array}{r} 26 \\ \times\ 8 \\ \hline 208 \end{array}$

He will plant 208 carrot plants this year.
My answer is reasonable because it is
very close to my estimate of 200 plants.

EUREKA
MATH

Module 3:   Multi-Digit Multiplication and Division

201

©2015 Great Minds. eureka-math.org
G4-M3-TE-B2-1.3.1-01.2016

Mathematics Curriculum

4 GRADE

Topic E

Division of Tens and Ones with Successive Remainders

4.NBT.6, 4.OA.3

Focus Standard:	4.NBT.6	Find whole-number quotients and remainders with up to four-digit dividends and one-digit divisors, using strategies based on place value, the properties of operations, and/or the relationship between multiplication and division. Illustrate and explain the calculation by using equations, rectangular arrays, and/or area models.
Instructional Days:	8	
Coherence -Links from:	G3–M1	Properties of Multiplication and Division and Solving Problem with Units of 2–5 and 10
-Links to:	G3–M3	Multiplication and Division with Units of 0, 1, 6–9, and Multiples of 10
	G5–M2	Multi-Digit Whole Number and Decimal Fraction Operations

In Topic E, students synthesize their Grade 3 knowledge of division types (*group size unknown* and *number of groups unknown*) with their new, deeper understanding of place value.

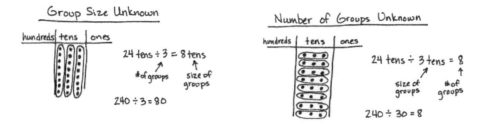

Students focus on interpreting the remainder within division problems both in word problems and long division (**4.OA.3**). A remainder of 1, as exemplified below, represents a leftover flower in the first situation and a remainder of 1 ten in the second situation.[1]

---

[1]Note that care must be taken in the interpretation of remainders. Consider the fact that $7 \div 3$ is not equal to $5 \div 2$ because the remainder of 1 is in reference to a different whole amount ($2\frac{1}{3}$ is not equal to $2\frac{1}{2}$).

EUREKA MATH™

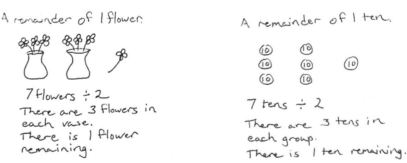

While we have no reason to subdivide a remaining flower, there are good reasons to subdivide a remaining ten. Students apply this simple idea to divide two-digit numbers unit by unit: dividing the tens units first, finding the remainder (the number of tens unable to be divided), and decomposing remaining tens into ones to then be divided.

Lesson 14 begins Topic E by having students solve division word problems involving remainders. In Lesson 15, students deepen their understanding of division by solving problems with remainders using both arrays and the area model. Students practice dividing two-digit dividends with a remainder in the ones place using place value disks in Lesson 16 and continue that modeling in Lesson 17 where the remainder in the tens place is decomposed into ones.

The long division algorithm[2] is introduced in Lesson 16 by directly relating the steps of the algorithm to the steps involved when dividing using place value disks. Introducing the algorithm in this manner helps students to understand how place value plays a role in the steps of the algorithm. The same process of relating the standard algorithm to the concrete representation of division continues in Lesson 17.

Lesson 18 moves students to the abstract level by requiring them to solve division problems numerically without drawing. In Lesson 19, students explain the successive remainders of the algorithm by using place value understanding and place value disks. Finally, in Lessons 20 and 21, students use the area model to solve division problems and then compare the standard algorithm to the area model (**4.NBT.6**). Lesson 20 focuses on division problems without remainders, while Lesson 21 involves remainders.

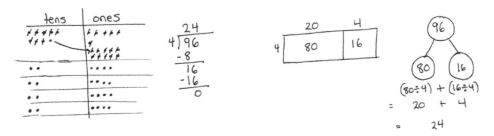

Quotients and remainders are independent of each other but must both be included to give a complete response. A quotient and a remainder cannot be recorded after an equal sign because the symbol R or the words *with a remainder of* are invalid in an equation. Therefore, a quotient and a remainder can be written as a statement such as *seven divided by two is three with a remainder of one*, or *the quotient is three and the remainder is one*. It is mathematically correct to record the quotient and the remainder together at the top of the long division algorithm.

---

[2]Students become fluent with the standard division algorithm in Grade 6 (6.NS.2). For adequate practice in reaching fluency, students are introduced to, but not assessed on, the division algorithm in Grade 4 as a general method for solving division problems.

A Teaching Sequence Toward Mastery of Division of Tens and Ones with Successive Remainders

Objective 1: Solve division word problems with remainders.
(Lesson 14)

Objective 2: Understand and solve division problems with a remainder using the array and area models.
(Lesson 15)

Objective 3: Understand and solve two-digit dividend division problems with a remainder in the ones place by using place value disks.
(Lesson 16)

Objective 4: Represent and solve division problems requiring decomposing a remainder in the tens.
(Lesson 17)

Objective 5: Find whole number quotients and remainders.
(Lesson 18)

Objective 6: Explain remainders by using place value understanding and models.
(Lesson 19)

Objective 7: Solve division problems without remainders using the area model.
(Lesson 20)

Objective 8: Solve division problems with remainders using the area model.
(Lesson 21)

Lesson 14

Objective: Solve division word problems with remainders.

Suggested Lesson Structure

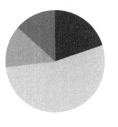

- ▨ Application Problem   (8 minutes)
- ■ Fluency Practice   (12 minutes)
- ▨ Concept Development   (32 minutes)
- ■ Student Debrief   (8 minutes)
- **Total Time**   **(60 minutes)**

Application Problem (8 minutes)

Tyler planted potatoes, oats, and corn. He planted 23 acres of potatoes. He planted 3 times as many acres of oats as potatoes, and he planted 4 times as many acres of corn as oats. How many acres did Tyler plant with potatoes, oats, and corn in all?

Note: This Application Problem reviews the objective of Lesson 13: *Use multiplication, addition, or subtraction to solve multi-step word problems*. It precedes the Fluency Practice and Concept Development as a review of multiplication skills prior to work with division in Grade 4, which starts in this lesson.

**NOTES ON
MULTIPLE MEANS
OF REPRESENTATION:**

English language learners and others may benefit from a brief explanation of the term *acre*.

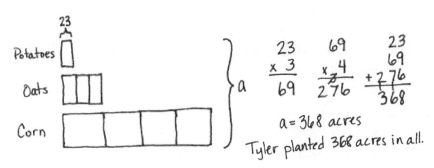

**EUREKA
MATH**™

Lesson 14:   Solve division word problems with remainders.

205

©2015 Great Minds. eureka-math.org
G4-M3-TE-B2-1.3.1-01.2016

Fluency Practice (12 minutes)

- Group Count to Divide **4.OA.1**   (4 minutes)
- Number Sentences in an Array **4.NBT.5**   (4 minutes)
- Divide with Remainders **4.NBT.6**   (4 minutes)

Group Count to Divide (4 minutes)

Note: This fluency activity prepares students to divide with remainders during this lesson's Concept Development.

- T: (Write $8 \div 2 = \_\_$.) Let's find the quotient, counting by twos. Show a finger for each multiple you count by.
- S: 2 (show 1 finger), 4 (show 2 fingers), 6 (show 3 fingers), 8 (show 4 fingers).
- T: What's $8 \div 2$?
- S: $8 \div 2 = 4$.

Continue with the following possible sequence: $12 \div 2$, $18 \div 2$, $14 \div 2$, $15 \div 5$, $25 \div 5$, $40 \div 5$, $30 \div 5$, $9 \div 3$, $15 \div 3$, $27 \div 3$, $21 \div 3$, $16 \div 4$, $24 \div 4$, $32 \div 4$, and $36 \div 4$.

Number Sentences in an Array (4 minutes)

Materials: (S) Personal white board

Note: This fluency activity prepares students for Lesson 15's Concept Development.

- T: (Project a 3×4 array.) How many boxes do you see altogether?
- S: 12.
- T: Let's count by threes to check. (Point at columns as students count.)
- S: 3, 6, 9, 12.
- T: Let's count by fours to check. (Point at rows as students count.)
- S: 4, 8, 12.
- T: On your personal white board, write two multiplication sentences to show how many boxes are in this array.
- S: (Write $3 \times 4 = 12$ and $4 \times 3 = 12$.)
- T: (Write $12 \div \_\_ = \_\_$. Write $12 \div \_\_ = \_\_$.) Write two division sentences for this array.
- S: (Write $12 \div 3 = 4$ and $12 \div 4 = 3$.)

Continue with the following possible sequence: 5×2 array and 7×3 array.

Divide with Remainders (4 minutes)

Note: This fluency activity prepares students for this lesson's Concept Development.

- T: How many groups of 2 are in 10?
- S: 5.

T: Let's prove it by counting by twos. Use your fingers as you count.

S: (Show one finger for each multiple.) 2, 4, 6, 8, 10.

T: Show and say how many groups of 2 are in 10.

S: (Show 5 fingers.) 5.

T: (Write 11 ÷ 2.) Let's find out how many groups of 2 are in 11. Count with me.

S: (Show one finger for each multiple.) 2, 4, 6, 8, 10.

T: How many groups?

S: 5.

T: How many left?

S: 1.

Continue with the following possible sequence: 8 ÷ 4 and 9 ÷ 4, 12 ÷ 3 and 13 ÷ 3, 15 ÷ 5 and 17 ÷ 5, 20 ÷ 4 and 23 ÷ 4, and 50 ÷ 10 and 55 ÷ 10.

Concept Development (32 minutes)

Materials: (S) Personal white board

Problem 1: Divide a two-digit number by a one-digit number modeled with an array.

There are 12 students in PE class separated into 4 equal teams. How many students are on each team?

T: Read the problem, and draw an array to represent the division.

S: (Draw an array as pictured below to the right.)

T: Tell me a division expression that matches the situation.

S: 12 ÷ 4.

T: What is the quotient?

S: The quotient is 3.

T: How many students are on each team?

S: There are 3 students on each team.

T: How can you check to make sure your division was correct?

S: I can count by three 4 times to get 12. → I can multiply 3 times 4 to get 12.

T: Does this quotient tell us the size of the group or the number of groups?

S: The size of the group.

T: Let's revise the story a bit. Again, there are 12 students in PE class, but now 3 students are needed on each team. How many teams can be made? (Point to the same array.) What is the division expression for this new story?

> **NOTES ON MULTIPLE MEANS OF REPRESENTATION:**
>
> Some learners may want to model 12 ÷ 4 as a tape diagram. At times, autonomy, creativity, and diversity are celebrated in modeling; in this case, however, a specific instructional model for representing the quotient and the remainder has been chosen. This model could also be represented concretely by having the students in the class simulate the actions of the students in Problems 1 and 2.

There are 3 students on each team.

12÷4=3

3×4=12

-or-

There are 4 teams of 3 students.

12÷3=4

4×3=12

Lesson 14:   Solve division word problems with remainders.   **207**

©2015 Great Minds. eureka-math.org
G4-M3-TE-B2-1.3.1-01.2016

S: 12 ÷ 3.

T: Does the quotient tell us the size of the group or the number of groups?

S: The number of groups.

T: The same array can represent a situation with the group size unknown or the number of groups unknown.

Problem 2: Divide a two-digit number by a one-digit number with a remainder modeled with an array.

13 ÷ 4

T: One more student joined the class described at the beginning of Problem 1. There are now 13 students to be divided into 4 equal teams. Draw an array to find how many students are on each team. What did you find?

S: I can represent 13 in four groups. → Four groups of 3 make 12, but I have 1 left over. → One student won't be on a team.

T: Tell me an expression to represent this problem.

S: 13 ÷ 4.

T: When we divide a number into equal groups, sometimes there is an amount leftover. We call the number that we have left a **remainder**.

T: What is the quotient?

S: The quotient is 3.

T: What is the amount left over, the remainder?

S: 1.

T: We state our answer by saying the quotient and then the remainder. The quotient is 3. The remainder is 1. We can also say or write, "The quotient is 3 with a remainder of 1."

T: Discuss with your partner how you can use multiplication to check your work for this answer.

S: Four threes is 12. That doesn't prove our answer is right. → We can add the remainder to the product. Four times 3 is 12. Add 1 to get 13.

T: Let's return again to a second story. There are 13 students in PE class. Exactly 3 students are needed on each team. How many teams can be made?

T: Tell me the new expression.

S: 13 ÷ 3.

T: State the quotient and remainder.

T: The quotient is 4, and the remainder is 1.

A NOTE ON
THE RECORDING
OF QUOTIENTS AND
REMAINDERS:

When writing 13 ÷ 4 = 3 R1, one may conclude that since 7 ÷ 2 = 3 R1, the following must be true: 7 ÷ 2 = 13 ÷ 4. However, this translates into $3\frac{1}{2} = 3\frac{1}{3}$, which is a false number sentence. To avoid this incorrect use of the equal sign and the misconceptions it creates, the remainder is stated separately from the quotient, and the R notation directly following the equal sign is not used.

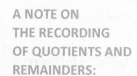

13 ÷ 4

There are 3 in each group with 1 remaining.
The quotient is 3.
The remainder is 1.

13 ÷ 3

There are 4 groups with 1 remaining.
The quotient is 4.
The remainder is 1.

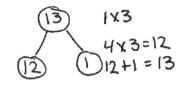

1 × 3
4 × 3 = 12
12 + 1 = 13

EUREKA
MATH

T: Talk to your partner. What do the quotient and the remainder mean in the second story?

S: Four teams can be made, and there is 1 extra person.

Draw the number bond as shown, and have students compare it with the quotient and the remainder. Notice the part on the left represents the equal groups, and the part on the right is the remainder.

Problem 3: Divide a two-digit number by a one-digit number with a remainder modeled with a tape diagram.

Kristy bought 13 roses. If she puts 6 roses in each vase, how many vases will she use? Will there be any roses left over?

T: Draw an array. Solve for 13 ÷ 6.

S: I can't because 13 is an odd number, and 6 + 6 = 12. An even number plus an even number won't give you an odd number. → You can divide by 6, but there will be 1 extra flower left over. → I can fill 2 vases and have 1 flower left over.

T: Tell your partner a statement that tells the quotient and remainder for this problem.

S: The quotient is 2, and the remainder is 1.

T: Describe to your partner what that statement tells us.

13 ÷ 6   Kristy will use 2 vases.
          There will be 1 rose left over.

                   or

13 ÷ 2   There will be 6 roses in each vase.
          There will be 1 rose left over.

S: We started with 13 and made groups of 6. We made 2 groups with 1 rose remaining. → Kristy can fill 2 vases. She will have 1 rose left over.

T: Again, let's revise our story a bit. Now, Kristy bought 13 roses and wants to put them equally in 2 vases. How many roses will be in each vase? Is this the same array?

S: Yes.

T: Talk to your partner. How has our interpretation of the array changed?

S: In the first story, we didn't know the number of vases. In the second story, we didn't know the number in each vase. → We changed the story from finding the number of groups to finding the size of the group.

T: How can we check our work for both situations?

S: We can draw a number bond to show 2 groups of 6, and then 1 more. → Two times 6 is 12, and 12 plus 1 is 13.

T: Let's turn our array into a tape diagram to show 13 in 2 groups of 6 with a remainder of 1. (Demonstrate.)

T: Using the array, draw a rectangle around the flowers. Erase the flowers, and label the diagram.

S: You should divide the bar into two parts. I know each part is worth 6, but 6 plus 6 isn't 13.

2×6

2×6=12
12+1=13

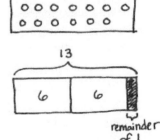

T: Our tape diagram must have a third part to represent the remainder. Let's separate the bar into two equal parts and make a very small third part. Shade to show the remaining flower. (Demonstrate.)

T: With your partner, draw a tape diagram to show 13 roses divided equally into 4 vases.

Students draw a tape diagram, dividing it into four parts. Using their basic facts, they know 13 cannot be divided into four equal parts. They shade a fifth part of the tape diagram to show the remainder.

S: The quotient is 3. The remainder is 1. → We can check our work by drawing a number bond and adding the parts or multiplying 4 times 3 and adding 1. Whatever method we use, we get back to the original total when our quotient and remainder are correct.

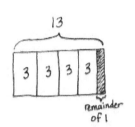

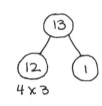

T: Look at your tape diagram. Is the model the same when we don't know the number of groups, when we know that there are 3 flowers in each vase, but we don't know the number of vases?

S: Yes!

Problem 4: Divide a two-digit number by a one-digit number, interpreting the remainder.

Allison has 22 meters of fabric to sew dresses. She uses 3 meters of fabric for each dress. After how many dresses will Allison need to buy more fabric?

T: Let's represent this problem using a tape diagram together. (Model for the students as you talk.) We don't know the number of groups or the number of dresses she will make. We know each dress uses 3 meters, so let's draw one group and label it as *fabric for 1 dress.* We don't know how many dresses she can make or how many threes there are, so we label that with a question mark. We do know there will be a remainder because we know our facts of 3. 22 isn't a multiple of 3. Solve this problem.

S: Twenty-two divided by 3 is 7 with a remainder of 1.

T: With your partner, discuss your answer to the question. After how many dresses will Allison need to buy more fabric?

S: Well, she can make 7 dresses. I guess she'll have only 1 meter to make her next dress. → No, the problem says she must have 3 meters of fabric for each dress, so after 7 dresses she will have to buy more fabric. → She can make 7 dresses, but to make an eighth dress, she will need to buy 2 more meters of fabric. I can prove that my tape diagram is correct by drawing an array. See, there are 7 threes. Each group represents 1 dress. That means that there are 7 dresses. The 1 left over means that to make the eighth dress, she will need 2 more meters. I can see that by looking at the array.

MP.4

©2015 Great Minds. eureka-math.org
G4-M3-TE-B2-1.3.1-01.2016

EUREKA MATH™

Problem Set (10 minutes)

Students should do their personal best to complete the Problem Set within the allotted 10 minutes. For some classes, it may be appropriate to modify the assignment by specifying which problems they work on first. Some problems do not specify a method for solving. Students should solve these problems using the RDW approach used for Application Problems.

Student Debrief (8 minutes)

Lesson Objective: Solve division word problems with remainders.

The Student Debrief is intended to invite reflection and active processing of the total lesson experience.

Invite students to review their solutions for the Problem Set. They should check work by comparing answers with a partner before going over answers as a class. Look for misconceptions or misunderstandings that can be addressed in the Debrief. Guide students in a conversation to debrief the Problem Set and process the lesson.

Any combination of the questions below may be used to lead the discussion.

- In Problem 3, there are 2 extra chairs. How can the **remainder** help you to find how many more chairs are needed to set up 1 more complete table?

- In Problem 4, how many full days of baking can be done? How much more flour is needed to bake on the sixth day?

- In Problem 6, 45 ÷ 7 equals 6 with a remainder of 3. What do the quotient and remainder represent in this problem? If 6 vans are full with 3 people remaining, why do we need 7 vans? Does the quotient always give the final answer? Why is it important to think carefully about the remainder? How would a model support your answer of 7 vans?

- How does an array help you to determine a remainder? Use the problems 12 ÷ 3, 13 ÷ 3, and 13 ÷ 2 in your conversation. How do the arrays with the whole 12 and 13 differ?

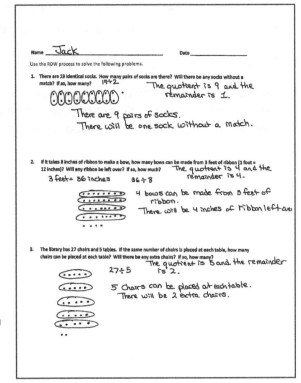

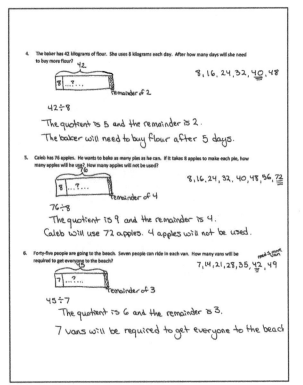

- What complications are there in modeling a division problem with a remainder using a tape diagram?
- What new math vocabulary did we use today to communicate precisely?

Exit Ticket (3 minutes)

After the Student Debrief, instruct students to complete the Exit Ticket. A review of their work will help with assessing students' understanding of the concepts that were presented in today's lesson and planning more effectively for future lessons. The questions may be read aloud to the students.

©2015 Great Minds. eureka-math.org
G4-M3-TE-B2-1.3.1-01.2016

Name _____ Date _____

Use the RDW process to solve the following problems.

1. There are 19 identical socks. How many pairs of socks are there? Will there be any socks without a match? If so, how many?

2. If it takes 8 inches of ribbon to make a bow, how many bows can be made from 3 feet of ribbon (1 foot = 12 inches)? Will any ribbon be left over? If so, how much?

3. The library has 27 chairs and 5 tables. If the same number of chairs is placed at each table, how many chairs can be placed at each table? Will there be any extra chairs? If so, how many?

©2015 Great Minds. eureka-math.org
G4-M3-TE-B2-1.3.1-01.2016

4. The baker has 42 kilograms of flour. She uses 8 kilograms each day. After how many days will she need to buy more flour?

5. Caleb has 76 apples. He wants to bake as many pies as he can. If it takes 8 apples to make each pie, how many apples will he use? How many apples will not be used?

6. Forty-five people are going to the beach. Seven people can ride in each van. How many vans will be required to get everyone to the beach?

Lesson 14:   Solve division word problems with remainders.

Name _____   Date _____

Use the RDW process to solve the following problem.

Fifty-three students are going on a field trip. The students are divided into groups of 6 students. How many groups of 6 students will there be? If the remaining students form a smaller group, and one chaperone is assigned to every group, how many total chaperones are needed?

Name _____ Date _____

Use the RDW process to solve the following problems.

1. Linda makes booklets using 2 sheets of paper. She has 17 sheets of paper. How many of these booklets can she make? Will she have any extra paper? How many sheets?

2. Linda uses thread to sew the booklets together. She cuts 6 inches of thread for each booklet. How many booklets can she stitch with 50 inches of thread? Will she have any unused thread after stitching up the booklets? If so, how much?

3. Ms. Rochelle wants to put her 29 students into groups of 6. How many groups of 6 can she make? If she puts any remaining students in a smaller group, how many students will be in that group?

Lesson 14: Solve division word problems with remainders.

EUREKA
MATH™

4. A trainer gives his horse, Caballo, 7 gallons of water every day from a 57-gallon container. How many days will Caballo receive his full portion of water from the container? On which number day will the trainer need to refill the container of water?

5. Meliza has 43 toy soldiers. She lines them up in rows of 5 to fight imaginary zombies. How many of these rows can she make? After making as many rows of 5 as she can, she puts the remaining soldiers in the last row. How many soldiers are in that row?

6. Seventy-eight students are separated into groups of 8 for a field trip. How many groups are there? The remaining students form a smaller group of how many students?

Lesson 15

Objective: Understand and solve division problems with a remainder using the array and area models.

Suggested Lesson Structure

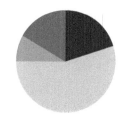

■ Fluency Practice   (12 minutes)
░ Application Problem   (5 minutes)
░ Concept Development   (33 minutes)
■ Student Debrief   (10 minutes)

   Total Time   **(60 minutes)**

Fluency Practice (12 minutes)

- Show Values with Place Value Disks **4.NBT.1**   (4 minutes)
- Divide with Remainders **4.NBT.6**   (4 minutes)
- Number Sentences in an Array **4.NBT.**   (4 minutes)

Show Values with Place Value Disks (4 minutes)

Materials: (T) Thousands place value chart (Lesson 4 Template) (S) Personal white board, thousands place value chart (Lesson 4 Template)

Note: This fluency activity prepares students for Lesson 16's Concept Development.

   T: (Project the place value chart with 2 tens disks and 4 ones disks.) On your personal white board, write the number in standard form.
   S: (Write 24.)

Repeat process for 5 tens and 3 ones, 4 tens and 1 one, 3 tens and 11 ones, and 3 tens and 17 ones.

   T: (Write 32.) Say the number.
   S: 32.
   T: Show 32 using place value disks.
   S: (Draw disks for 3 tens and 2 ones.)

Continue with the following possible sequence: 21 and 43.

Divide with Remainders (4 minutes)

Note: This fluency activity provides maintenance of the fluency introduced in Lesson 14.

Repeat the process from Lesson 14 for the following possible sequence: $6 \div 2$ and $7 \div 2$; $24 \div 3$ and $25 \div 3$, $12 \div 4$ and $15 \div 4$, $18 \div 6$ and $21 \div 6$, and $45 \div 5$ and $49 \div 5$.

Number Sentences in an Array (4 minutes)

Materials: (S) Personal white board

Note: This fluency activity prepares students for this lesson's Concept Development.

T: (Project a 5 × 3 + 1 array.) How many boxes do you see altogether?

S: 16.

T: Let's count by fives to check. (Point at columns as students count.)

S: 5, 10, 15.

T: Plus 1? (Point to the extra square outside of the rectangle.)

S: 16.

T: Count by threes to check.

S: 3, 6, 9, 12, 15.

T: Plus 1? (Point to the extra square outside of the rectangle.)

S: 16.

T: On your personal white board, write two multiplication number sentences to show how many boxes are in this array.

S: (Write (5 × 3) + 1 = 16 and (3 × 5) + 1 = 16.)

T: Write two division sentences for this array.

S: (Write 16 ÷ 3 = 5 with a remainder of 1 and 16 ÷ 5 = 3 with a remainder of 1.)

Repeat using the following possible sequence: (3 × 6) + 1 and (3 × 4) + 2.

Application Problem (5 minutes)

Chandra printed 38 photos to put into her scrapbook. If she can fit 4 photos on each page, how many pages will she use for her photos?

Note: This Application Problem relates to the objective of Lesson 14 in that students solve a division word problem with a remainder. Here, students interpret the remainder to determine the total number of scrapbook pages needed. This anticipates the last problem in this lesson.

> **NOTES ON MULTIPLE MEANS OF REPRESENTATION:**
>
> Modeling the array (rather than the tape diagram) may give students a clearer picture of the solution to the Application Problem. Encourage students to use the labels *photo* and *page,* if beneficial. Discuss how the equation informs the solution, yet the picture reveals the solution.

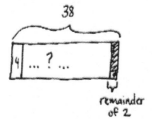

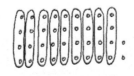

38 ÷ 4   9 × 4 = 36
Q = 9   36 + 2 = 38
R = 2

Chandra will need 10 pages because 9 pages only fits 36 photos, so the 10th page will fit the remaining 2 photos.

Lesson 15:   Understand and solve division problems with a remainder using the array and area models.

219

©2015 Great Minds. eureka-math.org
G4-M3-TE-B2-1.3.1-01.2016

Concept Development (33 minutes)

Materials: (T/S) Square grid paper

Problem 1: Solve a division problem with and without a remainder using the area model.

Display 10 ÷ 2.

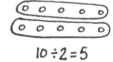

- T: Draw an array to represent 10 ÷ 2. Explain to your partner how you solved.
- S: (Draw.) I drew 2 circles and placed 10 dots evenly among the circles. → I drew 10 dots as 2 rows of 5 dots.

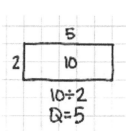

- T: Let's use grid paper to draw a rectangle with an area of 10 square centimeters and one side length of 2 centimeters. Tell your partner how we can find the unknown side length.
- S: The area is 10, so we know it is 5. → If the width is 2 centimeters, that means the length is 5 centimeters, and 2 centimeters times 5 centimeters gives an area of 10 square centimeters. → We can count and mark off by twos until we get to 10.
- T: Discuss with your partner how the length of 5 centimeters is represented in the area model.
- S: The length is 5, and the quotient is 5. → The length of the area model represents the quotient of this division problem.

Display 11 ÷ 2.

- T: With your partner, discuss how you would draw an area model for 11 ÷ 2.

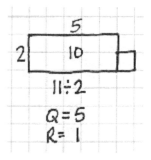

- S: Two can be the length or the width. → I can't just draw 2 rows of square units because of the remainder. → If I mark off 2 squares at a time, I count 2, 4, 6, 8, 10. I can't do another group of 2 because it would be 12. There aren't enough.
- T: Eleven square centimeters is the total area. Let's draw a rectangle starting with a width of 2 centimeters. We'll continue lengthening it until we get as close to 11 square centimeters as we can.
- S: A length of 5 centimeters and width of 2 centimeters is as close as we can get to 11 square centimeters. → We can't do 2 × 6 because that's 12 square centimeters, and the total area is 11 square centimeters.
- T: We can show a total area of 11 square centimeters by modeling 1 more square centimeter. The remainder of 1 represents 1 more square centimeter.

Repeat for 16 ÷ 3 and 23 ÷ 4.

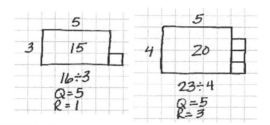

Lesson 15:   Understand and solve division problems with a remainder using the array and area models.

©2015 Great Minds. eureka-math.org
G4-M3-TE-B2-1.3.1-01.2016

EUREKA
MATH™

Problem 2: Solve a division problem using an array and the area model.

Display 38 ÷ 4.

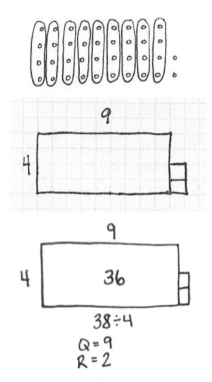

T: In the Application Problem, you drew an array (pictured to the right) to solve. Represent the same problem using the area model on grid paper. (Allow two minutes to work.)

T: What do you notice about the array compared to the area model on graph paper?

S: The area model is faster to draw. Thirty-eight dots is a lot to draw. → There are the same number of dots and squares when I used graph paper. → Both get us the same answer of a quotient 9 with a remainder of 2.

MP.4

T: Let's represent 38 ÷ 4 even more efficiently without grid paper since it's hard to come by grid paper every time you want to solve a problem.

T: (Give students one minute to draw.) Talk to your partner about how the array model and grid paper model supported you in drawing the rectangle with a given structure.

S: I knew the length was a little more than twice the width. → I knew that the remainder was half a column. → I knew that there was a remainder. It was really obvious with the array and grid paper.

Problem Set (10 minutes)

Students should do their personal best to complete the Problem Set within the allotted 10 minutes. For some classes, it may be appropriate to modify the assignment by specifying which problems they work on first. Some problems do not specify a method for solving. Students should solve these problems using the RDW approach used for Application Problems.

Student Debrief (10 minutes)

Lesson Objective: Understand and solve division problems with a remainder using the array and area models.

The Student Debrief is intended to invite reflection and active processing of the total lesson experience.

Invite students to review their solutions for the Problem Set. They should check work by comparing answers with a partner before going over answers as a class. Look for misconceptions or misunderstandings that can be addressed in the Debrief. Guide students in a conversation to debrief the Problem Set and process the lesson.

> **NOTES ON MULTIPLE MEANS OF REPRESENTATION:**
>
> Help English language learners distinguish between terms used for division: *division, divisor, quotient,* and *whole.* Label a division equation, and post for future reference. Make a word web of synonyms for division that students can interchange, if desired. Encourage students to speak these words as they participate in the Student Debrief.

Lesson 15:   Understand and solve division problems with a remainder using the array and area models.

221

©2015 Great Minds. eureka-math.org
G4-M3-TE-B2-1.3.1-01.2016

Any combination of the questions below may be used to lead the discussion.

- What does the quotient represent in the area model?

- When does the area model present a challenge in representing division problems?

- How can Problem 3 and Problem 4 have the same remainder?

- How could you change the 43 in Problem 5 so that there would be the same quotient but with no remainder?

- The quotient represents a side length. The remainder consists of square units. Why?

- How is the whole represented in an area model?

- What new math vocabulary did we use today to communicate precisely?

- How did the Application Problem connect to today's lesson?

Exit Ticket (3 minutes)

After the Student Debrief, instruct students to complete the Exit Ticket. A review of their work will help with assessing students' understanding of the concepts that were presented in today's lesson and planning more effectively for future lessons. The questions may be read aloud to the students.

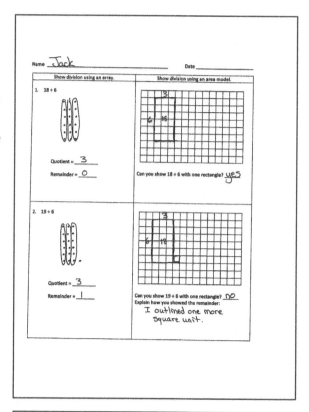

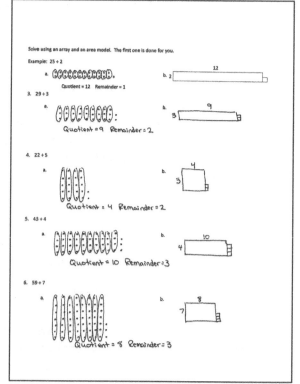

Lesson 15:   Understand and solve division problems with a remainder using the array and area models.

©2015 Great Minds. eureka-math.org
G4-M3-TE-B2-1.3.1-01.2016

EUREKA MATH

Name _____ Date _____

Show division using an array.	**Show** division using an area model.
1. 18 ÷ 6 Quotient = _____ Remainder = _____	 Can you show 18 ÷ 6 with one rectangle? _____
2. 19 ÷ 6 Quotient = _____ Remainder = _____	 Can you show 19 ÷ 6 with one rectangle? _____ Explain how you showed the remainder:

Lesson 15:   Understand and solve division problems with a remainder using the
array and area models.

223

©2015 Great Minds. eureka-math.org
G4-M3-TE-B2-1.3.1-01.2016

Solve using an array and an area model. The first one is done for you.

Example: 25 ÷ 2

a.
• • • • • • • • • • • • •
• • • • • • • • • • • • •

Quotient = 12   Remainder = 1

b.

```
        12
   ┌──────────────────┐ ┐
2  │                  │ │
   └──────────────────┘ ┘
```

3. 29 ÷ 3

a.   b.

4. 22 ÷ 5

a.   b.

5. 43 ÷ 4

a.   b.

6. 59 ÷ 7

a.   b.

Lesson 15:   Understand and solve division problems with a remainder using the array and area models.

EUREKA
MATH™

Name _____   Date _____

Solve using an array and area model.

1. 27 ÷ 5

   a.   b.

2. 32 ÷ 6

   a.   b.

Lesson 15:   Understand and solve division problems with a remainder using the array and area models.

©2015 Great Minds. eureka-math.org
G4-M3-TE-B2-1.3.1-01.2016

225

Name _____ Date _____

Show division using an array.	Show division using an area model.
1. 24 ÷ 4	
Quotient = _____	Can you show 24 ÷ 4 with one rectangle? _____
Remainder = _____	
2. 25 ÷ 4	
Quotient = _____	Can you show 25 ÷ 4 with one rectangle? _____
Remainder = _____	Explain how you showed the remainder:

Lesson 15: Understand and solve division problems with a remainder using the array and area models.

©2015 Great Minds. eureka-math.org
G4-M3-TE-B2-1.3.1-01.2016

EUREKA
MATH

Solve using an array and area model. The first one is done for you.

Example: 25 ÷ 3

a.

Quotient = 8   Remainder = 1

b.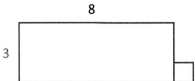

3. 44 ÷ 7

a.

b.

4. 34 ÷ 6

a.

b.

5. 37 ÷ 6

a.

b.

6. 46 ÷ 8

a.

b.

Lesson 16

Objective: Understand and solve two-digit dividend division problems with a remainder in the ones place by using place value disks.

Suggested Lesson Structure

■ Fluency Practice   (8 minutes)
▫ Concept Development   (42 minutes)
■ Student Debrief   (10 minutes)
   Total Time   **(60 minutes)**

Fluency Practice (8 minutes)

▪ Group Counting **4.OA.1**   (4 minutes)
▪ Divide with Remainders **4.NBT.6**   (4 minutes)

Group Counting (4 minutes)

Note: This fluency activity prepares students to divide with remainders during today's Concept Development.

Direct students to count forward and backward, occasionally changing the direction of the count.

▪   Twos to 20
▪   Threes to 30
▪   Fours to 40
▪   Fives to 50

> **NOTES ON MULTIPLE MEANS OF ACTION AND EXPRESSION:**
>
> Since learners differ in their physical abilities, provide options for modeling and crossing out small dots, such as concrete place value disks in an enlarged place value chart, drawing larger circles, drawing tick marks, or using fingerprints. Adjust response time accordingly.

Divide with Remainders (4 minutes)

Note: This fluency activity prepares students for today's Concept Development.

Repeat the process from Lessons 14 and 15 using the following possible sequence: $6 \div 2$, $20 \div 5$, $16 \div 4$, $18 \div 3$, $15 \div 2$, $18 \div 5$, $11 \div 3$, $13 \div 4$, and $33 \div 4$.

Lesson 16:   Understand and solve two-digit dividend division problems with a
                          remainder in the ones place by using place value disks.

©2015 Great Minds. eureka-math.org
G4-M3-TE-B2-1.3.1-01.2016

EUREKA MATH™

Concept Development (42 minutes)

Materials: (T) Tens place value chart (Template) (S) Personal white board, tens place value chart (Template)

Problem 1

6 ones ÷ 3

3 tens 6 ones ÷ 3

Display 6 ÷ 3 on the board.

T: 6 ones represents what?

S: The whole. → The total. → What you are dividing.

T: Show 6 using place value disks. What is the number we are dividing by?

S: 3.

T: Let's assume it's telling us how many groups to make. Draw 3 groups below. Can we distribute 6 ones into 3 groups? Think of it like dealing cards evenly among 3 players. (Model as students follow along.) First, put one in each group. Cross off the ones one at a time as you distribute them evenly. Next, put another one in each group if you are able. Continue this until all of the ones are distributed.

S: We can put 2 ones in each group.

T: Are there any ones left over?

S: No.

T: How many ones are in each of our 3 groups?

S: 2 ones.

T: What is 6 ones ÷ 3? Give me the number sentence.

S: 6 ones ÷ 3 equals 2 ones.

T: Let's represent 6 ÷ 3 in a new way. Let's record the whole and the **divisor**. (Record with long division symbol as shown above.) Look back to your model. 6 ones divided by 3 is…?

S: 2 ones.

T: (Record 2 ones.)

T: (Point to the place value chart.) You distributed 2 ones 3 times. 2 ones times 3 is…?

S: 6 ones.

T: (Refer to the numbers carefully, pointing to 2 ones and the divisor, and recording 6 ones.)

T: (Point to the place value chart.) We divided 6 ones and have no ones remaining. 6 ones minus 6 ones equals 0 ones. (Write the subtraction line.) What does this zero mean?

S: There is no remainder. → All the ones were divided with none left over. → We subtracted the total number distributed from the total number of ones.

T: We can see the 3 groups of 2 both in our model and in our numbers and know our answer is correct since 3 times 2 equals 6.

Lesson 16:   Understand and solve two-digit dividend division problems with a remainder in the ones place by using place value disks.

229

Display 36 ÷ 3 on the board.

T: 3 tens and 6 ones represents what?

S: The whole.

T: Show 36 using place value disks. What is the number we are dividing by?

S: 3.

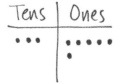

T: Make room for 3 groups below. Let's start dividing with the largest units. What is the largest unit?

S: The tens.

T: 3 tens divided by 3 is?

S: 1 ten.

T: Distribute the 3 tens, and cross them off to show they are now divided equally into the 3 groups.

T: Are there any tens left over?

S: No.

T: 6 ones divided by 3 is…?

S: 2 ones. We did that in the last problem. We distribute the ones evenly, one at a time, into each group. We cross off the ones, one at a time, as we distribute them.

T: Are there any ones left over?

S: No.

T: How many tens and ones are in each of our 3 groups?

S: 1 ten and 2 ones.

T: What is 36 ÷ 3?

S: 12.

T: Let's represent 36 ÷ 3 using numbers. Record the whole and the divisor.

T: Look back to your model. 3 tens divided by 3 is…?

S: 1 ten.

T: (Record 1 ten. Point to the place value chart.) You distributed 1 ten 3 times. Give a multiplication sentence that says that.

S: 1 ten times 3 equals 3 tens. (As students speak, refer to the algorithm.)

T: (Point to the place value chart.) How many tens are remaining to be distributed?

S: None. → Zero.

T: 3 tens minus 3 tens equals 0 tens. (Refer to the written problem.)

T: What of our whole amount remains to be divided?

S: 6 ones.

NOTES ON MULTIPLE MEANS OF ENGAGEMENT:

A student whose pace is ahead of the class may be engaged by journaling a response to the following:

- Compare the quotients of 36 ÷ 3 and 6 ÷ 3. What do you notice?

- Write three equations to check 36 ÷ 3 = 12.

- Compare the models of division (i.e., array, area model, etc.).

Lesson 16:   Understand and solve two-digit dividend division problems with a remainder in the ones place by using place value disks.

T: (Record 6 ones next to 0 tens.) Say a division sentence to divide 6 ones into 3 groups.

S: 6 ones divided by 3 equals 2 ones. (As students speak, refer to the problem.)

T: (Point to the place value chart.) You recorded 2 ones 3 times. Say a multiplication sentence that tells that.

S: 2 ones times 3 equals 6 ones. (As students speak, refer to the problem.)

T: (Point to the place value chart.) We started with 6 ones, distributed 6 ones, and have no ones remaining. Say a subtraction sentence for that.

S: 6 ones minus 6 ones equals 0 ones.

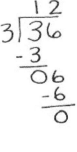

Have students notice the 3 groups of 12 and relate that to the checking equation of 3 twelves or 3 times 12.

Problem 2

5 ones ÷ 4

4 tens 5 ones ÷ 4

Display 5 ÷ 4 on the board.

T: With your partner, represent the whole and the divisor, 4, on the place value chart, and record the written problem.

S: (Draw 5 ones and 4 groups below in the place value chart, and record the written problem.)

T: 5 ones divided by 4 equals?

S: It doesn't divide evenly. → I can place 1 one in each group, but I will have 1 one left over.

T: Distribute as many ones as you can, crossing off the ones you use. What is the quotient for 5 ones divided by 4?

S: 1 one.

T: Record your quotient numerically. Say a multiplication sentence for how many ones were distributed.

S: 1 one times 4 equals 4 ones.

T: Record 4 ones numerically and subtract.

S: 5 ones minus 4 ones is 1 one.

T: Record 1 one numerically. How many ones are remaining in the place value chart?

S: 1 one.

T: Circle 1 one. Tell your partner why 1 one is a remainder.

S: It is what is left over after we made our groups. → Our groups must be equal. If we put this 1 one into a group, the groups will not be equal.

T: Watch as I record the remainder numerically using *R1*.

Lesson 16: Understand and solve two-digit dividend division problems with a remainder in the ones place by using place value disks.

231

©2015 Great Minds. eureka-math.org
G4-M3-TE-B2-1.3.1-01.2016

Display 45 ÷ 4 on the board.

T: Represent 45 using place value disks. Prepare to represent 45 ÷ 4 numerically.

T: 4 tens divided by 4 equals…?

S: 1 ten.

T: Cross off and distribute your tens below in each of the 4 groups. Record 1 ten in the tens column. Tell your partner the next numerical steps.

S: 1 ten times 4 is 4 tens. We subtract 4 tens from 4 tens and get 0 tens. We have 5 ones remaining, so we record those next to the 0 tens.

T: 5 ones divided by 4 equals…?

S: 1 one. → We can place 1 one in each group. But we will have 1 one remaining.

T: Distribute the disks, crossing off the 4 you use. Then, tell your partner how to record that using numbers.

S: 5 ones divided by 4 is 1 one. 1 one times 4 is 4 ones. 5 ones minus 4 ones is 1 one. Hey, we have 1 one left in the place value chart!

T: Correct. Circle that 1 one. It is your remainder. Show your partner how to record the remainder.

T: What is 45 ÷ 4?

S: 11 with a remainder of 1.

T: What do you notice about using numbers, or **long division**, and place value disks?

S: Both help us get to the same answer. → In the place value chart, we can see the remainder of 1. Then, we can write out all of the steps we did with the disks and still show the quotient of 11 and the remainder of 1. → We started with the largest units and went to the smallest with the disks and the numbers.

Problem 3

       8 ones ÷ 3

6 tens 8 ones ÷ 3

Display 8 ÷ 3 on the board.

T: Solve for 8 ÷ 3 using place value disks. Represent the problem using long division with your partner.

Circulate. Listen for students using place value as they divide, multiply, and subtract.

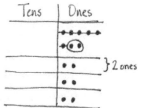

S: The quotient is 2 and the remainder is 2.

T: How do we use multiplication and addition to check our quotient and remainder in division?

S: Two times 3 is 6. Six plus 2 is 8. → We multiply the quotient times the divisor and add the remainder. → We multiply the number in each group by the number of groups and then add the remainder.

Lesson 16:   Understand and solve two-digit dividend division problems with a remainder in the ones place by using place value disks.

©2015 Great Minds. eureka-math.org
G4-M3-TE-B2-1.3.1-01.2016

EUREKA
MATH™

Display 68 ÷ 3 on the board.

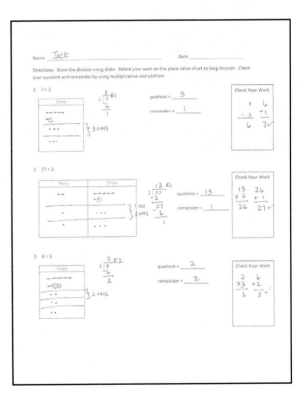

- T: Solve for 68 ÷ 3 using place value disks. Represent the problem using numbers, or long division, with your partner.
- S: I got 22 with a remainder of 2.
- T: How can we check if 22 with a remainder of 2 is the correct answer?
- S: We can multiply to check because we know that multiplication and division are related. → We can multiply 22 × 3 to check, and then we need to add 2.
- T: 22 × 3 is...?
- S: 66.
- T: Plus 2?
- S: 68. Our answer was right!

MP.4

Problem Set (10 minutes)

Students should do their personal best to complete the Problem Set within the allotted 10 minutes. For some classes, it may be appropriate to modify the assignment by specifying which problems they work on first. Some problems do not specify a method for solving. Students should solve these problems using the RDW approach used for Application Problems.

Student Debrief (10 minutes)

Lesson Objective: Understand and solve two-digit dividend division problems with a remainder in the ones place by using place value disks.

The Student Debrief is intended to invite reflection and active processing of the total lesson experience.

Invite students to review their solutions for the Problem Set. They should check work by comparing answers with a partner before going over answers as a class. Look for misconceptions or misunderstandings that can be addressed in the Debrief. Guide students in a conversation to debrief the Problem Set and process the lesson.

Lesson 16:   Understand and solve two-digit dividend division problems with a
              remainder in the ones place by using place value disks.

©2015 Great Minds. eureka-math.org
G4-M3-TE-B2-1.3.1-01.2016

233

Any combination of the questions below may be used to lead the discussion.

- How did solving Problem 1 prepare you for solving Problem 2?

- Explain to your partner why only 6 ones could be distributed in Problem 3. What happens to the remaining ones?

- Solve 12 divided by 3. Solve 12 divided by 4. As a **divisor** gets larger, what will happen to the quotient if the whole stays the same?

- Was the remainder ever larger than the divisor? Why not?

- In the Problem Set, we only had remainders of 1 and 2. Give me an example of a problem that might have a larger remainder.

- Explain the connection between using place value disks and **long division**. Why do you think it is called long division?

- What new math vocabulary did we use today to communicate precisely?

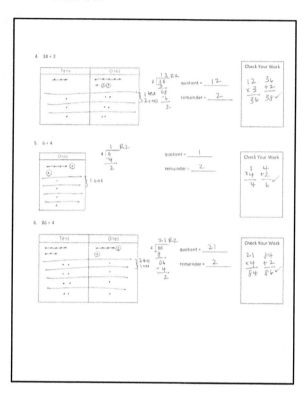

Exit Ticket (3 minutes)

After the Student Debrief, instruct students to complete the Exit Ticket. A review of their work will help with assessing students' understanding of the concepts that were presented in today's lesson and planning more effectively for future lessons. The questions may be read aloud to the students.

Lesson 16: Understand and solve two-digit dividend division problems with a remainder in the ones place by using place value disks.

©2015 Great Minds. eureka-math.org
G4-M3-TE-B2-1.3.1-01.2016

Name _____ Date _____

Show the division using disks. Relate your work on the place value chart to long division. Check your quotient and remainder by using multiplication and addition.

1. $7 \div 2$

Ones

$2 \overline{) 7}$

quotient = _____

remainder = _____

Check Your Work

3

$\times\ 2$

_____

2. $27 \div 2$

Tens	Ones

$2 \overline{) 27}$

quotient = _____

remainder = _____

Check Your Work

Lesson 16:   Understand and solve two-digit dividend division problems with a
remainder in the ones place by using place value disks.

235

©2015 Great Minds. eureka-math.org
G4-M3-TE-B2-1.3.1-01.2016

3. 8 ÷ 3

Ones

3)‾8‾

quotient = _____

remainder = _____

Check Your Work

4. 38 ÷ 3

Tens	Ones

3)‾3‾8‾

quotient = _____

remainder = _____

Check Your Work

Lesson 16:   Understand and solve two-digit dividend division problems with a remainder in the ones place by using place value disks.

©2015 Great Minds. eureka-math.org
G4-M3-TE-B2-1.3.1-01.2016

EUREKA MATH

5. 6 ÷ 4

Ones

4 ⟌ 6

quotient = _____

remainder = _____

Check Your Work

6. 86 ÷ 4

Tens	Ones

4 ⟌ 86

quotient = _____

remainder = _____

Check Your Work

Lesson 16:   Understand and solve two-digit dividend division problems with a
remainder in the ones place by using place value disks.

237

©2015 Great Minds. eureka-math.org
G4-M3-TE-B2-1.3.1-01.2016

Name _____   Date _____

Show the division using disks. Relate your work on the place value chart to long division. Check your quotient and remainder by using multiplication and addition.

1. 5 ÷ 3

Ones

3 | 5

Check Your Work

quotient = _____

remainder = _____

2. 65 ÷ 3

Tens	Ones

3 | 65

Check Your Work

quotient = _____

remainder = _____

Lesson 16:   Understand and solve two-digit dividend division problems with a remainder in the ones place by using place value disks.

Name _____ Date _____

Show the division using disks. Relate your work on the place value chart to long division. Check your quotient and remainder by using multiplication and addition.

1. 7 ÷ 3

Ones

3 ⟌ 7

quotient = _____

remainder = _____

Check Your Work

```
      2
    × 3
  _____
```

2. 67 ÷ 3

Tens	Ones

3 ⟌ 6 7

quotient = _____

remainder = _____

Check Your Work

Lesson 16:   Understand and solve two-digit dividend division problems with a remainder in the ones place by using place value disks.

239

©2015 Great Minds. eureka-math.org
G4-M3-TE-B2-1.3.1-01.2016

3. 5 ÷ 2

Ones

2 ⟌ 5

quotient = _____

remainder = _____

Check Your Work

4. 85 ÷ 2

Tens	Ones

2 ⟌ 85

quotient = _____

remainder = _____

Check Your Work

EUREKA
MATH™

5. 5 ÷ 4

Ones

4 ⟌ 5

quotient = _____

remainder = _____

Check Your Work

6. 85 ÷ 4

Tens	Ones

4 ⟌ 8 5

Check Your Work

quotient = _____

remainder = _____

Lesson 16:   Understand and solve two-digit dividend division problems with a
remainder in the ones place by using place value disks.

241

©2015 Great Minds. eureka-math.org
G4-M3-TE-B2-1.3.1-01.2016

tens	ones

_____

tens place value chart

Lesson 16: Understand and solve two-digit dividend division problems with a remainder in the ones place by using place value disks.

©2015 Great Minds. eureka-math.org
G4-M3-TE-B2-1.3.1-01.2016

EUREKA
MATH™

Lesson 17

Objective: Represent and solve division problems requiring decomposing a remainder in the tens.

Suggested Lesson Structure

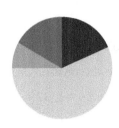

■ Fluency Practice   (11 minutes)
▨ Application Problem   (5 minutes)
▧ Concept Development   (34 minutes)
■ Student Debrief   (10 minutes)

Total Time   **(60 minutes)**

Fluency Practice (11 minutes)

- Group Counting **4.OA.1**   (2 minutes)
- Divide Mentally **4.NBT.6**   (4 minutes)
- Divide Using the Standard Algorithm **4.NBT.6**   (5 minutes)

Group Counting (2 minutes)

Note: This fluency activity prepares students to divide with remainders during the Concept Development.

Direct students to count forward and backward, occasionally changing the direction of the count.

- Twos to 20
- Threes to 30
- Fours to 40
- Fives to 50

Divide Mentally (4 minutes)

Note: This fluency activity reviews Lesson 16's content.

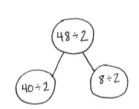

T: (Write 40 ÷ 2.) Say the completed division sentence in unit form.

S: 4 tens divided by 2 equals 2 tens.

T: (To the right, write 8 ÷ 2.) Say the completed division sentence in unit form.

S: 8 ones divided by 2 equals 4 ones.

T: (Above both equations, write 48 ÷ 2. Draw a number bond to connect the two original problems to this new problem.) Say the completed division sentence in unit form.

EUREKA
MATH™

Lesson 17:   Represent and solve division problems requiring decomposing a
              remainder in the tens.

©2015 Great Minds. eureka-math.org
G4-M3-TE-B2-1.3.1-01.2016

S: 4 tens 8 ones divided by 2 equals 2 tens 4 ones.

T: Say the division sentence in standard form.

S: 48 divided by 2 equals 24.

Continue with the following possible sequence: 93 ÷ 3 and 88 ÷ 4.

Divide Using the Standard Algorithm (5 minutes)

Materials: (S) Personal white board

Note: This fluency activity reviews Lesson 16's content.

T: (Write 24 ÷ 2.) On your boards, solve the division problem using long division.

Continue with the following possible sequence: 36 ÷ 3, 37 ÷ 3, 55 ÷ 5, 57 ÷ 5, 88 ÷ 4, 87 ÷ 4, 96 ÷ 3, and 95 ÷ 3.

Application Problem (5 minutes)

Audrey and her sister found 9 dimes and 8 pennies. If they share the money equally, how much money will each sister get?

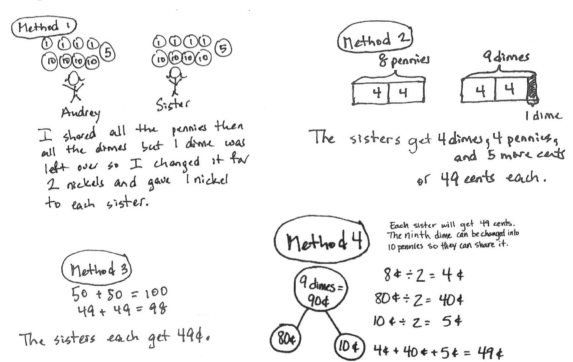

Note: This Application Problem reviews division of ones. Sharing 9 dimes connects to Problems 1 and 2 of today's Concept Development, asking students to decompose 1 ten for 10 ones.

EUREKA
MATH™

Concept Development (34 minutes)

Materials: (T) Tens place value chart (Lesson 16 Template) (S) Personal white board, tens place value chart (Lesson 16 Template)

Problem 1: Divide two-digit numbers by one-digit numbers using place value disks, regrouping in the tens.

3 ones ÷ 2

3 tens ÷ 2

Display 3 ÷ 2 on the board.

MP.4

- T: (Have students model on the place value chart.) 3 ones divided by 2 is…?
- S: One with a remainder of 1.
- T: Record 3 ÷ 2 as long division.

Students complete the problem. Encourage students to share the relationship of their model to the steps of the algorithm.

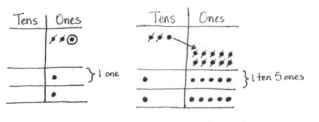

Display 30 ÷ 2 on the board.

- T: Using mental math, tell your partner the answer to 30 ÷ 2.
- S: Thirty divided by 2 is 15.
- T: Let's confirm your quotient. Represent 30 on the place value chart. Tell your partner how many groups below are needed.
- S: Two. (Draw.)
- T: 3 tens divided by 2 is…? Distribute your disks, and cross off what what's been distributed. The answer is…?
- S: 1 ten with a remainder of 1 ten. That's an interesting answer.
- T: Can we rename the leftover ten?
- S: Yes! Change 1 ten for 10 ones.
- T: Let's rename 1 ten. Now, rename and distribute the 10 ones with your partner.
- S: Our answer is 1 ten 5 ones, or 15.
- T: Why didn't we stop when we had a remainder of 1 ten?
- S: Because 1 ten is just 10 ones, and you can keep dividing.
- T: So, why did we stop when we got a remainder of 1 one?
- S: The ones are the smallest unit on our place value chart, so we stopped there and made a remainder.
- T: Let's solve 30 ÷ 2 using long division.
- T: 3 tens divided by 2?
- S: 1 ten.

Lesson 17:   Represent and solve division problems requiring decomposing a remainder in the tens.

©2015 Great Minds. eureka-math.org
G4-M3-TE-B2-1.3.1-01.2016

245

T: (Record 1 ten. Point to the place value chart.) You recorded 1 ten, twice. Say a multiplication equation that tells that.

S: 1 ten times 2 equals 2 tens.

As students say the multiplication equation, refer to the problem, pointing to 1 ten and the divisor, and record 2 tens.

T: (Point to the place value chart.) We started with 3 tens, distributed 2 tens, and have 1 ten remaining. Tell me a subtraction equation for that.

S: 3 tens minus 2 tens equals 1 ten.

As students say the subtraction equation, refer to the problem, pointing to the tens column, drawing a subtraction line, and recording 1 ten.

T: (Point to the place value chart.) How many ones remain to be divided?

S: 10 ones.

T: Yes. We changed 1 ten for 10 ones. Say a division equation for how you distributed 1 ten or 10 ones.

S: 10 ones divided by 2 equals 5 ones.

As students say the division equation, refer to the problem, pointing to the 10 ones and the divisor, and record 5 ones.

T: (Point to the place value chart.) You recorded 5 ones twice. Say a multiplication equation that tells that.

S: 5 ones times 2 equals 10 ones.

As students say the multiplication equation, refer to the problem, pointing to 5 ones and the divisor, and record 10 ones.

T: (Point to the place value chart.) We renamed 10 ones, distributed 10 ones, and have no ones remaining. Say a subtraction equation for that.

S: 10 ones minus 10 ones equals 0 ones.

As students say the subtraction equation, refer to the problem, drawing a subtraction line, and record 0 ones.

Have students share with a partner how the model matches the steps of the algorithm. Note that both show equal groups and how both can be used to check their work using multiplication.

Problem 2

4 ones ÷ 3

4 tens 2 ones ÷ 3

Display 4 ÷ 3 on the board.

T: Represent 4 ones on the place value chart. With your partner, solve 4 ÷ 3 using place value disks and long division.

S: The quotient is 1, and the remainder is 1.

Lesson 17: Represent and solve division problems requiring decomposing a remainder in the tens.

©2015 Great Minds. eureka-math.org
G4-M3-TE-B2-1.3.1-01.2016

Display 42 ÷ 3 on the board.

T: Represent 4 tens 2 ones on the place value chart, and get ready to solve using long division.

T: 4 tens divided by 3 is …? Distribute your disks, and cross off what is used. The answer is…?

S: 1 ten with a remainder of 1 ten. Oh! I remember from last time, we need to change 1 ten for 10 ones.

T: (With students, draw an arrow to show 1 ten decomposed as 10 ones in the place value chart, and show 12 ones in the algorithm.) How many ones remain?

S: 12.

T: Yes. 10 ones + 2 ones is 12 ones.

T: Show 12 ones divided by 3. Complete the remaining steps. What is the quotient?

S: Our quotient is 1 ten 4 ones, or 14.

Have students share with a partner how the model matches the steps of the algorithm, paying particular attention to the decomposition of 1 ten and how it is combined with the ones. Note that this is just the same process the students use in subtraction. We decompose a larger unit into smaller units.

Problem 3

8 tens 4 ones ÷ 3

Display 84 ÷ 3 on the board.

T: Solve for 84 ÷ 3 by using place value disks and long division.

S: The quotient is 28.

T: What was different about the place value chart with this problem?

S: There were a lot more disks! → We had to decompose 2 tens this time.

T: How many ones did you have after decomposing your 2 tens?

S: 24 ones.

T: Show your partner where to find 24 ones in the numerical representation.

S: (Students point to the 2 tens remaining that were bundled, as ones, with the 4 ones.)

T: Check your answer using multiplication.

S: 28 times 3 is 84. Our answer is right!

NOTES ON
MULTIPLE MEANS
OF ENGAGEMENT:

Students working above grade level and others can be encouraged to solve without place value charts to become more efficient at solving long division problems. Allow them to share and explain their method with others.

EUREKA
MATH™

Lesson 17:   Represent and solve division problems requiring decomposing a remainder in the tens.

©2015 Great Minds. eureka-math.org
G4-M3-TE-B2-1.3.1-01.2016

247

Problem Set (10 minutes)

Students should do their personal best to complete the Problem Set within the allotted 10 minutes. For some classes, it may be appropriate to modify the assignment by specifying which problems they work on first. Some problems do not specify a method for solving. Students should solve these problems using the RDW approach used for Application Problems.

Student Debrief (10 minutes)

Lesson Objective: Represent and solve division problems requiring decomposing a remainder in the tens.

The Student Debrief is intended to invite reflection and active processing of the total lesson experience.

Invite students to review their solutions for the Problem Set. They should check work by comparing answers with a partner before going over answers as a class. Look for misconceptions or misunderstandings that can be addressed in the Debrief. Guide students in a conversation to debrief the Problem Set and process the lesson.

Any combination of the questions below may be used to lead the discussion.

- How did Problem 2 allow you to see only the remaining 1 ten in the ones column?

- Explain why 1 ten remains in Problem 4.

- How is the long division recording different in today's lesson compared to yesterday's lesson?

- What different words are we using to describe what we do when we have a remaining ten or tens? (*Break apart, unbundle, change, rename, decompose, regroup*) Which of these words are you most comfortable using yourself?

- What other operation involves changing 1 ten for 10 ones at times? (Subtraction.) What operations involve the opposite, changing 10 ones for 1 ten at times?

- What would happen if we divided the ones before the tens?

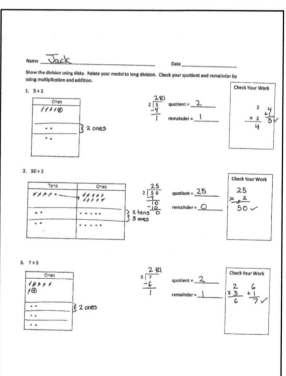

Lesson 17:   Represent and solve division problems requiring decomposing a
remainder in the tens.

**EUREKA
MATH™**

- What connection can you find between the written division and the multiplication you used to check your work?
- Why are we learning long division after addition, subtraction, and multiplication?
- How did the Application Problem connect to today's lesson?

Exit Ticket (3 minutes)

After the Student Debrief, instruct students to complete the Exit Ticket. A review of their work will help with assessing students' understanding of the concepts that were presented in today's lesson and planning more effectively for future lessons. The questions may be read aloud to the students.

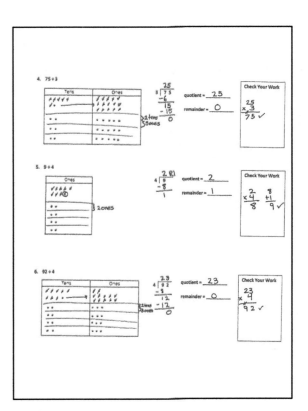

Lesson 17:   Represent and solve division problems requiring decomposing a remainder in the tens.

©2015 Great Minds. eureka-math.org
G4-M3-TE-B2-1.3.1-01.2016

249

Name _____ Date _____

Show the division using disks. Relate your model to long division. Check your quotient and remainder by using multiplication and addition.

1. 5 ÷ 2

Ones

2 ⟌ 5

Check Your Work

$\quad\quad 2$
$\times\ 2$
———

quotient = _____

remainder = _____

2. 50 ÷ 2

Tens	Ones

2 ⟌ 5 0

Check Your Work

quotient = _____

remainder = _____

Lesson 17:   Represent and solve division problems requiring decomposing a remainder in the tens.

EUREKA MATH

3. 7 ÷ 3

Ones

3 ⟌ 7

Check Your Work

quotient = _____

remainder = _____

4. 75 ÷ 3

Tens	Ones

3 ⟌ 7 5

Check Your Work

quotient = _____

remainder = _____

Lesson 17:   Represent and solve division problems requiring decomposing a
remainder in the tens.

©2015 Great Minds. eureka-math.org
G4-M3-TE-B2-1.3.1-01.2016

251

5. 9 ÷ 4

Ones

4 ⟌ 9

Check Your Work

quotient = _____

remainder = _____

6. 92 ÷ 4

Tens	Ones

4 ⟌ 9 2

Check Your Work

quotient = _____

remainder = _____

EUREKA
MATH™

Name _____   Date _____

Show the division using disks. Relate your model to long division. Check your quotient by using multiplication and addition.

1. 5 ÷ 4

Ones

4 | 5

quotient = _____

remainder = _____

Check Your Work

2. 56 ÷ 4

Tens	Ones

4 | 5 6

quotient = _____

remainder = _____

Check Your Work

Lesson 17: Represent and solve division problems requiring decomposing a remainder in the tens.

253

©2015 Great Minds. eureka-math.org
G4-M3-TE-B2-1.3.1-01.2016

Name _____   Date _____

Show the division using disks. Relate your model to long division. Check your quotient and remainder by using multiplication and addition.

1. 7 ÷ 2

Ones

2 ⟌ 7

Check Your Work

quotient = _____

remainder = _____

2. 73 ÷ 2

Tens	Ones

2 ⟌ 7 3

Check Your Work

quotient = _____

remainder = _____

Lesson 17:   Represent and solve division problems requiring decomposing a remainder in the tens.

©2015 Great Minds. eureka-math.org
G4-M3-TE-B2-1.3.1-01.2016

3. 6 ÷ 4

Ones

4 ⟌ 6

Check Your Work

quotient = _____

remainder = _____

4. 62 ÷ 4

Tens	Ones

4 ⟌ 6 2

Check Your Work

quotient = _____

remainder = _____

Lesson 17: Represent and solve division problems requiring decomposing a remainder in the tens.

255

©2015 Great Minds. eureka-math.org
G4-M3-TE-B2-1.3.1-01.2016

5. 8 ÷ 3

Ones

3 | 8

Check Your Work

quotient = _____

remainder = _____

6. 84 ÷ 3

Tens	Ones

3 | 8 4

Check Your Work

quotient = _____

remainder = _____

Lesson 17:   Represent and solve division problems requiring decomposing a remainder in the tens.

©2015 Great Minds. eureka-math.org
G4-M3-TE-B2-1.3.1-01.2016

Lesson 18

Objective: Find whole number quotients and remainders.

Suggested Lesson Structure

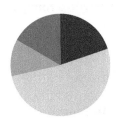

- ■ Fluency Practice   (12 minutes)
- ▨ Application Problem   (7 minutes)
- ▢ Concept Development   (31 minutes)
- ■ Student Debrief   (10 minutes)

  Total Time   **(60 minutes)**

Fluency Practice (12 minutes)

- ▪ Group Counting **4.OA.1**   (4 minutes)
- ▪ Divide Mentally **4.NBT.6**   (4 minutes)
- ▪ Divide Using the Standard Algorithm **4.NBT.6**   (4 minutes)

Group Counting (4 minutes)

Note: This fluency activity prepares students to divide with remainders during this lesson's Concept Development.

Direct students to count forward and backward, occasionally changing the direction of the count.

- ▪ Fours to 40
- ▪ Sixes to 60

Divide Mentally (4 minutes)

Note: This fluency activity reviews content from Lessons 16 and 17.

Repeat the process from Lesson 17 using the following possible sequence: $48 \div 2$, $55 \div 5$, $96 \div 3$, and $84 \div 4$.

Divide Using the Standard Algorithm (4 minutes)

Materials: (S) Personal white board

Note: This fluency activity reviews Lesson 17's content.

Repeat the process from Lesson 17 using the following possible sequence: $20 \div 3$, $50 \div 2$, $43 \div 3$, and $64 \div 5$.

Application Problem (7 minutes)

Malory's family is going to buy oranges. The Grand Market sells oranges at 3 pounds for 87 cents. How much does 1 pound of oranges cost at Grand Market?

Note: This Application Problem reviews division with a remainder in the tens from Lesson 17.

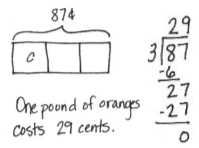

Concept Development (31 minutes)

Materials: (T) Tens place value chart (Lesson 16 Template) (S) Personal white board, tens place value chart (Lesson 16 Template)

Problem 1: Divide a two-digit number by a one-digit divisor with a remainder in the tens place.

5 tens 7 ones ÷ 3

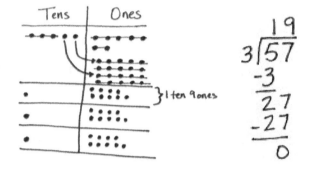

T: (Write 57 ÷ 3.) Let's divide 57 into 3 equal groups. Break 57 into tens and ones.

S: 5 tens 7 ones.

T: Let's divide 5 tens first. Why?

S: When we divide, we always start with the larger units. → We divide the tens first because we may have to change tens for ones.

T: 5 tens divided by 3…?

S: (Record the steps of the algorithm.) 1 ten in each group, with 2 tens remaining.

T: We've distributed 3 tens. Let's write 3 in the tens place. We also write that there are 2 tens remaining because 5 tens minus 3 tens is 2 tens.

T: How do we divide the remaining 2 tens?

S: We unbundle the 2 tens as 20 ones.

T: Yes. So, how many ones do we have altogether?

S: 27.

T: Yes, 20 ones plus 7 ones is 27 ones.

T: You know your threes facts. Get ready for some mental math. What's 27 ones divided by 3?

S: 9 ones!

T: 9 ones in each group is recorded above, in the ones place. Record the remaining steps. Read the quotient.

NOTES ON MULTIPLE MEANS OF ACTION AND EXPRESSION:

Scaffold long division with the following options:

- Provide graph paper for easy alignment of tens and ones.
- Label the tens and ones places.
- Write zeros as place holders.

EUREKA MATH

S: (Record the remaining steps.) 19.

T: Say the division sentence.

S: 57 divided by 3 is 19.

T: Check with multiplication. What's 19 times 3?

S: 57.

Problem 2: Divide with a remainder in the tens and ones places using the division algorithm.

8 tens 6 ones ÷ 5

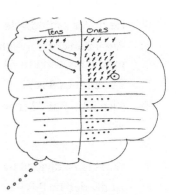

T: (Write 86 ÷ 5.) You solved 57 divided by 3 by unbundling tens. Let's try a more challenging problem. How many groups will we divide 86 into?

S: 5.

T: What is the first step?

S: Start with the tens. Divide 8 tens into 5 groups. That's 1 ten in each group with 3 tens remaining.

T: Show me on your personal white board using long division, or the division algorithm, how you recorded the distributed tens and the remaining tens.

T: What will you do with the 3 remaining tens?

S: Unbundle 3 tens as 30 ones.

T: How many ones altogether?

S: 36.

T: Next step?

S: Divide 36 ones into 5 groups. That's 7 ones in each group, with 1 one remaining.

T: How did you record what you distributed? What remains? Check your neighbor's work. Thumbs up if you agree.

T: I see you've written 35 ones distributed under the 36 ones you had at first. Did you write R1? Read your quotient. Read your remainder. What is 86 divided by 5?

S: 17 with a remainder of 1.

T: How could you prove your division is correct?

S: Multiply 17 by 5, and then add 1 more.

T: Work with your partner to check with multiplication.

Problem 3: Use mental math to divide and calculate a remainder.

7 tens 4 ones ÷ 8

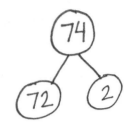

T: (Write 74 ÷ 8.) You've unbundled tens, and you've written remainders in the quotient. Now, take a look at this problem. What's tricky here?

S: Hey! We can't divide 7 tens into 8 groups! What will we do?

T: We'll think of our eights facts. I'm thinking of an eights fact whose product is close to 74. Can you guess?

S: 72. 8 times 9 is 72.

T: Nice job! But 72 is only part of 74. What's the other part?

S: 2.

T: What is 74 divided by 8?

S: 74 divided by 8 is 9 with a remainder of 2.

Continue with 87 ÷ 9 and 64 ÷ 7. Gradually omit the number bond, and encourage mental math.

Problem Set (10 minutes)

Students should do their personal best to complete the Problem Set within the allotted 10 minutes. For some classes, it may be appropriate to modify the assignment by specifying which problems they work on first. Some problems do not specify a method for solving. Students should solve these problems using the RDW approach used for Application Problems.

Student Debrief (10 minutes)

Lesson Objective: Find whole number quotients and remainders.

The Student Debrief is intended to invite reflection and active processing of the total lesson experience.

Invite students to review their solutions for the Problem Set. They should check work by comparing answers with a partner before going over answers as a class. Look for misconceptions or misunderstandings that can be addressed in the Debrief. Guide students in a conversation to debrief the Problem Set and process the lesson.

NOTES ON MULTIPLE MEANS OF ENGAGEMENT:

Students who have not memorized eights or nines facts may not be ready to use mental math to solve 74 ÷ 8. Adjust the numbers, or provide a multiplication chart. Approach Problems 11 and 12 of the Problem Set similarly if students have not memorized sevens and eights facts.

MP.5

©2015 Great Minds. eureka-math.org
G4-M3-TE-B2-1.3.1-01.2016

Any combination of the questions below may be used to lead the discussion.

- Compare the remainders to the divisors on the Problem Set. What do you find is true? Which always has a larger value? Why is that?

- How did the zero effect your division in Problem 9?

- What did you notice about the divisor, the whole, and quotients in Problems 9 and 10?

- Can you predict whether or not there will be a remainder? How?

- The whole is the same in Problems 11 and 12. Why is the quotient smaller in Problem 11?

Exit Ticket (3 minutes)

After the Student Debrief, instruct students to complete the Exit Ticket. A review of their work will help with assessing students' understanding of the concepts that were presented in today's lesson and planning more effectively for future lessons. The questions may be read aloud to the students.

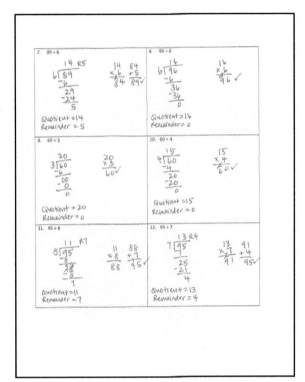

Name _____ Date _____

Solve using the standard algorithm. Check your quotient and remainder by using multiplication and addition.

1. $46 \div 2$	2. $96 \div 3$
3. $85 \div 5$	4. $52 \div 4$
5. $53 \div 3$	6. $95 \div 4$

Lesson 18:   Find whole number quotients and remainders.

EUREKA MATH™

7. 89 ÷ 6

8. 96 ÷ 6

9. 60 ÷ 3

10. 60 ÷ 4

11. 95 ÷ 8

12. 95 ÷ 7

Name _____ Date _____

Solve using the standard algorithm. Check your quotient and remainder by using multiplication and addition.

1. $93 \div 7$

2. $99 \div 8$

Lesson 18:   Find whole number quotients and remainders.

**EUREKA
MATH™**

Name _____ Date _____

Solve using the standard algorithm. Check your quotient and remainder by using multiplication and addition.

1. 84 ÷ 2	2. 84 ÷ 4
3. 48 ÷ 3	4. 80 ÷ 5
5. 79 ÷ 5	6. 91 ÷ 4

©2015 Great Minds. eureka-math.org
G4-M3-TE-B2-1.3.1-01.2016

7. 91 ÷ 6	8. 91 ÷ 7
9. 87 ÷ 3	10. 87 ÷ 6
11. 94 ÷ 8	12. 94 ÷ 6

Lesson 18:   Find whole number quotients and remainders.

Lesson 19

Objective: Explain remainders by using place value understanding and models.

Suggested Lesson Structure

■ Fluency Practice   (12 minutes)
▨ Application Problem   (8 minutes)
▢ Concept Development   (25 minutes)
▨ Student Debrief   (15 minutes)

   Total Time   **(60 minutes)**

Fluency Practice (12 minutes)

- Sprint: Mental Division **4.NBT.6**   (8 minutes)
- Divide Using the Standard Algorithm **4.NBT.6**   (4 minutes)

Sprint: Mental Division (8 minutes)

Materials: (S) Mental Division Sprint

Note: This Sprint reviews content from previous lessons and reinforces place value used in the division algorithm.

Divide Using the Standard Algorithm (4 minutes)

Materials: (S) Personal white board

Note: This fluency activity reviews Lesson 17's content.

Repeat the process from Lesson 17 using the following possible sequence: $37 ÷ 2$, $45 ÷ 3$, $26 ÷ 4$, and $58 ÷ 3$.

Application Problem (8 minutes)

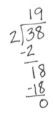

Each friend will receive $19 as 1 $10 bill, 1 $5 bill, and 4 $1 bills.

Two friends start a business writing and selling comic books. After 1 month, they have earned $38. Show how they can share their earnings fairly, using $1, $5, $10, and $20 bills.

Note: Students practice decomposing a ten using long division from Lesson 17 and with a money model. Other acceptable answers are 1 ten 9 ones, 19 ones, 3 fives 4 ones, or 2 fives 9 ones.

Lesson 19:   Explain remainders by using place value understanding and models.

©2015 Great Minds. eureka-math.org
G4-M3-TE-B2-1.3.1-01.2016

Concept Development (25 minutes)

Materials: (T) Tens place value chart (Lesson 16 Template) (S) Personal white board, tens place value chart (Lesson 16 Template)

Problem 1: Model division with remainders in the tens and ones places using place value disks.

$41 \div 3$

T: (Write $41 \div 3$.) What disks will you draw to represent 41?

S: 4 tens 1 one.

T: How many equal groups will we divide 41 into?

S: 3.

T: Draw 3 groups, and let's share 4 tens equally. How many tens in each group? Draw place value disks as you distribute 4 tens into 3 groups like you're dealing cards to 3 players.

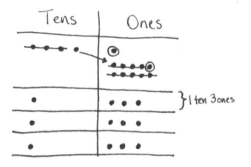

S: 1 ten in each group, with 1 ten remaining.

T: How can we divide the remaining ten?

S: Unbundle 1 ten as 10 ones.

T: Let's see you draw that. (Allow students time to draw.) What did you do?

S: I drew an arrow from the remaining tens disk in the tens place and drew 10 ones in the ones place.

T: How many ones do you have now?

S: 11 ones.

T: Let's divide those 11 ones equally into 3 groups. Divide 11 ones into 3 groups by distributing 1 to each group. How many ones are remaining?

S: 8.

T: Are there enough to distribute again?

S: Yes. We can distribute another one to each group.

T: How many are left now?

S: Five. We can distribute again. We will have 2 remaining.

T: Explain what happened.

S: 2 ones are left after distributing the rest equally. We had to keep distributing until we didn't have enough to distribute evenly again.

T: Now, your place value disks clearly show the solution for $41 \div 3$. Tell me the quotient. Tell me the remainder.

**NOTES ON
MULTIPLE MEANS
OF ACTION AND
EXPRESSION:**

Some learners may need less guidance to model $41 \div 3$ and, after solving quickly and independently, may benefit more from writing a step-by-step script for solving $41 \div 3$ in preparation for Problem 5 of the Problem Set. This script might be used in a video of the student supporting his peers as they learn long division.

        Lesson 19:   Explain remainders by using place value understanding and models.

S: 41 divided by 3 is 13 with a remainder of 2.

T: With your partner, write an equation we can use to check your division.

S: (13 × 3) + 2 = 41.

T: With your partner, find where 13, 3, 2, and 41 are represented in the place value chart.

S: Thirteen is the 1 ten and 3 ones in each group. Three is the number of groups we made. Two is the remaining 2 ones from the whole. Forty-one is the whole.

Problem 2: Share $64 as 6 tens and 4 ones equally among 4 friends.

T: Tell your partner what happens when we have an extra ten we can't distribute.

S: We break the ten apart into 10 ones. Then, we add the 10 ones to the ones that are already there. Then, we can distribute the ones into 4 equal groups.

T: Can you think of a real-life situation in which you might change a ten for 10 ones?

S: Yeah! When you're getting change for 10 dollars! → If the soda machine doesn't take tens, you need to change out for ones.

T: Let's say I give 4 students $64 to share equally—6 ten-dollar bills and 4 one-dollar bills. Write an equation and draw place value disks to show how to divide the money.

T: What happens when you try to share 6 ten-dollar bills equally with 4 people?

MP.8

S: Each person gets 1 ten-dollar bill, but then you have 2 ten-dollar bills left.

T: What do you do?

S: Make change! Cash in those 2 ten-dollar bills for 20 ones. Then, we can share the money fairly. → Or, they could change the 2 tens for 4 fives. That would work, too.

T: You're both correct. Either approach would work. Since we're using a place value chart to show division, let's pretend they changed the 2 tens for 20 ones and model that. Since we have so many ones, model with quick dots as you distribute like a fast card dealer. How will you distribute the ones?

S: I will keep distributing them until I can't distribute them equally anymore. This time, I was able to distribute evenly.

T: Why do you have to keep distributing?

S: If I don't keep distributing, there will be too many remaining. That means that you would be able to distribute again but didn't.

T: How much money does each student receive?

S: $16.

T: Check your quotient with your partner using multiplication.

S: 16 × 4 = 64. I see 4 groups of 1 ten 6 ones, which is 64.

Lesson 19:   Explain remainders by using place value understanding and models.

©2015 Great Minds. eureka-math.org
G4-M3-TE-B2-1.3.1-01.2016

269

Problem Set (15 minutes)

Students should do their personal best to complete the Problem Set within the allotted 15 minutes. For some classes, it may be appropriate to modify the assignment by specifying which problems they work on first. Some problems do not specify a method for solving. Students should solve these problems using the RDW approach used for Application Problems.

Student Debrief (15 minutes)

Lesson Objective: Explain remainders by using place value understanding and models.

The Student Debrief is intended to invite reflection and active processing of the total lesson experience.

Invite students to review their solutions for the Problem Set. They should check work by comparing answers with a partner before going over answers as a class. Look for misconceptions or misunderstandings that can be addressed in the Debrief. Guide students in a conversation to debrief the Problem Set and process the lesson.

Any combination of the questions below may be used to lead the discussion.

- In Problem 2, Cayman's remainder is larger than the divisor. What rule can you suggest to Cayman so he doesn't make this mistake again? Was his answer completely wrong? Why not?

- In Problem 4, the friends have to make change for the 1 ten-dollar bill. Why can't they tear the bill in half? How does that relate to the place value disks?

- In Problem 5, how did your script describe the remainder in the tens and ones?

- Select a few students to share and compare their scripts for solving 45 ÷ 3.

- Compare using place value disks and other methods to divide. Which do you prefer? Why?

- We related a remainder in the tens place to making change with money. What other real-life situations can you relate it to? Is this similar to mixed metric units, such as having 5 liters of water to share among 4 people?

- With money, sometimes we might use units other than ones and tens, such as fives or twenties. Why do you think we use only ones and tens to model division on the place value chart?

NOTES ON MULTIPLE MEANS OF ACTION AND EXPRESSION:

Support English language learners as they write a script to explain how to solve 45 ÷ 3. Provide a word bank with corresponding pictures. The following are possible words to include in the word bank:

cross out	distribute	share	draw
tens	ones	four	five
three	unbundle	divide	equal
fairly	next	then	last

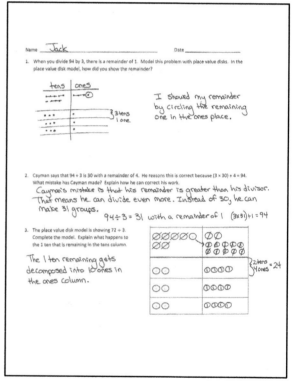

©2015 Great Minds. eureka-math.org
G4-M3-TE-B2-1.3.1-01.2016

EUREKA MATH™

Exit Ticket (3 minutes)

After the Student Debrief, instruct students to complete the Exit Ticket. A review of their work will help with assessing students' understanding of the concepts that were presented in today's lesson and planning more effectively for future lessons. The questions may be read aloud to the students.

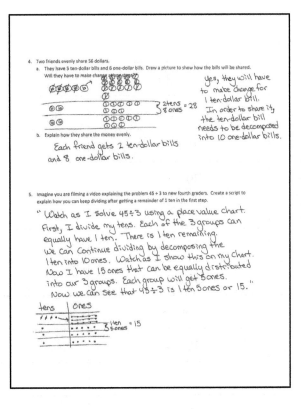

Lesson 19:   Explain remainders by using place value understanding and models.

271

©2015 Great Minds. eureka-math.org
G4-M3-TE-B2-1.3.1-01.2016

A

Number Correct: _____

Mental Division

1.	20 ÷ 2 =	
2.	4 ÷ 2 =	
3.	24 ÷ 2 =	
4.	30 ÷ 3 =	
5.	6 ÷ 3 =	
6.	36 ÷ 3 =	
7.	40 ÷ 4 =	
8.	8 ÷ 4 =	
9.	48 ÷ 4 =	
10.	2 ÷ 2 =	
11.	40 ÷ 2 =	
12.	42 ÷ 2 =	
13.	3 ÷ 3 =	
14.	60 ÷ 3 =	
15.	63 ÷ 3 =	
16.	4 ÷ 4 =	
17.	80 ÷ 4 =	
18.	84 ÷ 4 =	
19.	40 ÷ 5 =	
20.	50 ÷ 5 =	
21.	60 ÷ 5 =	
22.	70 ÷ 5 =	

23.	68 ÷ 2 =	
24.	96 ÷ 3 =	
25.	86 ÷ 2 =	
26.	93 ÷ 3 =	
27.	88 ÷ 4 =	
28.	99 ÷ 3 =	
29.	66 ÷ 3 =	
30.	66 ÷ 2 =	
31.	40 ÷ 4 =	
32.	80 ÷ 4 =	
33.	60 ÷ 4 =	
34.	68 ÷ 4 =	
35.	20 ÷ 2 =	
36.	40 ÷ 2 =	
37.	30 ÷ 2 =	
38.	36 ÷ 2 =	
39.	30 ÷ 3 =	
40.	39 ÷ 3 =	
41.	45 ÷ 3 =	
42.	60 ÷ 3 =	
43.	57 ÷ 3 =	
44.	51 ÷ 3 =	

Lesson 19: Explain remainders by using place value understanding and models.

©2015 Great Minds. eureka-math.org
G4-M3-TE-B2-1.3.1-01.2016

EUREKA
MATH™

B

Number Correct: _____

Improvement: _____

Mental Division

1.	30 ÷ 3 =	
2.	9 ÷ 3 =	
3.	39 ÷ 3 =	
4.	20 ÷ 2 =	
5.	6 ÷ 2 =	
6.	26 ÷ 2 =	
7.	80 ÷ 4 =	
8.	4 ÷ 4 =	
9.	84 ÷ 4 =	
10.	2 ÷ 2 =	
11.	60 ÷ 2 =	
12.	62 ÷ 2 =	
13.	3 ÷ 3 =	
14.	90 ÷ 3 =	
15.	93 ÷ 3 =	
16.	8 ÷ 4 =	
17.	40 ÷ 4 =	
18.	48 ÷ 4 =	
19.	50 ÷ 5 =	
20.	60 ÷ 5 =	
21.	70 ÷ 5 =	
22.	80 ÷ 5 =	

23.	86 ÷ 2 =	
24.	69 ÷ 3 =	
25.	68 ÷ 2 =	
26.	96 ÷ 3 =	
27.	66 ÷ 3 =	
28.	99 ÷ 3 =	
29.	88 ÷ 4 =	
30.	88 ÷ 2 =	
31.	40 ÷ 4 =	
32.	80 ÷ 4 =	
33.	60 ÷ 4 =	
34.	64 ÷ 4 =	
35.	20 ÷ 2 =	
36.	40 ÷ 2 =	
37.	30 ÷ 2 =	
38.	38 ÷ 2 =	
39.	30 ÷ 3 =	
40.	36 ÷ 3 =	
41.	42 ÷ 3 =	
42.	60 ÷ 3 =	
43.	54 ÷ 3 =	
44.	48 ÷ 3 =	

EUREKA MATH™

Lesson 19:   Explain remainders by using place value understanding and models.

273

Name _____ Date _____

1. When you divide 94 by 3, there is a remainder of 1. Model this problem with place value disks. In the place value disk model, how did you show the remainder?

2. Cayman says that 94 ÷ 3 is 30 with a remainder of 4. He reasons this is correct because (3 × 30) + 4 = 94. What mistake has Cayman made? Explain how he can correct his work.

©2015 Great Minds. eureka-math.org
G4-M3-TE-B2-1.3.1-01.2016

3. The place value disk model is showing $72 \div 3$. Complete the model. Explain what happens to the 1 ten that is remaining in the tens column.

4. Two friends evenly share 56 dollars.

   a. They have 5 ten-dollar bills and 6 one-dollar bills. Draw a picture to show how the bills will be shared. Will they have to make change at any stage?

   b. Explain how they share the money evenly.

Lesson 19: Explain remainders by using place value understanding and models.

275

5. Imagine you are filming a video explaining the problem 45 ÷ 3 to new fourth graders. Create a script to explain how you can keep dividing after getting a remainder of 1 ten in the first step.

Explain remainders by using place value understanding and models.

EUREKA
MATH™

©2015 Great Minds. eureka-math.org
G4-M3-TE-B2-1.3.1-01.2016

Name _____   Date _____

1. Molly's photo album has a total of 97 pictures. Each page of the album holds 6 pictures. How many pages can Molly fill? Will there be any pictures left? If so, how many? Use place value disks to solve.

2. Marti's photo album has a total of 45 pictures. Each page holds 4 pictures. She said she can only fill 10 pages completely. Do you agree? Explain why or why not.

EUREKA MATH

Lesson 19:   Explain remainders by using place value understanding and models.

277

©2015 Great Minds. eureka-math.org
G4-M3-TE-B2-1.3.1-01.2016

Name _____ Date _____

1. When you divide 86 by 4, there is a remainder of 2. Model this problem with place value disks. In the place value disk model, how can you see that there is a remainder?

2. Francine says that 86 ÷ 4 is 20 with a remainder of 6. She reasons this is correct because (4 × 20) + 6 = 86. What mistake has Francine made? Explain how she can correct her work.

Lesson 19:   Explain remainders by using place value understanding and models.

©2015 Great Minds. eureka-math.org
G4-M3-TE-B2-1.3.1-01.2016

3. The place value disk model is showing 67 ÷ 4. Complete the model. Explain what happens to the 2 tens that are remaining in the tens column.

⊘ ⊘ ⊘ ⊘ ⑩ ⑩	① ① ① ① ① ① ①
⑩	
⑩	
⑩	
⑩	

4. Two friends share 76 blueberries.

   a. To count the blueberries, they put them into small bowls of 10 blueberries. Draw a picture to show how the blueberries can be shared equally. Will they have to split apart any of the bowls of 10 blueberries when they share them?

   b. Explain how the friends can share the blueberries fairly.

Lesson 19: Explain remainders by using place value understanding and models.

279

5. Imagine you are drawing a comic strip showing how to solve the problem 72 ÷ 4 to new fourth graders. Create a script to explain how you can keep dividing after getting a remainder of 3 tens in the first step.

Lesson 19:   Explain remainders by using place value understanding and models.

EUREKA
MATH™

Lesson 20

Objective: Solve division problems without remainders using the area model.

Suggested Lesson Structure

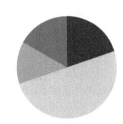

■ Fluency Practice   (12 minutes)
▨ Application Problem   (8 minutes)
▨ Concept Development   (30 minutes)
■ Student Debrief   (10 minutes)

   Total Time   **(60 minutes)**

Fluency Practice (12 minutes)

- Divide Using the Standard Algorithm **4.NBT.6**   (4 minutes)
- Find the Unknown Factor **4.OA.4**   (5 minutes)
- Mental Multiplication **4.NBT.5**   (3 minutes)

Divide Using the Standard Algorithm (4 minutes)

Materials: (S) Personal white board

Note: This fluency activity reviews Lesson 17's content.

Repeat the process from Lesson 17 using the following possible sequence: 67 ÷ 2, 60 ÷ 4, 29 ÷ 3, and 77 ÷ 4.

Find the Unknown Factor (5 minutes)

Materials: (S) Personal white board

Note: This fluency activity prepares students for Lesson 22's Concept Development

   T: (Write 5 × ___ = 15.) Say the unknown factor.
   S: 3.
   T: (Write 15 ÷ 5.) On your personal white board, write the division problem.
   S: (Write 15 ÷ 5 = 3.)

Continue with the following possible sequence: 3 × ___ = 12, 4 × ___ = 12, 5 × ___ = 35, 6 × ___ = 36, 7 × ___ = 49, 9 × ___ = 81, 6 × ___ = 48, 7 × ___ = 42, and 9 × ___ = 54.

EUREKA
MATH™

Lesson 20:   Solve division problems without remainders using the area model.

©2015 Great Minds. eureka-math.org
G4-M3-TE-B2-1.3.1-01.2016

281

Mental Multiplication (3 minutes)

Note: This fluency activity reviews content taught earlier in the module.

> T: (Write 3 × 2 = __.) Say the complete multiplication sentence in unit form.
>
> S: 3 ones × 2 = 6 ones.
>
> T: (Write 3 × 2 = 6. To the right, write 30 × 2 = __.) Say the complete multiplication sentence in unit form.
>
> S: 3 tens × 2 = 6 tens.
>
> T: (Write 30 × 2 = 60. To the right, write 30 × 20 = __.) Say the complete multiplication sentence in unit form.
>
> S: 3 tens × 2 tens = 6 hundreds.
>
> T: (Write 30 × 20 = 600.)

> **NOTES ON MULTIPLE MEANS OF EXPRESSION:**
>
> As with any mental math, some students do better when having the option to write. This aids in their processing of the oral commands and reduces stress, which, though beneficial to some, may be crippling to others.

Continue with the following possible sequence: 4 × 2, 40 × 2, 40 × 20, 5 × 3, 50 × 3, and 50 × 30.

Application Problem (8 minutes)

Write an expression to find the unknown length of each rectangle. Then, find the sum of the two unknown lengths.

a.

4 cm | 40 square cm | 8 square cm

$(40 \div 4) + (8 \div 4)$
$10 + 2 = 12$ 12 centimeters

b.

4 cm | 80 square cm | 16 square cm

$(80 \div 4) + (16 \div 4)$
$20 + 4 = 24$ 24 centimeters

Note: This Application Problem serves as an introduction to today's Concept Development, in which students find the total unknown length of a rectangle with an area of 48, corresponding to Part (a), and 96, corresponding to Part (b).

Lesson 20:   Solve division problems without remainders using the area model.

EUREKA MATH™

Concept Development (30 minutes)

Materials: (S) Personal white board

Problem 1: Decompose 48 ÷ 4 from whole to part.

T: Draw a rectangle with an area of 48 square units and a width of 4 units.

S: (Draw.)

T: Draw a new rectangle with the same area directly below but partitioned to match the areas of the rectangles in Part (a) of the Application Problem.

T: Let's draw a number bond to match the whole and parts of the rectangle.

S/T: (Draw the bond as pictured below.)

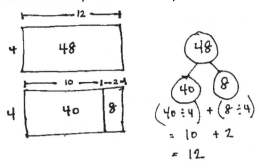

T: Let's find the unknown side lengths of the smaller rectangles and add them. (Show as the distribution of the quotients shown above.) What is 40 ÷ 4?

S: 10.

T: What is 8 ÷ 4?

S: 2.

T: What is 10 and 2?

S: 12.

T: What is 48 divided by 4?

S: 12.

T: What is the length of the unknown side?

S: 12 units.

T: Take a moment to record the number sentences, reviewing with your partner their connection to both the number bond and the area model.

T: Work with your partner to partition the same area of 48 as 2 twenties and 8. When you are finished, try to find another way to partition the area of 48 so it's easy to divide.

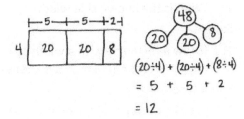

T: (Allow students to work for about four minutes.) Did anyone find another way to partition the area of 48 so it's easy to divide?

S: Yes! 24 + 24. 24 divided by 4 is 6. 6 + 6 is 12. → 30 and 18 don't work well because 30 has a remainder when you divide it by 4. → I did it by using 4 rectangles, each with an area of 12 square units. → Oh, yeah, 12 + 12 + 12 + 12.

T: Explain to your partner why different ways of partitioning give us the same correct side length.

S: You are starting with the same amount of area but just chopping it up differently. → The sum of the lengths is the same as the whole length. → You can take a total, break it into parts, and divide each of them separately. → I use the same break apart and distribute strategy to find the answer to 56 ÷ 8. 40 ÷ 8 is 5. 16 ÷ 8 is 2. 5 and 2 makes 7.

Problem 2: Decompose 96 ÷ 4 from whole to part.

Repeat the same process with Part (b) from the Application Problem.

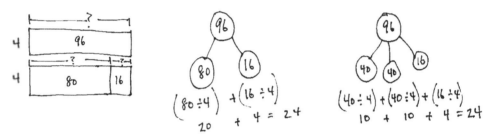

T: How did you partition the area of 96?

S: We chopped 96 into 40 + 40 + 16. → It was just like 48 ÷ 4. We saw that we could partition 96 into 4 twenties and 2 eights. → We made 96 into 2 forty-eights and used our answer from 48 ÷ 4. All we had to do was double it.

T: Discuss with your partner why we do not decompose 96 as 90 and 6.

S: 9 tens ÷ 4 gives a remainder.

T: True!

Problem 3: Compose 96 ÷ 4 from part to whole.

T: (Write 96 ÷ 4.) Thinking about area, let's try a new way to divide. The expression 96 ÷ 4 can describe a rectangle with an area of 96 square units. We are trying to find out the length of the unknown side.

T: What is the known side width?

S: 4.

T: (Draw a rectangle with a width of 4.) Four times how many tens gets us as close as possible to an area of 9 tens? (Point to the 9 tens of the dividend.)

S: 2 tens.

T: Let's give 2 tens to the length. (Label 2 tens above the rectangle.) Let's record the 2 tens in the tens place.

284   Lesson 20:   Solve division problems without remainders using the area model.

©2015 Great Minds. eureka-math.org
G4-M3-TE-B2-1.3.1-01.2016

EUREKA
MATH™

T: What is 4 times 2 tens?

S: 8 tens. (Record 8 below the 9 tens.)

T: How many square units is that?

S: 80 square units. (Record 80 square units in the rectangle.)

T: How many tens remain?

S: 1 ten.

T: (Record 1 ten below the 8 tens.) Let's add the remaining ten to the 6 ones. What is 1 ten + 6 ones? (Record the 6 ones to the right of the 1 ten.)

S: 16.

T: We have 16 square units remaining with a width of 4. (Point to the 16 in the problem.) Four times how many ones gets us as close as possible to an area of 16 square units?

S: 4 ones.

T: Let's give 4 ones to the length.

T: What is 4 times 4?

S: 16. We have 16 square units.

T: (Record 16 square units in the rectangle.) We had 16 square units to divide, and we did. (Record 16 in the problem, and subtract to get zero.) We have no more area to divide.

T: Tell me the length of the unknown side.

S: 24.

T: Our quotient tells us that length.

T: How can we express the length of the unknown side using the distributive property?

S: $(80 \div 4) + (16 \div 4)$.

T: With your partner, draw arrows to connect the distributive property and the area model.

T: Review our four drawings and our process with your partner. Try to reconstruct what we did step-by-step before we try another one.

T: (Allow time for students to review.) We solved 96 divided by 4 in two very different ways using the area model. First, we started with the whole rectangle and partitioned it. The second way was to go one place value at a time and make the whole rectangle from parts.

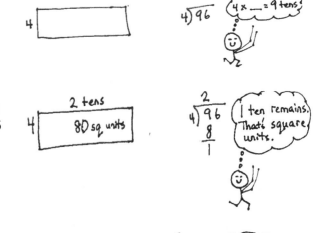

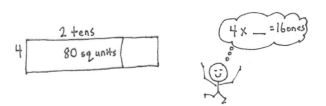

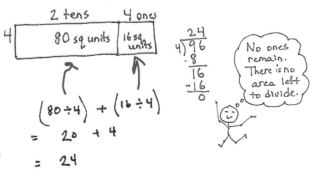

©2015 Great Minds. eureka-math.org
G4-M3-TE-B2-1.3.1-01.2016

Problem Set (10 minutes)

Students should do their personal best to complete the Problem Set within the allotted 10 minutes. For some classes, it may be appropriate to modify the assignment by specifying which problems they work on first. Some problems do not specify a method for solving. Students should solve these problems using the RDW approach used for Application Problems.

Student Debrief (10 minutes)

Lesson Objective: Solve division problems without remainders using the area model.

The Student Debrief is intended to invite reflection and active processing of the total lesson experience.

Invite students to review their solutions for the Problem Set. They should check work by comparing answers with a partner before going over answers as a class. Look for misconceptions or misunderstandings that can be addressed in the Debrief. Guide students in a conversation to debrief the Problem Set and process the lesson.

Any combination of the questions below may be used to lead the discussion.

- In Problem 2, did you partition the rectangle the same way as your partner? Why were we able to go from whole to part?

- Explain the connection between the written method, the number bond, and the area model in Problem 3.

- In the last problem, explain the connection between the algorithm and the area model.

- Each time we divide, what happens to the amount of area we still have left to divide?

- Even though division is messy, I think it is the most interesting operation of all because— imagine this—sometimes that little piece that is left to divide is always there, even though it gets infinitely small! Talk to your partner about what you think I might mean by that.

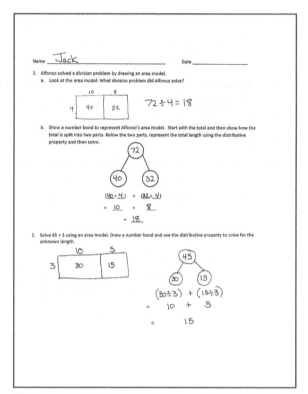

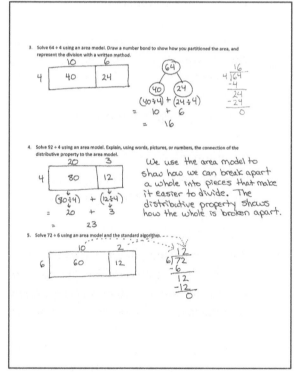

Lesson 20:   Solve division problems without remainders using the area model.

EUREKA
MATH™

Exit Ticket (3 minutes)

After the Student Debrief, instruct students to complete the Exit Ticket. A review of their work will help with assessing students' understanding of the concepts that were presented in today's lesson and planning more effectively for future lessons. The questions may be read aloud to the students.

Lesson 20:   Solve division problems without remainders using the area model.

287

©2015 Great Minds. eureka-math.org
G4-M3-TE-B2-1.3.1-01.2016

Name _____ Date _____

1. Alfonso solved a division problem by drawing an area model.

   a. Look at the area model. What division problem did Alfonso solve?

   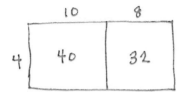

   b. Show a number bond to represent Alfonso's area model. Start with the total, and then show how the total is split into two parts. Below the two parts, represent the total length using the distributive property, and then solve.

   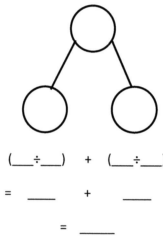

   (___÷___) + (___÷___)

   = ____ + ____

   = ____

2. Solve 45 ÷ 3 using an area model. Draw a number bond, and use the distributive property to solve for the unknown length.

Lesson 20: Solve division problems without remainders using the area model.

3. Solve 64 ÷ 4 using an area model. Draw a number bond to show how you partitioned the area, and represent the division with a written method.

4. Solve 92 ÷ 4 using an area model. Explain, using words, pictures, or numbers, the connection of the distributive property to the area model.

5. Solve 72 ÷ 6 using an area model and the standard algorithm.

Lesson 20:   Solve division problems without remainders using the area model.

289

©2015 Great Minds. eureka-math.org
G4-M3-TE-B2-1.3.1-01.2016

Name _____ Date _____

1. Tony drew the following area model to find an unknown length. What division equation did he model?

$$
\begin{array}{c c}
 & \overset{20}{} \quad \overset{4}{} \\
3 \; \boxed{\; 60 \; | \; 12 \;}
\end{array}
$$

2. Solve 42 ÷ 3 using the area model, a number bond, and a written method.

Lesson 20:   Solve division problems without remainders using the area model.

Name _____ Date _____

1. Maria solved a division problem by drawing an area model.

   a. Look at the area model. What division problem did Maria solve?

   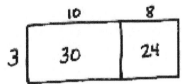

   b. Show a number bond to represent Maria's area model. Start with the total, and then show how the total is split into two parts. Below the two parts, represent the total length using the distributive property, and then solve.

   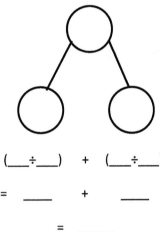

   (___÷___)   +   (___÷___)

   =   _____   +   _____

   =   _____

2. Solve $42 ÷ 3$ using an area model. Draw a number bond, and use the distributive property to solve for the unknown length.

EUREKA MATH™

Lesson 20: Solve division problems without remainders using the area model.

291

©2015 Great Minds. eureka-math.org
G4-M3-TE-B2-1.3.1-01.2016

3. Solve 60 ÷ 4 using an area model. Draw a number bond to show how you partitioned the area, and represent the division with a written method.

4. Solve 72 ÷ 4 using an area model. Explain, using words, pictures, or numbers, the connection of the distributive property to the area model.

5. Solve 96 ÷ 6 using an area model and the standard algorithm.

Lesson 20:   Solve division problems without remainders using the area model.

©2015 Great Minds. eureka-math.org
G4-M3-TE-B2-1.3.1-01.2016

Lesson 21

Objective: Solve division problems with remainders using the area model.

Suggested Lesson Structure

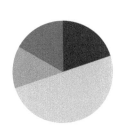

■ Fluency Practice   (12 minutes)
▨ Application Problem   (8 minutes)
▢ Concept Development   (30 minutes)
■ Student Debrief   (10 minutes)
   Total Time   **(60 minutes)**

Fluency Practice (12 minutes)

- Sprint: Division with Remainders **4.NBT.6**   (8 minutes)
- Find the Unknown Factor **4.OA.4**   (4 minutes)

Sprint: Division with Remainders (8 minutes)

Materials: (S) Division with Remainders Sprint

Note: This Sprint reviews content from Topic E, including division with and without remainders.

Find the Unknown Factor (4 minutes)

Materials: (S) Personal white board

Note: This fluency activity prepares students for Lesson 22's Concept Development

  T: (Write 6 × ___ = 18.) Say the unknown factor.
  S: 3.
  T: (Write 18 ÷ 6.) On your personal white board, complete the division sentence.
  S: (Write 18 ÷ 6 = 3.)

Continue with the following possible sequence: 3 × ___ = 21, 4 × ___ = 20, 5 × ___ = 25, 6 × ___ = 42, 7 × ___ = 56, 9 × ___ = 72, 6 × ___ = 54, 7 × ___ = 63, and 9 × ___ = 63.

Lesson 21:   Solve division problems with remainders using the area model.

293

©2015 Great Minds. eureka-math.org
G4-M3-TE-B2-1.3.1-01.2016

Application Problem (8 minutes)

A rectangle has an area of 36 square units and a width of 2 units. What is the unknown side length?

Method 1:

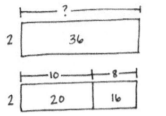

Method 2:

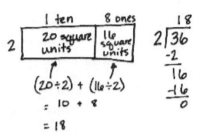

The unknown side length is 18 units.

Note: This Application Problem serves as an introduction to Problem 1 in the Concept Development, in which students find the total unknown length of a rectangle with an area of 37 and a width of 2. In today's Concept Development, students move on to the complexity of using the area model when there is a remainder.

Concept Development (30 minutes)

Materials: (T) Square grid paper (S) Problem Set

Note: Use the Problem Set for Lesson 21 to record work for Problems 1 and 2 of this Concept Development. Use the remaining problems on the Problem Set for class instruction or independent practice.

Problem 1: 37 ÷ 2

- T: (Display the Application Problem with an area of 36 square units on grid paper.) This rectangle has a side length of 18. What would be the area of a rectangle with a width of 2 units and a length of 19 units? (Draw on grid paper.)

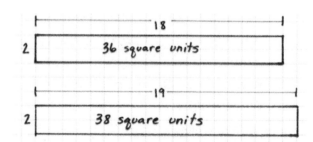

- S: 38 square units.
- T: So, we cannot represent a rectangle with a width of 2 and an area of 37 square units. Let's get as close as we can to 37 square units by building a rectangle part to whole as we did yesterday.

©2015 Great Minds. eureka-math.org
G4-M3-TE-B2-1.3.1-01.2016

T: Draw a rectangle. Label the width as 2 units. Two times how many tens gets us as close as possible to an area of 3 tens?

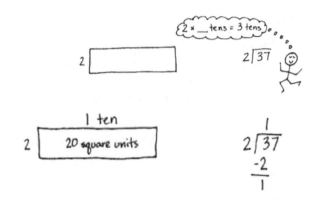

S: 1 ten.

T: Label this rectangle with a length of 1 ten. Record 1 ten in the tens place. What is 1 ten times 2?

S: 2 tens.

T: How many square units of area is that?

S: 20 square units.

T: (Record 20 square units in the rectangle.) How many tens remain?

S: 1 ten. (Record 1 ten below 2 tens. Record 7 ones next to the 1 ten.)

T: 17 ones remain. Two times how many ones gives us an area close to 17 square units?

S: 8 ones.

T: Extend the rectangle, and label its length as 8 ones. 8 ones times 2 is…?

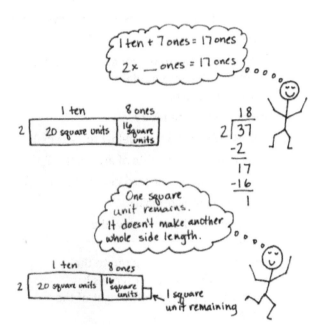

S: 16 ones.

T: 16 ones represents the area of this rectangle. (Label as 16 square units.) How many ones remain?

S: 1 one.

T: To make a new length unit, we must have 2 square units. We only have 1. Let's draw the remaining 1 square unit.

T: Let's validate our drawing and algorithm using the distributive property. 20 square units divided by 2 is…?

S: 10.

T: 10 length units. 16 square units divided by 2 is…?

S: 8 length units.

T: 10 length units plus 8 length units is…?

S: 18 length units.

T: Let's solve for the area. 18 length units times 2 length units equals?

S: 36 square units.

T: We see that in our area model. Add 1 square unit, our remainder.

S: 37 square units.

The length of the unknown side is 18 units. One square unit was leftover.

$$(20 \div 2) + (16 \div 2)$$
$$= 10 + 8$$
$$= 18$$

$$(18 \times 2) + 1 = 37$$

Problem 2: 76 ÷ 3

T: (Write 76 ÷ 3.) I'm going to represent this with an area model moving from part to whole by place value, just as we did with 37 ÷ 2. What should the total area be?

S: 76 square units.

T: (Draw a rectangle.) What is the width or the known side length?

S: 3 length units.

T: (Label a width of 3.) Three times how many tens gets us as close as possible to an area of 7 tens? (Point to the 7 tens of the dividend.)

S: 2 tens.

T: Let's give 2 tens to the length. (Write the length on the area model.) Let's record 2 tens in the tens place.

T: What is 2 tens times 3?

S: 6 tens. (Record 6 tens below the 7 tens.)

T: How many square units of area is that?

S: 60 square units. (Record in the rectangle.)

T: How many tens remain?

S: 1 ten. (Record 1 ten below the 6 tens.)

T: Let's add the remaining ten to the 6 ones. What is 1 ten + 6 ones? (Record the 6 ones to the right of the 1 ten.)

S: 16 ones.

T: We have an area of 16 square units remaining with a width of 3. (Point to the 16 in the algorithm.) Three times how many ones gets us as close as possible to an area of 16?

S: 5 ones.

T: Let's give 5 ones to the length. (Label the length.)

T: This rectangle has an area of…?

S: 15 square units.

T: How many square units remain?

S: 1 square unit.

T: What is the unknown length, and how many square units remain?

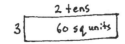

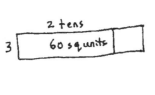

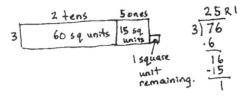

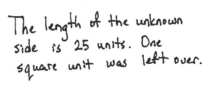

Lesson 21:   Solve division problems with remainders using the area model.

EUREKA
MATH™

S: The unknown length is 25 with a remainder of 1 square unit.

T: 60 square units divided by a side length of 3 (record with the distributive property as shown to the right) gave us a side length of...?

S: 20.

T: Let's say "length units."

S: 20 length units.

T: 15 square units divided by a side length of 3 (record) gave us a side length of...?

S: 5 length units.

T: The total length was...?

S: 25 length units.

T: With 1 square unit, we did not add on to the length.

T: We built the area one rectangle at a time by place value. Each time after we divide, we have some area remaining. After dividing the tens, we had 16 square units remaining. (Point to the model and long division.) After dividing the ones, we had 1 square unit remaining. (Point to the model and long division.) Later, when we study fractions more, we will be able to make a little more length from that area, but for now, we are just going to leave it as 1 square unit of area remaining. (Optional: See the Student Debrief for a way of understanding the remainder as length.)

T: Review with your partner how we solved this problem step by step.

Have students proceed through the balance of the Problem Set, supported as necessary.

Problem Set (10 minutes)

Students should do their personal best to complete the remainder of the Problem Set within the allotted 10 minutes. For some classes, it may be appropriate to modify the assignment by specifying which problems they work on first. Some problems do not specify a method for solving. Students should solve these problems using the RDW approach used for Application Problems.

$$(60 \div 3) + (15 \div 3)$$
$$= 20 + 5$$
$$= 25$$
$$(25 \times 3) + 1 = 76$$

NOTES ON MULTIPLE MEANS OF REPRESENTATION:

To draw the area models, consider giving students the option of using graph paper, which gives the concreteness of the squares that make up the area.

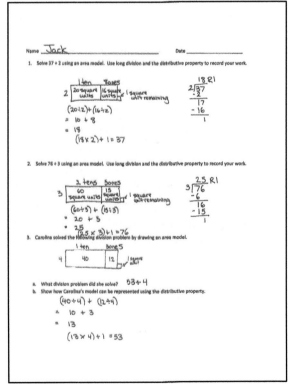

Lesson 21: Solve division problems with remainders using the area model.

297

©2015 Great Minds. eureka-math.org
G4-M3-TE-B2-1.3.1-01.2016

Student Debrief (10 minutes)

Lesson Objective: Solve division problems with remainders using the area model.

The Student Debrief is intended to invite reflection and active processing of the total lesson experience.

Invite students to review their solutions for the Problem Set. They should check work by comparing answers with a partner before going over answers as a class. Look for misconceptions or misunderstandings that can be addressed in the Debrief. Guide students in a conversation to debrief the Problem Set and process the lesson.

Any combination of the questions below may be used to lead the discussion.

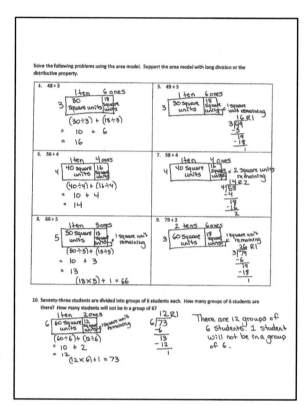

- Explain to your partner the connection between the distributive property and the area model in Problem 3.

- Because we often have remainders when we divide, we have to use the area model by building up from part to whole. What did the first rectangle you drew in Problem 1 represent? The next chunk of the rectangle?

- Each time we divide, what happens to the amount of area we still have left to divide?

- Why don't we have this complication of leftovers or remainders with multiplication?

- In Problem 4, we didn't know if we were going to have a remainder in the ones place, so instead we built up to the area working with one place value unit at a time. How might the problems with remainders have been challenging if you started with the whole area, like in Lesson 20?

- (Optional.) Let's look back at Problem 2, 76 ÷ 3. What if we cut this remaining square unit into 3 equal parts with vertical lines? What is the length of one of these units? What if we stack them to add more area? What is the total length of the new rectangle, including this tiny piece?

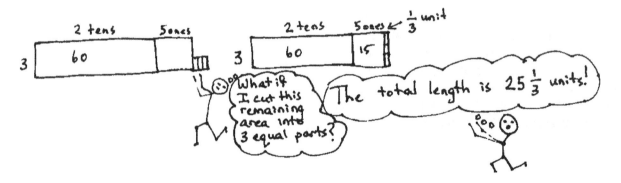

©2015 Great Minds. eureka-math.org
G4-M3-TE-B2-1.3.1-01.2016

Exit Ticket (3 minutes)

After the Student Debrief, instruct students to complete the Exit Ticket. A review of their work will help with assessing students' understanding of the concepts that were presented in today's lesson and planning more effectively for future lessons. The questions may be read aloud to the students.

Lesson 21:   Solve division problems with remainders using the area model.

299

A

Number Correct: _____

Division with Remainders

1.	8 ÷ 2	Q = _____	R = _____
2.	9 ÷ 2	Q = _____	R = _____
3.	4 ÷ 4	Q = _____	R = _____
4.	5 ÷ 4	Q = _____	R = _____
5.	7 ÷ 5	Q = _____	R = _____
6.	8 ÷ 5	Q = _____	R = _____
7.	5 ÷ 3	Q = _____	R = _____
8.	6 ÷ 3	Q = _____	R = _____
9.	8 ÷ 4	Q = _____	R = _____
10.	9 ÷ 4	Q = _____	R = _____
11.	2 ÷ 2	Q = _____	R = _____
12.	3 ÷ 2	Q = _____	R = _____
13.	7 ÷ 3	Q = _____	R = _____
14.	8 ÷ 3	Q = _____	R = _____
15.	9 ÷ 3	Q = _____	R = _____
16.	8 ÷ 6	Q = _____	R = _____
17.	9 ÷ 6	Q = _____	R = _____
18.	5 ÷ 5	Q = _____	R = _____
19.	6 ÷ 5	Q = _____	R = _____
20.	8 ÷ 8	Q = _____	R = _____
21.	9 ÷ 8	Q = _____	R = _____
22.	9 ÷ 9	Q = _____	R = _____

23.	6 ÷ 2	Q = _____	R = _____
24.	7 ÷ 2	Q = _____	R = _____
25.	3 ÷ 3	Q = _____	R = _____
26.	4 ÷ 3	Q = _____	R = _____
27.	6 ÷ 4	Q = _____	R = _____
28.	7 ÷ 4	Q = _____	R = _____
29.	6 ÷ 6	Q = _____	R = _____
30.	7 ÷ 6	Q = _____	R = _____
31.	4 ÷ 2	Q = _____	R = _____
32.	5 ÷ 2	Q = _____	R = _____
33.	9 ÷ 3	Q = _____	R = _____
34.	9 ÷ 5	Q = _____	R = _____
35.	7 ÷ 7	Q = _____	R = _____
36.	9 ÷ 9	Q = _____	R = _____
37.	13 ÷ 4	Q = _____	R = _____
38.	18 ÷ 5	Q = _____	R = _____
39.	21 ÷ 6	Q = _____	R = _____
40.	24 ÷ 7	Q = _____	R = _____
41.	29 ÷ 8	Q = _____	R = _____
42.	43 ÷ 6	Q = _____	R = _____
43.	53 ÷ 6	Q = _____	R = _____
44.	82 ÷ 9	Q = _____	R = _____

Lesson 21:   Solve division problems with remainders using the area model.

EUREKA
MATH™

B

Number Correct: _____

Improvement: _____

Division with Remainders

1.	9 ÷ 8	Q = _____	R = _____
2.	8 ÷ 8	Q = _____	R = _____
3.	9 ÷ 6	Q = _____	R = _____
4.	8 ÷ 6	Q = _____	R = _____
5.	5 ÷ 5	Q = _____	R = _____
6.	6 ÷ 5	Q = _____	R = _____
7.	7 ÷ 4	Q = _____	R = _____
8.	6 ÷ 4	Q = _____	R = _____
9.	5 ÷ 3	Q = _____	R = _____
10.	6 ÷ 3	Q = _____	R = _____
11.	2 ÷ 2	Q = _____	R = _____
12.	3 ÷ 2	Q = _____	R = _____
13.	3 ÷ 3	Q = _____	R = _____
14.	4 ÷ 3	Q = _____	R = _____
15.	8 ÷ 7	Q = _____	R = _____
16.	9 ÷ 7	Q = _____	R = _____
17.	4 ÷ 4	Q = _____	R = _____
18.	5 ÷ 4	Q = _____	R = _____
19.	6 ÷ 2	Q = _____	R = _____
20.	7 ÷ 2	Q = _____	R = _____
21.	8 ÷ 5	Q = _____	R = _____
22.	7 ÷ 5	Q = _____	R = _____

23.	4 ÷ 2	Q = _____	R = _____
24.	5 ÷ 2	Q = _____	R = _____
25.	8 ÷ 4	Q = _____	R = _____
26.	9 ÷ 4	Q = _____	R = _____
27.	9 ÷ 3	Q = _____	R = _____
28.	8 ÷ 3	Q = _____	R = _____
29.	9 ÷ 5	Q = _____	R = _____
30.	6 ÷ 6	Q = _____	R = _____
31.	7 ÷ 6	Q = _____	R = _____
32.	9 ÷ 9	Q = _____	R = _____
33.	7 ÷ 7	Q = _____	R = _____
34.	9 ÷ 2	Q = _____	R = _____
35.	8 ÷ 2	Q = _____	R = _____
36.	37 ÷ 8	Q = _____	R = _____
37.	50 ÷ 9	Q = _____	R = _____
38.	17 ÷ 6	Q = _____	R = _____
39.	48 ÷ 7	Q = _____	R = _____
40.	51 ÷ 8	Q = _____	R = _____
41.	68 ÷ 9	Q = _____	R = _____
42.	53 ÷ 6	Q = _____	R = _____
43.	61 ÷ 8	Q = _____	R = _____
44.	70 ÷ 9	Q = _____	R = _____

Name _____   Date _____

1. Solve 37 ÷ 2 using an area model. Use long division and the distributive property to record your work.

2. Solve 76 ÷ 3 using an area model. Use long division and the distributive property to record your work.

3. Carolina solved the following division problem by drawing an area model.

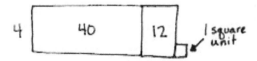

a. What division problem did she solve?

b. Show how Carolina's model can be represented using the distributive property.

Lesson 21:   Solve division problems with remainders using the area model.

©2015 Great Minds. eureka-math.org
G4-M3-TE-B2-1.3.1-01.2016

Solve the following problems using the area model. Support the area model with long division or the distributive property.

4. $48 \div 3$	5. $49 \div 3$
6. $56 \div 4$	7. $58 \div 4$
8. $66 \div 5$	9. $79 \div 3$

Lesson 21:   Solve division problems with remainders using the area model.

10. Seventy-three students are divided into groups of 6 students each. How many groups of 6 students are there? How many students will not be in a group of 6?

Name _____   Date _____

1. Kyle drew the following area model to find an unknown length. What division equation did he model?

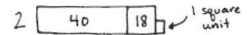

2. Solve 93 ÷ 4 using the area model, long division, and the distributive property.

Lesson 21:   Solve division problems with remainders using the area model.

305

©2015 Great Minds. eureka-math.org
G4-M3-TE-B2-1.3.1-01.2016

Name _____   Date _____

1. Solve 35 ÷ 2 using an area model. Use long division and the distributive property to record your work.

2. Solve 79 ÷ 3 using an area model. Use long division and the distributive property to record your work.

3. Paulina solved the following division problem by drawing an area model.

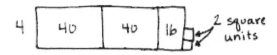

a. What division problem did she solve?

b. Show how Paulina's model can be represented using the distributive property.

Lesson 21:   Solve division problems with remainders using the area model.

©2015 Great Minds. eureka-math.org
G4-M3-TE-B2-1.3.1-01.2016

Solve the following problems using the area model. Support the area model with long division or the distributive property.

4. $42 \div 3$	5. $43 \div 3$
6. $52 \div 4$	7. $54 \div 4$
8. $61 \div 5$	9. $73 \div 3$

10. Ninety-seven lunch trays were placed equally in 4 stacks. How many lunch trays were in each stack? How many lunch trays will be left over?

Mathematics Curriculum

Topic F
Reasoning with Divisibility

4.OA.4

Focus Standard:	4.OA.4	Find all factor pairs for a whole number in the range 1–100. Recognize that a whole number is a multiple of each of its factors. Determine whether a given whole number in the range 1–100 is a multiple of a given one-digit number. Determine whether a given whole number in the range 1–100 is prime or composite.
Instructional Days:	4	
Coherence -Links from:	G3–M1	Properties of Multiplication and Division and Solving Problems with Units of 2–5 and 10
	G3–M3	Multiplication and Division with Units of 0, 1, 6–9, and Multiples of 10
-Links to:	G5–M2	Multi-Digit Whole Number and Decimal Fraction Operations
	G5–M3	Addition and Subtraction of Fractions

In Topic F, armed with an understanding of remainders, students explore factors, multiples, and prime and composite numbers within 100 (**4.OA.4**). Students gain valuable insights into patterns of divisibility as they test for primes and find factors and multiples, at times using their new skill of dividing double-digit dividends. This prepares them for Topic G's work with dividends of up to four digits.

Lesson 22 has students find factor pairs for numbers to 100 and then use their understanding of factors to determine whether numbers are prime or composite. In Lesson 23, students use division to examine numbers to 100 for factors and make observations about patterns they observe, for example, "When 2 is a factor, the numbers are even." Lesson 24 transitions the work with factors into a study of multiples, encouraging students to notice that the set of multiples of a number is infinite while the set of factors is finite.

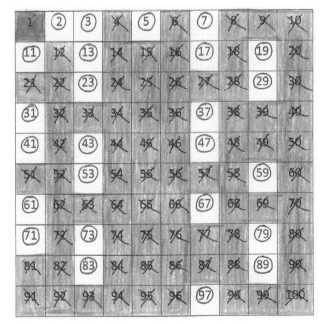

In Lesson 25, the Sieve of Eratosthenes uses multiples to enable students to identify and explore the properties of prime and composite numbers to 100.

A Teaching Sequence Toward Mastery of Reasoning with Divisibility

Objective 1: Find factor pairs for numbers to 100, and use understanding of factors to define prime and composite.
(Lesson 22)

Objective 2: Use division and the associative property to test for factors and observe patterns.
(Lesson 23)

Objective 3: Determine if a whole number is a multiple of another number.
(Lesson 24)

Objective 4: Explore properties of prime and composite numbers to 100 by using multiples.
(Lesson 25)

EUREKA
MATH™

Lesson 22

Objective: Find factor pairs for numbers to 100, and use understanding of factors to define prime and composite.

Suggested Lesson Structure

- ■ Fluency Practice   (12 minutes)
- ▨ Application Problem   (5 minutes)
- ▢ Concept Development   (33 minutes)
- ■ Student Debrief   (10 minutes)

  Total Time   **(60 minutes)**

Fluency Practice (12 minutes)

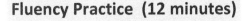

- ▪ Divide Using the Area Model **4.NBT.6**   (4 minutes)
- ▪ Find the Unknown Factor **4.OA.4**   (5 minutes)
- ▪ Mental Multiplication **4.NBT.5**   (3 minutes)

Divide Using the Area Model (4 minutes)

Materials: (S) Personal white board

Note: This fluency activity reviews content from Lesson 20.

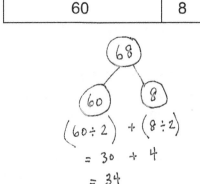

- T: (Project an area model that shows 68 ÷ 2.) Write a division expression for this area model.
- S: (Write 68 ÷ 2.)
- T: Label the length of each rectangle in the area model.
- S: (Write 30 above the 60 and 4 above the 8.)
- T: Solve using the standard algorithm or the distributive property with a number bond.

Continue with the following possible sequence: 96 ÷ 3, 72 ÷ 3, and 72 ÷ 4.

Find the Unknown Factor (5 minutes)

Note: This fluency activity prepares students for the Concept Development.

Repeat the process from Lesson 20 for 3 × ___ = 9, 4 × ___ = 16, 5 × ___ = 45, 6 × ___ = 42, 7 × ___ = 56, 9 × ___ = 72, 6 × ___ = 54, 7 × ___ = 63, and 9 × ___ = 54.

Lesson 22:   Find factor pairs for numbers to 100, and use understanding of factors
             to define prime and composite.

©2015 Great Minds. eureka-math.org
G4-M3-TE-B2-1.3.1-01.2016

311

Mental Multiplication (3 minutes)

Note: This fluency activity reviews content taught earlier in the module.

Repeat the process from Lesson 20 with the following possible sequence: 4×2, 4×20, 2×40, 20×40, 3×3, 3×30, 30×30, 3×4, 3×40, and 30×40.

Application Problem (5 minutes)

$8 \times \_\_\_\_ = 96$. Find the unknown side length, or factor. Use an area model to solve the problem.

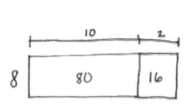

Note: This Application Problem applies the Topic E skill of dividing a two-digit dividend using an area model and serves as a lead-in to this lesson's Concept Development by using area models to illustrate the concept of factor pairs.

Concept Development (33 minutes)

Materials: (S) Personal white board

Problem 1: Identify the factors and product represented in an array.

Display a 1×8 array and a 2×4 array.

- T: Tell your partner the multiplication sentences that are represented by these arrays.
- S: $1 \times 8 = 8$ and $2 \times 4 = 8$.
- T: Yes, both arrays show a product of 8. The factors 1 and 8 and the factors 2 and 4 are multiplied to give a product of 8.
- T: 1, 2, 4, and 8 are all factors of 8.

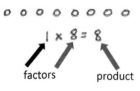

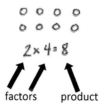

NOTES ON
MULTIPLE MEANS
OF ACTION AND
EXPRESSION:

Provide or guide students to make a table to find and organize the factor pairs of 8 and 18. Challenge students working above grade level to identify and present a method to their peers of finding factor pairs. Assist students working below grade level or those who need further concrete understanding of factor pairs to use tiles, creating arrays to find all of the factors of a given number.

Lesson 22:   Find factor pairs for numbers to 100, and use understanding of factors
to define prime and composite.

©2015 Great Minds. eureka-math.org
G4-M3-TE-B2-1.3.1-01.2016

EUREKA
MATH™

Display arrays for 1 × 18 and 2 × 9.

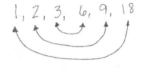

$1 \times 18 = 18$

T: What product is represented in both arrays?

S: 18.

T: Record the multiplication sentences for each array.

$2 \times 9 = 18$

S: 1 × 18 = 18 and 2 × 9 = 18.

T: Circle the factors. Write the factors of 18 that are represented in order from least to greatest.

$3 \times 6 = 18$

S: (Write 1, 2, 9, 18.)

T: With your partner, draw an array to represent another pair of factors with the product of 18.

1, 2, 3, 6, 9, 18

T: (Pause while students work.) What new factors of 18 did you find?

S: 3 and 6.

T: Revise your list of factors of 18.

S: 1, 2, 3, 6, 9, and 18.

T: How can we make sure we found all of the factors of 18?

3 is not a factor of 8, so I found all of the factors of 8!

1, 2, 4, 8

S: I can use my multiplication chart. → I can think through my multiplication facts. → But what if the number is really big, like 92? I don't know all the factors of 92. → I could draw arrays to find all the factors, making rows of 3, then 4, then 5, and all the way to 92. → That will take a long time.

T: Look at the list of factors for 18. Draw an arrow from 1 to 18. These are factor pairs because 1 × 18 = 18. With your partner, draw the rest of the arrows to connect the factor pairs.

S: (Draw as pictured to the right above.)

T: Notice that 3 and 6 are the middle pairs. We've checked everything up to 3, and the counting numbers between 3 and 6 are not factors of 18, so we found all the pairs. Try that with the factors of 8.

Problem 2: Identify factors to define prime and composite numbers.

Display the number sentence 2 × 8 = 16.

T: What are the factors?

S: 2 and 8.

T: What other multiplication sentences can you write using different factors that will give us the same product?

S: 1 × 16 = 16. 4 × 4 = 16.

T: So, what are all of the factors of 16?

S: 1, 2, 4, 8, and 16.

Lesson 22: Find factor pairs for numbers to 100, and use understanding of factors to define prime and composite.

©2015 Great Minds. eureka-math.org
G4-M3-TE-B2-1.3.1-01.2016

313

T: How do you know those are all of the factors of
    16?

S: I listed them in order. When I got to 8, I noticed
    I already had its factor pair. Two times 8 is 16, so
    I didn't have to go any further. → I stopped at 8,
    too, because it was half of 16. There isn't a
    factor between 1 and 2, so I guess we never need
    to go beyond the halfway point.

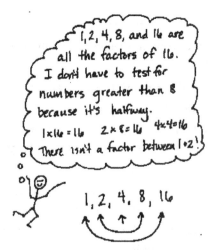

Display the equation $1 \times 7 = 7$.

T: What are the factors in this equation?

S: 1 and 7.

T: Find another factor pair for 7.

S: 7×1? → Those are the same factors. → If we drew arrays to represent factors of 7, the array for
    1×7 and 7×1 would look the same. → I can't find another pair. → There can't be another pair.
    2, 3, 4, 5, and 6 don't work.

T: I hear you saying that 1 and 7 are the only factors. Talk to your partner. How is that different from
    the factors of 8, 10, 16, and 18?

S: There are more factor pairs for 8, 10, 16, and 18 than there are for 7. → Seven has only one pair of
    factors, but the other numbers we looked at had more than one pair.

T: That's right! Now think about the number 5. Name a pair of factors that will give us a product of 5.

S: 1 and 5.

T: Are there any other factor pairs?

S: Nope. One times 5 makes 5 just like 1 times 7 is seven. → They both only have only one set of
    factors.

T: Numbers like 5 and 7 that have *exactly* two factors, 1 and the number itself, are called **prime
    numbers**.

T: With your partner, list at least two more prime numbers. (Allow time for students to discover and
    list. Review their findings for numbers such as 11, 13, and 17.)

T: (Refer to list just created.) If these are prime numbers, can you name a number that is not prime?

S: (Responses will vary.)

T: Yes! The numbers you mentioned have at least one factor other than 1 and the number itself.
    They are called **composite numbers**.

T: Let's use 6 as an example. Does 6 have more than two factors?

S: Yes! One and 6 are factors, but 2 and 3 are also factors.

T: So, what can we say about the number 6?

S: It is composite. It has more than two arrays to represent it. It has more than two factors.

Find factor pairs for numbers to 100, and use understanding of factors
              to define prime and composite.

©2015 Great Minds. eureka-math.org
G4-M3-TE-B2-1.3.1-01.2016

EUREKA
MATH™

Problem 3: Identify factors of numbers and determine if they are prime or composite.

Display the numbers 23, 35, and 48.

T: Let's use a table to record the factor pairs for 35. Say the first factor pair.

Guide students to complete the table as a class, using their multiplication facts.

T: Is 35 a prime or composite number? Why?

S: Composite, because it has more than one factor pair.

T: With your partner, use a table to list factors of 23 and 48 and tell if each one is prime or composite.

Factor Pairs for 35	
1	35
5	7

Allow three minutes for students to work.

T: Are any of these numbers prime numbers? How do you know?

S: Twenty-three is prime because we thought about all the possible factors, other than one, up to 11 and none worked.

T: Why can we stop at the number 11?

S: Eleven is the closest whole number to half of 23. Once I get halfway, I have found all of the factor pairs. After that, they just keep repeating.

T: Why is 48 composite?

S: There are more than two factors. → It has 6 and 8 as factors. → It also has 4 and 12. → I found 10 factors! It sure isn't prime!

Problem Set (10 minutes)

Students should do their personal best to complete the Problem Set within the allotted 10 minutes. For some classes, it may be appropriate to modify the assignment by specifying which problems they work on first. Some problems do not specify a method for solving. Students should solve these problems using the RDW approach used for Application Problems.

NOTES ON MULTIPLE MEANS OF ACTION AND EXPRESSION:

Provide concrete manipulatives for students to explore arrays as they classify each number in Problem 1 of the Problem Set as prime or composite. Numbers that can be arranged in more than one array pattern are composite.

Lesson 22:   Find factor pairs for numbers to 100, and use understanding of factors to define prime and composite.

315

©2015 Great Minds. eureka-math.org
G4-M3-TE-B2-1.3.1-01.2016

Student Debrief (10 minutes)

Lesson Objective: Find factor pairs for numbers to 100, and use understanding of factors to define prime and composite.

The Student Debrief is intended to invite reflection and active processing of the total lesson experience.

Invite students to review their solutions for the Problem Set. They should check work by comparing answers with a partner before going over answers as a class. Look for misconceptions or misunderstandings that can be addressed in the Debrief. Guide students in a conversation to debrief the Problem Set and process the lesson.

Any combination of the questions below may be used to lead the discussion.

- Compare the factors in Problem 1(e) and 1(l). Twenty-four is double 12. What do you notice about their factors? Compare the factors in Problem 1(d) and 1(i). Eighteen is double 9. What do you notice about their factors?

- In Problem 1, what numbers have an odd number of factors? Why is that so?

- Are all prime numbers odd? Explain what you would tell Bryan in Problem 3.

- Explain your answer to Problem 3(b). Are all even numbers composite? How many even numbers are not composite?

- We talked a lot about the number 1 today as being a factor of other numbers, but we have not classified it as **prime** or **composite**. Can 1 be composite? (No.) It turns out that it's not considered prime either!

NOTES ON PRIME NUMBERS:

Since 0 times any number is 0, it behaves differently than other numbers. Because of this difference, 0 is not classified as prime or composite.

Many students might reason that 1 should be prime since its only factors are 1 and itself. In fact, their logic is sound, and throughout history, many mathematicians would have agreed! However, choosing to define 1 as neither prime nor composite leads to simpler statements of theorems regarding the structure of the number system. This choice has become universally accepted in more recent times.

Name __Jack_____   Date _____

1. Record the factors of the given numbers as multiplication sentences and as a list in order from least to greatest. Classify each as prime (P) or composite (C). The first problem is done for you.

	Multiplication Sentences	Factors	P or C
a.	4 $1 \times 4 = 4$ $2 \times 2 = 4$	The factors of 4 are: 1, 2, 4	C
b.	6 $1 \times 6 = 6$ $2 \times 3 = 6$	The factors of 6 are: 1, 2, 3, 6	C
c.	7 $1 \times 7 = 7$	The factors of 7 are: 1, 7	P
d.	9 $1 \times 9 = 9$ $3 \times 3 = 9$	The factors of 9 are: 1, 3, 9	C
e.	12 $1 \times 12 = 12$ $2 \times 6 = 12$ $3 \times 4 = 12$	The factors of 12 are: 1, 2, 3, 4, 6, 12	C
f.	13 $1 \times 13 = 13$	The factors of 13 are: 1, 13	P
g.	15 $1 \times 15 = 15$ $3 \times 5 = 15$	The factors of 15 are: 1, 3, 5, 15	C
h.	16 $1 \times 16 = 16$ $2 \times 8 = 16$ $4 \times 4 = 16$	The factors of 16 are: 1, 2, 4, 8, 16	C
i.	18 $1 \times 18 = 18$ $2 \times 9 = 18$ $3 \times 6 = 18$	The factors of 18 are: 1, 2, 3, 6, 9, 18	C
j.	19 $1 \times 19 = 19$	The factors of 19 are: 1, 19	P
k.	21 $1 \times 21 = 21$ $3 \times 7 = 21$	The factors of 21 are: 1, 3, 7, 21	C
l.	24 $1 \times 24 = 24$ $4 \times 6 = 24$ $2 \times 12 = 24$ $3 \times 8 = 24$	The factors of 24 are: 1, 2, 3, 4, 6, 8, 12, 24	C

EUREKA MATH™

Exit Ticket (3 minutes)

After the Student Debrief, instruct students to complete the Exit Ticket. A review of their work will help with assessing students' understanding of the concepts that were presented in today's lesson and planning more effectively for future lessons. The questions may be read aloud to the students.

2. Find all factors for the following numbers and classify as prime or composite. Explain your classification of each as prime or composite.

Factor Pairs for 25		Factor Pairs for 28		Factor Pairs for 29	
1	25	1	28	1	29
5	5	2	14		
		4	7		

Composite
more than 2 factors

Composite
more than 2 factors

Prime
only 2 factors,
just 1 and itself (29)

3. Bryan says all prime numbers are odd numbers.
    a. List all of the prime numbers less than 20 in numerical order.

    2, 3, 5, 7, 11, 13, 17, 19

    b. Use your list to show that Bryan's claim is false.

    Bryan's claim is false because 2 is a prime number
    but it is an even number.

4. Sheila has 28 stickers to divide evenly among 3 friends. She thinks there will be no leftovers. Use what you know about factor pairs to explain if Sheila is correct.

    Sheila is incorrect. 3 is not a factor of 28. 3 is a
    factor of 27, so each friend could receive 9 stickers
    each, and there would be one sticker left over.
        3×9=27   27+1=28

Lesson 22: Find factor pairs for numbers to 100, and use understanding of factors to define prime and composite.

317

©2015 Great Minds. eureka-math.org
G4-M3-TE-B2-1.3.1-01.2016

Name _____ Date _____

1. Record the factors of the given numbers as multiplication sentences and as a list in order from least to greatest. Classify each as prime (P) or composite (C). The first problem is done for you.

	Multiplication Sentences	Factors	P or C
a.	4 $1 \times 4 = 4$ $2 \times 2 = 4$	The factors of 4 are: 1, 2, 4	C
b.	6	The factors of 6 are:	
c.	7	The factors of 7 are:	
d.	9	The factors of 9 are:	
e.	12	The factors of 12 are:	
f.	13	The factors of 13 are:	
g.	15	The factors of 15 are:	
h.	16	The factors of 16 are:	
i.	18	The factors of 18 are:	
j.	19	The factors of 19 are:	
k.	21	The factors of 21 are:	
l.	24	The factors of 24 are:	

Lesson 22: Find factor pairs for numbers to 100, and use understanding of factors to define prime and composite.

©2015 Great Minds. eureka-math.org
G4-M3-TE-B2-1.3.1-01.2016

EUREKA
MATH™

2. Find all factors for the following numbers, and classify each number as prime or composite. Explain your classification of each as prime or composite.

Factor Pairs for 25	

Factor Pairs for 28	

Factor Pairs for 29	

3. Bryan says all prime numbers are odd numbers.

   a. List all of the prime numbers less than 20 in numerical order.

   b. Use your list to show that Bryan's claim is false.

4. Sheila has 28 stickers to divide evenly among 3 friends. She thinks there will be no leftovers. Use what you know about factor pairs to explain if Sheila is correct.

EUREKA MATH™

Lesson 22: Find factor pairs for numbers to 100, and use understanding of factors to define prime and composite.

319

©2015 Great Minds. eureka-math.org
G4-M3-TE-B2-1.3.1-01.2016

Name _____ Date _____

Record the factors of the given numbers as multiplication sentences and as a list in order from least to greatest. Classify each as prime (P) or composite (C).

	Multiplication Sentences	Factors	Prime (P) or Composite (C)
a.	9	The factors of 9 are:	
b.	12	The factors of 12 are:	
c.	19	The factors of 19 are:	

Lesson 22: Find factor pairs for numbers to 100, and use understanding of factors to define prime and composite.

Name _____   Date _____

1. Record the factors of the given numbers as multiplication sentences and as a list in order from least to greatest. Classify each as prime (P) or composite (C). The first problem is done for you.

	Multiplication Sentences	Factors	P or C
a.	8 $1 \times 4 = 8$ $2 \times 4 = 8$	The factors of 8 are: 1, 2, 4, 8	C
b.	10	The factors of 10 are:	
c.	11	The factors of 11 are:	
d.	14	The factors of 14 are:	
e.	17	The factors of 17 are:	
f.	20	The factors of 20 are:	
g.	22	The factors of 22 are:	
h.	23	The factors of 23 are:	
i.	25	The factors of 25 are:	
j.	26	The factors of 26 are:	
k.	27	The factors of 27 are:	
l.	28	The factors of 28 are:	

Lesson 22:   Find factor pairs for numbers to 100, and use understanding of factors
                     to define prime and composite.

©2015 Great Minds. eureka-math.org
G4-M3-TE-B2-1.3.1-01.2016

2. Find all factors for the following numbers, and classify each number as prime or composite. Explain your classification of each as prime or composite.

Factor Pairs for 19	

Factor Pairs for 21	

Factor Pairs for 24	

3. Bryan says that only even numbers are composite.

   a. List all of the odd numbers less than 20 in numerical order.

   b. Use your list to show that Bryan's claim is false.

4. Julie has 27 grapes to divide evenly among 3 friends. She thinks there will be no leftovers. Use what you know about factor pairs to explain whether or not Julie is correct.

©2015 Great Minds. eureka-math.org
G4-M3-TE-B2-1.3.1-01.2016

EUREKA MATH

Lesson 23

Objective: Use division and the associative property to test for factors and observe patterns.

Suggested Lesson Structure

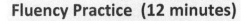

■ Fluency Practice   (12 minutes)

▨ Application Problem   (5 minutes)

▨ Concept Development   (33 minutes)

■ Student Debrief   (10 minutes)

    Total Time   **(60 minutes)**

Fluency Practice (12 minutes)

- Use Arrays to Find Factors **4.OA.4**   (6 minutes)
- Multiply Two Factors **4.NBT.5**   (4 minutes)
- Prime or Composite? **4.OA.4**   (2 minutes)

Use Arrays to Find Factors (6 minutes)

Materials: (S) Personal white board

Note: This fluency activity reviews Lesson 22's content. To challenge students, have them construct the arrays instead of having them projected.

T: (Project a 1 × 8 array.) What is the width of the array?

S: 1 unit.

T: (Write 1.) What's the length of the array?

S: 8 units.

T: (Write 8.) Write the multiplication sentence.

S: (Write 1 × 8 = 8.)

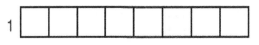

Repeat process for a 2 × 4 array.

T: List the factors of 8.

S: (Write factors of 8: 1, 2, 4, 8.)

Continue with following possible sequence: factors of 12, factors of 16, and factors of 18.

Lesson 23: Use division and the associative property to test for factors and observe patterns.

323

Multiply Two Factors (4 minutes)

Materials: (S) Personal white board

Note: This fluency activity reviews the Concept Development from Lessons 9, 10, and 22.

- T: (Write 174 × 2 = _____.) On your personal white board, solve the multiplication sentence using the standard algorithm.
- S: What are 4 factors of 348 you know right away?
- S: 1 and 348, 2 and 174.

Repeat the process using the following possible sequence: 348 × 2, 696 × 2, and 1,392 × 2. Students may realize that if 348 is a factor of 696, then 174 is, too!

Prime or Composite? (2 minutes)

Materials: (S) Personal white board

Note: This fluency activity reviews Lesson 22's Concept Development.

- T: (Write 7.) Is it prime or composite?
- S: Prime.
- T: Write the factor pair of 7.
- S: (Write 1 and 7.)
- T: (Write 12.) Is it prime or composite?
- S: Composite.
- T: Write the factor pairs of 12.
- S: (Write 1 and 12, 2 and 6, 3 and 4.)

Repeat the process for the following possible sequence: 15, 17, and 21.

**NOTES ON
MULTIPLE MEANS
OF ENGAGEMENT:**

Allow English language learners and others more time to compose their written response. Alternatively, have students discuss their reasoning with a partner.

Challenge students working above grade level to identify the prime and composite numbers in the seventies and sixties. Ask, "What do you notice?"

Application Problem (5 minutes)

Sasha says that every number in the twenties is a composite number because 2 is even. Amanda says there are two prime numbers in the twenties. Who is correct? How do you know?

Note: This Application Problem bridges Lesson 22's work with using division to determine prime and composite numbers to this lesson's objective of using division patterns to determine factors of numbers.

20 21 22 (23) 24 25 26 27 28 (29)
↓   ↓   ↓   Prime ↓   ↓   ↓   ↓   ↓   Prime
2×10 3×7 2×11 1×23 3×8 5×5 2×13 3×9 4×7 1×29

Amanda is correct. Sasha is only looking at the tens. You have to think about the whole number's value, not just one of its digits. I could think of factor pairs that weren't 1 and the number for the twenties, except 23 and 29. So those are prime numbers.

Concept Development (33 minutes)

Materials: (S) Personal white board

Problem 1: Use division to find factors of larger numbers.

T: Find the unknown factor: $28 = 7 \times$ ___.

S: 4.

T: How did you find the unknown factor?

S: I know my fours facts. → I divided 28 by 7.

T: Is 10 a factor of 28?

S: No.

T: How do you know?

S: Two times 10 is 20, and 3 times 10 is 30. → If you divide 28 by 10, you get a remainder.

T: How can I find out if 3 is a factor of 54?

S: We can divide 54 by 3.

T: What if I get a remainder?

S: If there is a remainder, then 3 isn't a factor. → As long as there's no remainder, you can write 54 as 3 times a whole number. → Yeah, it's 3 times the quotient.

Allow time for students to divide with their partner.

S: Fifty-four can be divided by 3 evenly. → Three is a factor of 54 because there is no remainder.

T: How can we determine if 2 is a factor of 54?

S: We can divide like we did for 3. → Two is an even number, so it goes evenly into 54. → Two is a factor of every even number and 54 is even, so 2 has to be one of its factors.

T: Use division to find out if 3 is a factor of 78, if 4 is a factor of 94, and if 3 is a factor of 87.

Quickly debrief the questions to ascertain that 3 is a factor of 78 and 87, but 4 is not a factor of 94.

Problem 2: Use the associative property to find additional factors of larger numbers.

T: Talk to your partner. Is it necessary to divide to figure out if 5 is a factor of 54?

S: Fifty-four can't be divided by 5 exactly. There is a remainder. → When you count by fives, each number ends with 5 or 0. Fifty-four does not end with 0 or 5. Five isn't a factor of 54.

T: We divided to determine if 3 was a factor of 54, but for 2 and 5 we don't need to divide. Explain to your partner why not.

S: The even numbers all have 2 for a factor. → If the digit in the ones place is odd, the number doesn't have 2 as a factor. → Numbers with 5 as a factor have 0 or 5 as a digit in the ones place. → We can use patterns for 2 and 5.

T: How can we know if 6 a factor of 54?

S: Six times 9 equals 54.

T: Earlier we saw that 2 and 3 are both factors of 54. Talk to your partner. Is this number sentence true?

T: (Write 54 = 6 × 9 = (2 × 3) × 9.)

S: (Share ideas.)

T: Let's write it vertically so that it is very easy to see how the factor 6 is related to 2 times 3.

T: (Write the problem as modeled to the right.) Now let's move the parentheses so that 3 associates with 9 rather than 2. Three times 9 is?

S: 27.

T: Find the product of 2 and 27. (Pause.) Is it true that 2 times 27 equals 54?

S: Yes!

T: We used the **associative property** to show that both 2 and 3 are factors of 54.

T: Let's test this method to see if it works with a number other than 54. Forty-two is 6 times…?

S: 7.

T: Let's use the associative property to see if 2 and 3 are also factors of 42.

T: (Write 42 = 6 × 7.) How will we rewrite 6?

S: 2 × 3.

T: (Beneath 6 × 7, write = (2 × 3) × 7.) Let's now move the parentheses to first multiply 3 times 7, to associate 3 with 7 rather than 2. 3 times 7 is?

S: 21.

T: Find the product of 2 and 21. (Pause.) Is it true that 2 times 21 equals 42?

S: Yes!

$$54 = 6 \times 9$$
$$= (2 \times 3) \times 9$$
$$= 2 \times (3 \times 9)$$
$$= 2 \times 27$$
$$= 54$$

$$42 = 6 \times 7$$
$$= (2 \times 3) \times 7$$
$$= 2 \times (3 \times 7)$$
$$= 2 \times 21$$
$$= 42$$

Record the thought process as shown to the right. Have students use the associative property to prove that since 6 is a factor of 60, both 2 and 3 are also factors.

Problem 3: Use division or the associative property to find factors of larger numbers.

T: Multiply 6 times 12. (Pause.) The answer is…?

S: 72.

T: Using either division or the associative property, work with your partner to prove that since 6 is a factor of 72, 2 and 3 are also factors.

S: Seventy-two is even, so 2 is a factor. I can use long division to find 72 divided by 3 is 24, so 3 is a factor. → I wrote 72 equals 6 times 12 as 72 equals 2 times 3 times 12. Using the associative property works. I know 2 and 3 are factors of 72 because 6 is a factor of 72.

$$72 = 6 \times 12$$
$$= (2 \times 3) \times 12$$
$$= 2 \times (3 \times 12)$$
$$= 2 \times 36$$
$$= 72$$

$$\begin{array}{r} 24 \\ 3\overline{)72} \\ -6 \\ \hline 12 \\ -12 \\ \hline 0 \end{array}$$

$$\begin{array}{r} 24 \\ \times\ 3 \\ \hline 72 \end{array}$$

Lesson 23:   Use division and the associative property to test for factors and observe patterns.

EUREKA
MATH™

Problem Set (10 minutes)

Students should do their personal best to complete the Problem Set within the allotted 10 minutes. For some classes, it may be appropriate to modify the assignment by specifying which problems they work on first. Some problems do not specify a method for solving. Students should solve these problems using the RDW approach used for Application Problems.

Student Debrief (10 minutes)

Lesson Objective: Use division and the associative property to test for factors and observe patterns.

The Student Debrief is intended to invite reflection and active processing of the total lesson experience.

Invite students to review their solutions for the Problem Set. They should check work by comparing answers with a partner before going over answers as a class. Look for misconceptions or misunderstandings that can be addressed in the Debrief. Guide students in a conversation to debrief the Problem Set and process the lesson.

Any combination of the questions below may be used to lead the discussion.

- How did answering Problem 1, Part (a) help you answer Problem 1, Part (b)? Was it necessary to divide?

- What relationship do you notice between Problem 1, Parts (a), (c), and (e)? What about between Problem 1, Parts (d), (f), and (h)?

- Discuss with your partner what is similar and what is different about Problem 1, Parts (a), (c), and (e) and Problem 1, Parts (d), (f), and (h).

- What's the difference between the statements in Problem 4? Why is one false and the other true?

- When we divided 72 by 3, we saw that there was no remainder. Another way to say that is "72 is divisible by 3." Is 24 divisible by 3? Is 25 divisible by 3?

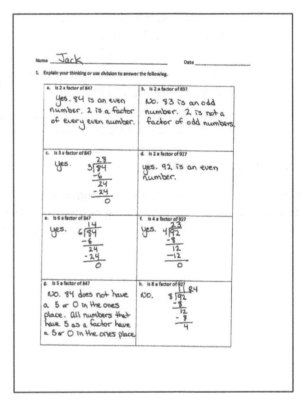

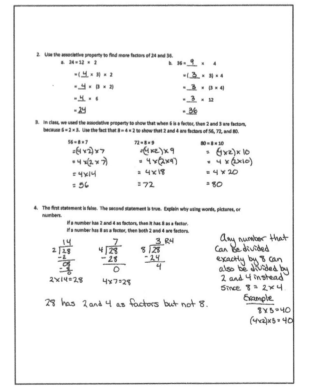

Lesson 23:   Use division and the associative property to test for factors and observe patterns.

327

©2015 Great Minds. eureka-math.org
G4-M3-TE-B2-1.3.1-01.2016

- We can use number patterns to determine if 2 and 5 are factors of other numbers. What other numbers do you think have patterns? Do you see a pattern for determining which numbers 3 is a factor of? Can you describe one?

- If 8 is a factor of 96, what other numbers must also be factors of 96? How can we use the **associative property** to prove this?

- Once someone tried to tell me that the two statements in Problem 4 say the same thing. How would you explain that the two statements are different?

Exit Ticket (3 minutes)

After the Student Debrief, instruct students to complete the Exit Ticket. A review of their work will help with assessing students' understanding of the concepts that were presented in today's lesson and planning more effectively for future lessons. The questions may be read aloud to the students.

Lesson 23:   Use division and the associative property to test for factors and observe patterns.

©2015 Great Minds. eureka-math.org
G4-M3-TE-B2-1.3.1-01.2016

Name _____   Date _____

1. Explain your thinking or use division to answer the following.

a. Is 2 a factor of 84?	b. Is 2 a factor of 83?
c. Is 3 a factor of 84?	d. Is 2 a factor of 92?
e. Is 6 a factor of 84?	f. Is 4 a factor of 92?
g. Is 5 a factor of 84?	h. Is 8 a factor of 92?

Lesson 23:   Use division and the associative property to test for factors and observe patterns.

329

©2015 Great Minds. eureka-math.org
G4-M3-TE-B2-1.3.1-01.2016

2. Use the associative property to find more factors of 24 and 36.

   a. $24 = 12 \times 2$

       $= (\underline{\hspace{1cm}} \times 3) \times 2$

       $= \underline{\hspace{1cm}} \times (3 \times 2)$

       $= \underline{\hspace{1cm}} \times 6$

       $= \underline{\hspace{1cm}}$

   b. $36 = \underline{\hspace{1cm}} \times 4$

       $= (\underline{\hspace{1cm}} \times 3) \times 4$

       $= \underline{\hspace{1cm}} \times (3 \times 4)$

       $= \underline{\hspace{1cm}} \times 12$

       $= \underline{\hspace{1cm}}$

3. In class, we used the associative property to show that when 6 is a factor, then 2 and 3 are factors, because $6 = 2 \times 3$. Use the fact that $8 = 4 \times 2$ to show that 2 and 4 are factors of 56, 72, and 80.

   $56 = 8 \times 7$ $72 = 8 \times 9$ $80 = 8 \times 10$

4. The first statement is false. The second statement is true. Explain why, using words, pictures, or numbers.

   If a number has 2 and 4 as factors, then it has 8 as a factor.
   If a number has 8 as a factor, then both 2 and 4 are factors.

Lesson 23:   Use division and the associative property to test for factors and observe patterns.

©2015 Great Minds. eureka-math.org
G4-M3-TE-B2-1.3.1-01.2016

EUREKA
MATH

Name _____   Date _____

1. Explain your thinking or use division to answer the following.

a. Is 2 a factor of 34?	b. Is 3 a factor of 34?
c. Is 4 a factor of 72?	d. Is 3 a factor of 72?

2. Use the associative property to explain why the following statement is true.
   Any number that has 9 as a factor also has 3 as a factor.

Lesson 23:   Use division and the associative property to test for factors and
observe patterns.

331

©2015 Great Minds. eureka-math.org
G4-M3-TE-B2-1.3.1-01.2016

Name _____ Date _____

1. Explain your thinking or use division to answer the following.

a. Is 2 a factor of 72?	b. Is 2 a factor of 73?
c. Is 3 a factor of 72?	d. Is 2 a factor of 60?
e. Is 6 a factor of 72?	f. Is 4 a factor of 60?
g. Is 5 a factor of 72?	h. Is 8 a factor of 60?

Lesson 23: Use division and the associative property to test for factors and observe patterns.

©2015 Great Minds. eureka-math.org
G4-M3-TE-B2-1.3.1-01.2016

2. Use the associative property to find more factors of 12 and 30.

a. $12 = 6 \times 2$

$= (\underline{} \times 2) \times 2$

$= \underline{} \times (2 \times 2)$

$= \underline{} \times \underline{}$

$= \underline{}$

b. $30 = \underline{} \times 5$

$= (\underline{} \times 3) \times 5$

$= \underline{} \times (3 \times 5)$

$= \underline{} \times 15$

$= \underline{}$

3. In class, we used the associative property to show that when 6 is a factor, then 2 and 3 are factors, because $6 = 2 \times 3$. Use the fact that $10 = 5 \times 2$ to show that 2 and 5 are factors of 70, 80, and 90.

$70 = 10 \times 7$ $80 = 10 \times 8$ $90 = 10 \times 9$

4. The first statement is false. The second statement is true. Explain why, using words, pictures, or numbers.

If a number has 2 and 6 as factors, then it has 12 as a factor.
If a number has 12 as a factor, then both 2 and 6 are factors.

EUREKA
MATH™

Lesson 23:   Use division and the associative property to test for factors and observe patterns.

333

©2015 Great Minds. eureka-math.org
G4-M3-TE-B2-1.3.1-01.2016

Lesson 24

Objective: Determine if a whole number is a multiple of another number.

Suggested Lesson Structure

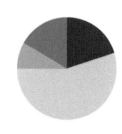

■ Fluency Practice   (12 minutes)
■ Application Problem   (5 minutes)
□ Concept Development   (33 minutes)
■ Student Debrief   (10 minutes)
  Total Time   **(60 minutes)**

Fluency Practice (12 minutes)

- Group Counting **4.OA.1**   (5 minutes)
- Prime or Composite? **4.OA.4**   (2 minutes)
- Test for Factors **4.OA.5**   (5 minutes)

Group Counting (5 minutes)

Note: Group counting reviews factors and patterns that students use during the Concept Development.

Direct students to count forward and backward, occasionally changing the direction of the count.

- Twos to 20
- Threes to 30
- Fours to 40
- Fives to 50
- Sixes to 60
- Tens to 100

Prime or Composite? (2 minutes)

Materials: (S) Personal white board

Note: This fluency activity reviews Lesson 22's Concept Development.

Repeat the process from Lesson 23 for the following possible sequence: 5, 15, 12, 19, and 24.

EUREKA
MATH™

Test for Factors (5 minutes)

Materials: (S) Personal white board

Note: This fluency activity reviews Lesson 23's content.

T: (Project 30, 45, 48, and 56.) On your personal white board, write the number that has 10 as a factor.
S: (Write 30.)
T: Write the division equations that prove both 5 and 2 are factors of 30.
S: (Write 30 ÷ 5 = 6 and 30 ÷ 2 = 15.)
T: Write the numbers that have 6 as a factor.
S: (Write 30 and 48.)
T: Prove that both 3 and 2 are factors of 30 and 48, using the associative property.
S: (Write 30 ÷ 3 = 10, 30 ÷ 2 = 15, 48 ÷ 3 = 16, and 48 ÷ 2 = 24.)
T: Write the numbers that have 8 as a factor.
S: (Write 48 and 56.)
T: Prove that both 4 and 2 are factors of 48 and 56, using the associative property.

Application Problem (5 minutes)

8 cm × 12 cm = 96 square centimeters. Imagine a rectangle with an area of 96 square centimeters and a side length of 4 centimeters. What is the length of its unknown side? How will it look when compared to the 8 centimeter by 12 centimeter rectangle? Draw and label both rectangles.

$$\begin{array}{r} 24 \\ 4\overline{)96} \\ 8 \\ \hline 16 \\ -16 \\ \hline 0 \end{array}$$

The length of the unknown side is 24 centimeters.

The 4 by 24 rectangle is 2 times as long and half as wide as the 8 by 12 rectangle.

24 cm
4 cm 96 sq. cm

12 cm
8 cm 96 sq. cm

Note: This Application Problem relates finding factors (Lessons 22 and 23) to multiples (Lesson 24). Consider leading students to visualize the columns of 4 or 8 square centimeters. When counting by the number of squares in those columns, will the count arrive exactly at 96? When counting by the number of squares in one row, 24 or 12, will the count also arrive exactly at 96? (Consider using graph paper to demonstrate for those students who would benefit from pictorial representation.)

Also consider showing students how the associative property beautifully illustrates how as the 8 is split in two, the 12 doubles (pictured to the right).

$$\begin{aligned} 96 &= 8 \times 12 \\ &= (4 \times 2) \times 12 \\ &= 4 \times (2 \times 12) \\ &= 4 \times 24 \\ &= 96 \end{aligned}$$

Lesson 24:   Determine if a whole number is a multiple of another number.   335

©2015 Great Minds. eureka-math.org
G4-M3-TE-B2-1.3.1-01.2016

Concept Development (33 minutes)

Materials: (S) Personal white board, crayons

Problem 1: Determine the meaning of the word *multiple*.

T: Turn to your partner and count by fours, taking turns with each new number. So, for example, you start by saying 0, your partner says 4, then you say 8. You have one minute. Ready? Begin.

S: (Skip-count with partners for one minute.)

T: Stop. What number did you count up to?

S: (Responses will vary.)

T: Good! Tell me some things you noticed.

S: We started by saying the 4 times table, then kept adding on 4. → There was a pattern with how the numbers ended. → When we got to 100, the counting started over again. Just like we started with 0, 4, 8, 12, after 100 it was 104, 108, 112, and so on.

T: Those are nice observations. Let's try that again, beginning where you left off. This time, as you count, think about what patterns there are. Ready? Begin.

S: (Skip-count with their partners for another minute.)

T: When we skip-count by a whole number, the numbers that we say are called *multiples*.

T: Talk to your partner about what you noticed.

S: All of the multiples of 4 were even numbers. → No matter how high we counted, we kept adding on 4 more. → The digit in the ones place of every number followed its own pattern. It went 0, 4, 8, 2, 6, over and over again.

T: Excellent discoveries! This pattern in the ones place continues forever! Why?

S: Because it is always 4 more. → If that's what has been happening, then the same things will keep happening. → It worked up to 1 hundred, and the ones and tens place will continue with the same pattern, so it will even work in the two hundreds and three hundreds. → Four times 25 is 100, so then in every hundred it repeats, so it just keeps going in a cycle!

T: How is a multiple different from a factor?

S: When we found the factors of a number, we listed them and then we were done. With multiples, we could keep going forever and ever!

Problem 2: Determine if one number is a multiple of another number, and list multiples of given numbers.

T: Why is 24 a multiple of 4?

S: When we count by fours we get to 24. → 4 times 6 is 24. → Four is a factor of 24.

T: Is 24 a multiple of 5?

S: No, because we can't skip-count by five to 24. → No, because 24 divided by 5 has a remainder. → No, because 5 is a not a factor of 24.

T: What about 8? Is 24 a multiple of 8?

S: Yes! Eight times 3 is 24. → Well, 8 is a factor of 24, so 24 must be a multiple of 8.

T: We know 96 is a multiple of 4 from our Application Problem, since 4 times 24 is 96. What did we do to figure that out?

S: I used long division. → I used the associative property.

T: Yes, because for some it is beyond mental math. How can we find out if 96 is a multiple of 3?

S: We can divide to see if 96 is divisible by 3. → We might use the associative property since we know that 8 times 12 and 4 times 24 are 96 from the Application Problem.

T: Try that.

Allow time for students to divide or use the associative property.

T: What did you discover?

S: There was no remainder, so 3 is a factor of 96. That makes 96 a multiple of 3.

T: What is the factor pair of 3?

S: 32.

T: If you count by 32 three times, will you get to 96?

S: Yes.

T: Is 96 a multiple of both 3 and 32?

S: Yes!

T: List the first five multiples of 3.

S: (Write 3, 6, 9, 12, 15.)

T: What number did you begin with?

S: 3.

T: But isn't 0 a multiple of 3? Should we start with 0 first?

S: No. It's less. → But 0 times 3 is 0, so maybe.

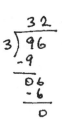

$$3 \overline{)96} \quad \begin{array}{r} 32 \\ \end{array}$$

$$\begin{array}{r} 3\,)\,96 \\ -9 \\ \hline 06 \\ -6 \\ \hline 0 \end{array}$$

$$96 = 12 \times 8$$
$$= (3 \times 4) \times 8$$
$$= 3 \times (4 \times 8)$$
$$= 3 \times 32$$
$$= 96$$

$$96 = 24 \times 4$$
$$= (3 \times 8) \times 4$$
$$= 3 \times (8 \times 4)$$
$$= 3 \times 32$$
$$= 96$$

NOTES ON MULTIPLE MEANS OF REPRESENTATION:

Students who struggle with the difference between a factor and a multiple might benefit from creating a three-column chart that lists numbers in the first column, factors in the second, and then multiples in the third, always followed by an ellipsis to remember the infinite number of multiples of any number. Students can refer to this visual representation as they complete the lesson and as they think about how factors and multiples are related.

#	factors	multiples
4	1, 2, 4	4, 8, 12, 16 …
9	1, 3, 9	9, 18, 27, 36 …
12	1, 2, 3, 4, 6, 12	12, 24, 36, 48 …

©2015 Great Minds. eureka-math.org
G4-M3-TE-B2-1.3.1-01.2016

T: Since zero times any number is zero, zero is a multiple of every number, so we *could* consider it the first multiple of every number. However, when we skip-count, we usually start with the number we're counting by. So, we usually think of the number itself, in this case 3, as the first multiple, instead of 0. That way, the first multiple is 1×3, the second is 2×3, and so on.

(Optional) Problem 3: Use the associative property to see that any multiple of 6 is also a multiple of 3 and 2.

T: Shout out a multiple of 6.

S: 12. → 30. → 60. → 24. → 600.

T: Is any multiple of 6 also a multiple of 2 and 3?

T: Let's use the associative property (and commutative property) to find out. (Write the following.)

T: $60 = 10 \times 6$

$= 10 \times (2 \times 3)$

$= (10 \times 2) \times 3 = 20 \times 3$

Yes, 60 is a multiple of 3. If we count by 3 twenty times, we get to 60.

$= (10 \times 3) \times 2 = 30 \times 2$

Yes, 60 is a multiple of 2. If we count by 2 thirty times, we get to 60.

T: Let's use a letter to represent the number of sixes to see if this is true for all sixes. (Write the following three equations on the board.)

$n \times 6 = n \times (2 \times 3)$

$n \times 6 = (n \times 2) \times 3$

$n \times 6 = (n \times 3) \times 2$

T: Discuss with your partner why these equations are true. You might try plugging in 4 or 5 as the number of sixes, n, to help you understand.

S: Wow! These equations are true. It's just that it takes twice as many threes to get to the multiple as sixes. → Yeah, it's double the number of multiples of six, $2 \times n$. → And it's three times as many twos to get there! It's because twos are smaller units so it takes more.

T: So, maybe the multiples of a number are also the multiples of its factors.

**NOTES ON
MULTIPLE MEANS
OF REPRESENTATION:**

When using the associative property, consider bringing the word to life by asking three students to stand at the front of the class in a line. Ask the person in the middle to associate with the person on the right. Ask them to associate with the person on their left. Ask those on the ends to associate.

▪ What changed? (The associations.)

Next, give each person an identity as a factor, perhaps 9, 2, and 5 respectively. Have the factor of 2 first associate with the 9 and then with the five. Then, have the 9 and 5 associate.

▪ Which is easiest: 18 times 5, 9 times 10, or 45 times 2?

If there is time, consider repeating the process with the multiples of 8 being multiples of both 2 and 4. Students might approach the generalization that the multiples of a given number include the multiples of the number's factors.

EUREKA
MATH™

Problem Set (10 minutes)

Students should do their personal best to complete the Problem Set within the allotted 10 minutes. For some classes, it may be appropriate to modify the assignment by specifying which problems they work on first.
Some problems do not specify a method for solving. Students should solve these problems using the RDW approach used for Application Problems.

Student Debrief (10 minutes)

Lesson Objective: Determine if a whole number is a multiple of another number.

The Student Debrief is intended to invite reflection and active processing of the total lesson experience.

Invite students to review their solutions for the Problem Set. They should check work by comparing answers with a partner before going over answers as a class. Look for misconceptions or misunderstandings that can be addressed in the Debrief. Guide students in a conversation to debrief the Problem Set and process the lesson.

Any combination of the questions below may be used to lead the discussion.

- What strategy did you use in Problem 2?
- In Problem 5, Parts (c) and (d), what patterns did you discover about multiples of 5 and 10?
- Explain the difference between factors and multiples.
- Which number is a multiple of *every* number?
- In Problem 1, which multiples were the easiest to write: the fives, fours, or sixes? Why?
- How can the associative property help you to know if a number is a multiple of another number?
- Did anybody answer *no* on Problem 4? What about 1? Are prime numbers multiples of 1?
- In the lesson, we found that when counting by fours, the multiples followed a pattern of having 0, 4, 8, 2, and 6 in the ones digit. Does that mean any even number is a multiple of 4?

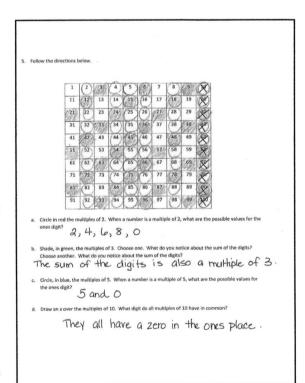

Lesson 24: Determine if a whole number is a multiple of another number.

339

©2015 Great Minds. eureka-math.org
G4-M3-TE-B2-1.3.1-01.2016

- Are the following true?
  - 3 is a factor of 12.
  - 12 is a multiple of 3.
  - 12 is divisible by 3.

Exit Ticket (3 minutes)

After the Student Debrief, instruct students to complete the Exit Ticket. A review of their work will help with assessing students' understanding of the concepts that were presented in today's lesson and planning more effectively for future lessons. The questions may be read aloud to the students.

©2015 Great Minds. eureka-math.org
G4-M3-TE-B2-1.3.1-01.2016

Name _____   Date _____

1. For each of the following, time yourself for 1 minute. See how many multiples you can write.

    a. Write the multiples of 5 starting from 100.

    b. Write the multiples of 4 starting from 20.

    c. Write the multiples of 6 starting from 36.

2. List the numbers that have 24 as a multiple.

3. Use mental math, division, or the associative property to solve. (Use scratch paper if you like.)

    a. Is 12 a multiple of 4? _____   Is 4 a factor of 12? _____

    b. Is 42 a multiple of 8? _____   Is 8 a factor of 42? _____

    c. Is 84 a multiple of 6? _____   Is 6 a factor of 84? _____

4. Can a prime number be a multiple of any other number except itself? Explain why or why not.

Lesson 24:   Determine if a whole number is a multiple of another number.

341

©2015 Great Minds. eureka-math.org
G4-M3-TE-B2-1.3.1-01.2016

5. Follow the directions below.

1	2	3	4	5	6	7	8	9	10
11	12	13	14	15	16	17	18	19	20
21	22	23	24	25	26	27	28	29	30
31	32	33	34	35	36	37	38	39	40
41	42	43	44	45	46	47	48	49	50
51	52	53	54	55	56	57	58	59	60
61	62	63	64	65	66	67	68	69	70
71	72	73	74	75	76	77	78	79	80
81	82	83	84	85	86	87	88	89	90
91	92	93	94	95	96	97	98	99	100

a. Circle in red the multiples of 2. When a number is a multiple of 2, what are the possible values for the ones digit?

b. Shade in green the multiples of 3. Choose one. What do you notice about the sum of the digits? Choose another. What do you notice about the sum of the digits?

c. Circle in blue the multiples of 5. When a number is a multiple of 5, what are the possible values for the ones digit?

d. Draw an X over the multiples of 10. What digit do all multiples of 10 have in common?

Lesson 24:   Determine if a whole number is a multiple of another number.

EUREKA
MATH

Name _____   Date _____

1. Fill in the unknown multiples of 11.

    5 × 11 = _____

    6 × 11 = _____

    7 × 11 = _____

    8 × 11 = _____

    9 × 11 = _____

2. Complete the pattern of multiples by skip-counting.

    7, 14, _____, 28, _____, _____, _____, _____, _____, _____

3. a. List the numbers that have 18 as a multiple.

    b. What are the factors of 18?

    c. Are your two lists the same? Why or why not?

Name _____ Date _____

1. For each of the following, time yourself for 1 minute. See how many multiples you can write.

    a. Write the multiples of 5 starting from 75.

    b. Write the multiples of 4 starting from 40.

    c. Write the multiples of 6 starting from 24.

2. List the numbers that have 30 as a multiple.

3. Use mental math, division, or the associative property to solve. (Use scratch paper if you like.)

    a. Is 12 a multiple of 3? _____ Is 3 a factor of 12? _____

    b. Is 48 a multiple of 8? _____ Is 48 a factor of 8? _____

    c. Is 56 a multiple of 6? _____ Is 6 a factor of 56? _____

4. Can a prime number be a multiple of any other number except itself? Explain why or why not.

Lesson 24:   Determine if a whole number is a multiple of another number.

©2015 Great Minds. eureka-math.org
G4-M3-TE-B2-1.3.1-01.2016

5. Follow the directions below.

1	2	3	4	5	6	7	8	9	10
11	12	13	14	15	16	17	18	19	20
21	22	23	24	25	26	27	28	29	30
31	32	33	34	35	36	37	38	39	40
41	42	43	44	45	46	47	48	49	50
51	52	53	54	55	56	57	58	59	60
61	62	63	64	65	66	67	68	69	70
71	72	73	74	75	76	77	78	79	80
81	82	83	84	85	86	87	88	89	90
91	92	93	94	95	96	97	98	99	100

a. Underline the multiples of 6. When a number is a multiple of 6, what are the possible values for the ones digit?

b. Draw a square around the multiples of 4. Look at the multiples of 4 that have an odd number in the tens place. What values do they have in the ones place?

c. Look at the multiples of 4 that have an even number in the tens place. What values do they have in the ones place? Do you think this pattern would continue with multiples of 4 that are larger than 100?

d. Circle the multiples of 9. Choose one. What do you notice about the sum of the digits?
Choose another one. What do you notice about the sum of the digits?

Lesson 24:   Determine if a whole number is a multiple of another number.

345

©2015 Great Minds. eureka-math.org
G4-M3-TE-B2-1.3.1-01.2016

Lesson 25

Objective: Explore properties of prime and composite numbers to 100 by using multiples.

Suggested Lesson Structure

■ Fluency Practice　　　　(12 minutes)

　Concept Development　　(30 minutes)

■ Student Debrief　　　　 (18 minutes)

　Total Time　　　　　　**(60 minutes)**

Fluency Practice (12 minutes)

- Test for Factors **4.OA.5**　　　　　　(5 minutes)
- Multiples Are Infinite **4.NBT.1**　　　(5 minutes)
- List Multiples and Factors **4.OA.4**　　(2 minutes)

Test for Factors (5 minutes)

Materials:　(S) Personal white board

Note: This fluency activity reviews Lesson 23's content.

　　T:　(Project 40, 64, 54, and 42.) On your personal white board, write the number that has 10 as a factor.

　　S:　(Write 40.)

　　T:　Use division to prove both 4 and 2 are factors of 40.

　　T:　Write the numbers that have 6 as a factor.

　　S:　(Write 54 and 42.)

　　T:　Prove that both 3 and 2 are factors of 54 and 42, using the associative property.

　　T:　Write the numbers that have 8 as a factor.

　　S:　(Write 40 and 64.)

　　T:　Prove that both 4 and 2 are factors of 40 and 64, using the associative property.

346　　　**Lesson 25:**　　Explore properties of prime and composite numbers to 100 by using multiples.

©2015 Great Minds. eureka-math.org
G4-M3-TE-B2-1.3.1-01.2016

EUREKA MATH™

Multiples Are Infinite (5 minutes)

Have students make groups of four. Assign each foursome a different number to count by starting at 0.
Allow students two minutes to count round robin in their groups.

T: Let's share our results. (Call on each group to share.)

T: Could you have kept counting by (assigned number) after I told you to stop?

S: Yes, because we just kept adding on (assigned number) more. → Yes, because you can keep
counting forever.

T: (Allow all groups to share.) We now know the multiples for *any* number are infinite—they go on
forever. How is that different from the factors of a number? Turn and talk to your partner about
this question.

S: Every number has only a certain amount of factors but an unlimited number of multiples. → The
number of factors any number has is finite, but the number of multiples is infinite.

List Multiples and Factors (2 minutes)

Materials: (S) Personal white board

Note: This fluency activity gives students practice in remembering the difference between factors and
multiples.

T: (Write 3.) List as many multiples of 3 as you can in the next 20 seconds. Take your mark. Get set.
Go.

S: (Write 3, 6, 9, 12, 15, 18, 21, 24, ….)

T: List the factors of 3.

S: (Write 1, 3.)

Continue with the following possible sequence: multiples of 4, factors of 4; multiples of 5, factors of 5.

Concept Development (30 minutes)

Materials: (T) Sieve (for the Student Debrief) (S) Problem Set, orange crayon, red crayon

Note: Use the Problem Set to guide this lesson's content.

T: Let's take a look at the number chart in front of you. What is the smallest prime number you see on
the chart?

S: Two.

T: What is the greatest composite number you see? How do you know?

S: One hundred, because it is even. → One hundred, because all even numbers greater than 2 have 2
as a factor, so they have to be composite numbers.

T: Excellent! Now, working with your partner, read and follow all of the directions at the top of the first
page of the Problem Set. Be sure to follow the directions in order, and check with each other to see
that you complete each activity the same way. If you find that you have different responses at
times, talk about it to see what the correct thing to do is.

Lesson 25:   Explore properties of prime and composite numbers to 100 by using
multiples.

©2015 Great Minds. eureka-math.org
G4-M3-TE-B2-1.3.1-01.2016

347

As students are charged with determining multiples that are greater than those in the times tables, some will choose to continue adding on, while others will choose to divide, and some will begin to rely on number patterns they have noticed. Encourage partners to compare strategies.

Note: At a certain point, the majority of students will have finished marking off multiples of 7. A few may have begun to notice that the multiples of the remaining numbers have already been crossed off. Interrupt the class at this point. Below is the suggested midpoint dialogue.

T: After you marked off multiples of 7, what was the next number that you circled?

S: 11.

T: Were there any multiples of 11 that hadn't been crossed out already?

S: No.

T: What about 13? Are there any multiples of 13 that still need to be crossed off?

S: No, they're already crossed off from before.

T: I wonder if that's true of the rest? Go back to 11. Let's see if we can figure out what happened. Count by elevens within 100 using the chart.

S: 11, 22, 33, 44, 55, …, 99.

T: Ninety-nine is how many elevens?

S: 9 elevens.

T: So, by the time we circled 11, is it true that we'd already marked all of the multiples of 2, 3, all the way up to 10?

S: Well, yeah, we circled 2, 3, 5, and 7, and crossed off their multiples. → We didn't have to do fours, because the fours got crossed out when we crossed out multiples of 2. → The same thing happened with the sixes, eights, nines, and tens.

T: Interesting, so we had already crossed out 2 × 11, 3 × 11, all the way up to 9 × 11. I wonder if the same thing happens with 13. Discuss with a partner: Will there be more or fewer groups of 13 than groups of 11 within a hundred?

S: More, because it is a bigger number. → Fewer, because it is a larger number so fewer will fit in 100. → Fewer because 9 × 11 is 99, so maybe 7 or 8 times 13 will be less than 100. → 9 × 13 is more than 100, so fewer groups.

T: Take a moment to figure out how many multiples of 13 are within 100.

S: (Might count by 13 or multiply.)

T: How many multiples of 13 are less than 100?

S: 7.

T: 7 times 13 is…?

S: 91.

T: We already marked off 91 because it is a multiple of 7. The same is true for 6 × 13, 5 × 13, and so on. Do we need to mark off multiples of 17?

S: No, because there will be even fewer groups, and we already marked off those factors.

T: Exactly. The highest multiple of 17 on the hundreds chart is 85. 5 seventeens is 85. We already marked 2 × 17 up to 5 × 17.

Following this dialogue, have students return to work. Once students have correctly completed page 1, have them continue to page 2. Allow students time to thoroughly discuss and answer each question. Circulate and offer assistance as needed. Be ready to initiate or prompt discussions when students seem unsure. Answer questions with questions to keep students thinking and analyzing.

Regroup, as the class completes page 2, to share responses to the Student Debrief questions.

Problem Set

Please note that the Problem Set comprises only questions used in the Concept Development. No additional time is allotted here since all problems are completed during the lesson. The Student Debrief has additional time allotted for the purpose of whole-class discussion of questions raised and discoveries made by the students during the Concept Development.

Student Debrief (18 minutes)

Lesson Objective: Explore properties of prime and composite numbers to 100 by using multiples.

The Student Debrief is intended to invite reflection and active processing of the total lesson experience.

Invite students to review their solutions for the Problem Set. They should check work by comparing answers with a partner before going over answers as a class. Look for misconceptions or misunderstandings that can be addressed in the Debrief. Guide students in a conversation to debrief the Problem Set and process the lesson.

Any combination of the questions below may be used to lead the discussion .

- Which numbers are circled? Which numbers are crossed out?
- We started this Problem Set by coloring number 1 red and beginning our work with the multiples of 2. Why didn't we cross out the multiples of 1?
- Are any prime numbers even? Are all odd numbers prime?
- We crossed off multiples of 2, 3, 5, and 7. Why didn't we have to cross off multiples of 4 or 6?
- How did you know some of the larger numbers, like 53 and 79, were prime?

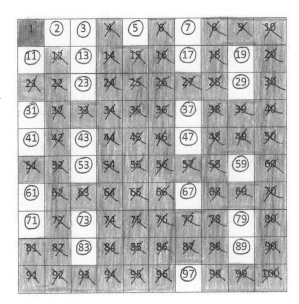

Lesson 25:   Explore properties of prime and composite numbers to 100 by using multiples.

349

©2015 Great Minds. eureka-math.org
G4-M3-TE-B2-1.3.1-01.2016

- How can we find the prime numbers between 1 and 200?

- The process of crossing out multiples to find primes is called the *sieve of Eratosthenes*. Eratosthenes was an ancient Greek mathematician. Why do you think this is called a sieve (show a sieve to the students)?

Exit Ticket (3 minutes)

After the Student Debrief, instruct students to complete the Exit Ticket. A review of their work will help with assessing students' understanding of the concepts that were presented in today's lesson and planning more effectively for future lessons. The questions may be read aloud to the students.

2.

a. List the circled numbers.

2,3,5,7,11,13,17,19,23,29,31,37,41,43,47,53,59,61,67,71,73,
79,83,89,97

b. Why weren't the circled numbers crossed off along the way?

The circled numbers were not crossed off along the way because they are not multiples of any other Numbers besides 1 and themselves.

c. Except for the number 1, what is similar about all of the numbers that were crossed off?

The crossed off numbers are all Composite numbers.

d. What is similar about all of the numbers that were circled?

The circled numbers are all prime numbers.

Lesson 25:   Explore properties of prime and composite numbers to 100 by using multiples.

©2015 Great Minds. eureka-math.org
G4-M3-TE-B2-1.3.1-01.2016

Name _____   Date _____

1. Follow the directions.

Shade the number 1 red.

a. Circle the first unmarked number.

b. Cross off every multiple of that number except the one you circled. If it's already crossed off, skip it.

c. Repeat Steps (a) and (b) until every number is either circled or crossed off.

d. Shade every crossed out number in orange.

1	2	3	4	5	6	7	8	9	10
11	12	13	14	15	16	17	18	19	20
21	22	23	24	25	26	27	28	29	30
31	32	33	34	35	36	37	38	39	40
41	42	43	44	45	46	47	48	49	50
51	52	53	54	55	56	57	58	59	60
61	62	63	64	65	66	67	68	69	70
71	72	73	74	75	76	77	78	79	80
81	82	83	84	85	86	87	88	89	90
91	92	93	94	95	96	97	98	99	100

Lesson 25:   Explore properties of prime and composite numbers to 100 by using multiples.

351

©2015 Great Minds. eureka-math.org
G4-M3-TE-B2-1.3.1-01.2016

2. a. List the circled numbers.

    b. Why were the circled numbers not crossed off along the way?

    c. Except for the number 1, what is similar about all of the numbers that were crossed off?

    d. What is similar about all of the numbers that were circled?

©2015 Great Minds. eureka-math.org
G4-M3-TE-B2-1.3.1-01.2016

EUREKA
MATH™

Name _____   Date _____

Use the calendar below to complete the following:

1. Cross off all composite numbers.

2. Circle all of the prime numbers.

3. List any remaining numbers.

Sunday	Monday	Tuesday	Wednesday	Thursday	Friday	Saturday
					1	2
3	4	5	6	7	8	9
10	11	12	13	14	15	16
17	18	19	20	21	22	23
24	25	26	27	28	29	30
31						

Lesson 25: Explore properties of prime and composite numbers to 100 by using
multiples.

©2015 Great Minds. eureka-math.org
G4-M3-TE-B2-1.3.1-01.2016

353

Name _____   Date _____

1. A student used the sieve of Eratosthenes to find all prime numbers less than 100. Create a step-by-step set of directions to show how it was completed. Use the word bank to help guide your thinking as you write the directions. Some words may be used just once, more than once, or not at all.

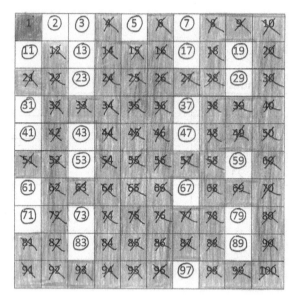

Word Bank

composite	cross out
number	shade
circle	X
multiple	prime

Directions for completing the sieve of Eratosthenes activity:

Lesson 25:   Explore properties of prime and composite numbers to 100 by using multiples.

©2015 Great Minds. eureka-math.org
G4-M3-TE-B2-1.3.1-01.2016

EUREKA
MATH™

2. What do all of the numbers that are crossed out have in common?

3. What do all of the circled numbers have in common?

4. There is one number that is neither crossed out nor circled. Why is it treated differently?

Lesson 25: Explore properties of prime and composite numbers to 100 by using multiples.

©2015 Great Minds. eureka-math.org
G4-M3-TE-B2-1.3.1-01.2016

355

Mathematics Curriculum

Topic G

Division of Thousands, Hundreds, Tens, and Ones

4.OA.3, 4.NBT.6, 4.NBT.1

Focus Standards:	4.OA.3	Solve multistep word problems posed with whole numbers and having whole-number answers using the four operations, including problems in which remainders must be interpreted. Represent these problems using equations with a letter standing for the unknown quantity. Assess the reasonableness of answers using mental computation and estimation strategies including rounding.
	4.NBT.6	Find whole-number quotients and remainders with up to four-digit dividends and one-digit divisors, using strategies based on place value, the properties of operations, and/or the relationship between multiplication and division. Illustrate and explain the calculation by using equations, rectangular arrays, and/or area models.
Instructional Days:	8	
Coherence -Links from:	G3–M1	Properties of Multiplication and Division and Solving Problems with Units of 2–5 and 10
	G3–M3	Multiplication and Division with Units of 0, 1, 6–9, and Multiples of 10
-Links to:	G5–M2	Multi-Digit Whole Number and Decimal Fraction Operations

Topic G extends to division with three- and four-digit dividends using place value understanding. Students begin the topic by connecting multiplication of 10, 100, and 1,000 by single-digit numbers from Topic B to division of multiples of 10, 100, and 1,000 in Lesson 26. Using unit language, students find their division facts allow them to divide much larger numbers.

12 ones ÷ 4 = 3 ones   12 tens ÷ 4 = 3 tens   12 hundreds ÷ 4 = 3 hundreds
12 ÷ 4 = 3   120 ÷ 4 = 30   1200 ÷ 4 = 300

In Lesson 27, place value disks support students visually as they decompose each unit before dividing. This lesson contains a first-use script on the steps of solving long division using place value disks and the algorithm in tandem for three- and four-digit dividends (**4.NBT.6**). Take note how patterning develops with these larger numbers.

EUREKA
MATH

Students then move to the abstract level in Lessons 28 and 29, recording long division with place value understanding, first of three-digit, then four-digit numbers using small divisors. In Lesson 30, students practice dividing when zeros are in the dividend or in the quotient.

Lessons 31 and 32 give students opportunities to apply their understanding of division by solving word problems (**4.OA.3**). In Lesson 31, students identify word problems as *number of groups unknown* or *group size unknown*, modeled using tape diagrams. Lesson 32 allows students to apply their place value understanding of solving long division using larger divisors of 6, 7, 8, and 9. Concluding this topic, Lesson 33 has students make connections between the area model and the standard algorithm for long division.

A Teaching Sequence Toward Mastery of Division of Thousands, Hundreds, Tens, and Ones

Objective 1: Divide multiples of 10, 100, and 1,000 by single-digit numbers.
(Lesson 26)

Objective 2: Represent and solve division problems with up to a three-digit dividend numerically and with place value disks requiring decomposing a remainder in the hundreds place.
(Lesson 27)

Objective 3: Represent and solve three-digit dividend division with divisors of 2, 3, 4, and 5 numerically.
(Lesson 28)

Objective 4: Represent numerically four-digit dividend division with divisors of 2, 3, 4, and 5, decomposing a remainder up to three times.
(Lesson 29)

Objective 5: Solve division problems with a zero in the dividend or with a zero in the quotient.
(Lesson 30)

Objective 6: Interpret division word problems as either *number of groups unknown* or *group size unknown*.
(Lesson 31)

Objective 7: Interpret and find whole number quotients and remainders to solve one-step division word problems with larger divisors of 6, 7, 8, and 9.
(Lesson 32)

Objective 8: Explain the connection of the area model of division to the long division algorithm for three- and four-digit dividends.
(Lesson 33)

Lesson 26

Objective: Divide multiples of 10, 100, and 1,000 by single-digit numbers.

Suggested Lesson Structure

■ Fluency Practice   (12 minutes)
■ Application Problem   (5 minutes)
■ Concept Development   (30 minutes)
■ Student Debrief   (13 minutes)

   Total Time   **(60 minutes)**

Fluency Practice (12 minutes)

- Show Values with Place Value Disks **4.NBT.1**   (4 minutes)
- Group Counting **4.OA.1**   (2 minutes)
- List Multiples and Factors **4.OA.4**   (2 minutes)
- List Prime Numbers **4.OA.4**   (4 minutes)

Show Values with Place Value Disks (4 minutes)

Materials: (T) Thousands place value chart (Lesson 4 Template) (S) Personal white board, thousands place value chart (Lesson 4 Template)

Note: This fluency activity prepares students for this lesson's Concept Development.

Repeat the process from Lesson 15 with the following possible sequence (projected or drawn).

- 1 hundreds disk, 2 tens disks, and 3 ones disks
- 4 hundreds disks, 1 tens disk, and 3 ones disks
- 3 hundreds disks, 15 tens disks, and 2 ones disks
- 2 hundreds disks, 15 tens disks, and 3 ones disks

Follow by having students draw disks for 524, 231, and 513.

Group Counting (2 minutes)

Note: Group counting reviews factors and multiples.

Direct students to count forward and backward, occasionally changing the direction of the count.

- Threes to 30
- Fours to 40
- Sixes to 60
- Eights to 80

List Multiples and Factors (2 minutes)

Materials: (S) Personal white board

Note: This fluency activity reviews Topic F's content and gives students practice in remembering the difference between factors and multiples.

Repeat the process from Lesson 25 with the following possible sequence: 4 multiples of 6 starting from 60, the 4 factors of 6, the 4 factors of 8, 4 multiples of 8 starting at 80, the 3 factors of 9, and 4 multiples of 9 starting at 90.

List Prime Numbers (4 minutes)

Materials: (S) Paper

Note: This fluency activity reviews Lesson 25's Concept Development.

- T: What's the smallest prime number?
- S: 2.
- T: On your paper, write 2.
- T: Are there any other even prime numbers?
- S: No.
- T: On your paper, list the prime numbers in order from least to greatest, beginning with 2. You have one minute.
- S: (List the prime numbers.)
- T: Compare your list with your partner's. Look for differences in your lists and decide who is correct. Make changes to your lists as needed. You have two minutes.

Lesson 26:   Divide multiples of 10, 100, and 1,000 by single-digit numbers.

©2015 Great Minds. eureka-math.org
G4-M3-TE-B2-1.3.1-01.2016

359

Application Problem (5 minutes)

A coffee shop uses 8-ounce mugs to make all of its coffee drinks. In one week, they served 30 mugs of espresso, 400 lattes, and 5,000 mugs of coffee. How many ounces of coffee drinks did they make in that one week?

8×30
$= 8 \times (3 \times 10)$
$= (8 \times 3) \times 10$
$= 24 \times 10$
$= 240$

8×400
$= 8 \times (4 \times 100)$
$= (8 \times 4) \times 100$
$= 32 \times 100$
$= 3,200$

8×5000
$= 8 \times (5 \times 1000)$
$= (8 \times 5) \times 1000$
$= 40 \times 1000$
$= 40,000$

$$\begin{array}{r} 40,000 \\ 3,200 \\ +\ \ \ 240 \\ \hline 43,440 \end{array}$$

The coffee shop made 43,440 ounces of coffee drinks in one week.

Note: By reviewing multiplication of 10, 100, and 1,000, this Application Problem leads up to today's Concept Development, which will explore division of multiples of 10, 100, and 1,000.

Concept Development (30 minutes)

Materials: (T) Thousands place value chart for dividing (Template) (S) Personal white board, thousands place value chart for dividing (Template)

Problem 1

$9 \div 3$ and $90 \div 3$

$900 \div 3$ and $9,000 \div 3$

Display $9 \div 3$ and $90 \div 3$.

>   T: Let's draw place value disks to represent these expressions. Solve. Compare your models to your partner's.
>   T: Give me a number sentence for each in unit form.
>   S: 9 ones ÷ 3 = 3 ones. 9 tens ÷ 3 = 3 tens.

Display $900 \div 3$ and $9,000 \div 3$.

>   T: Tell your partner how you might model these two expressions.
>   S: It's just like we did for the last problems. We represented 9 disks and divided them into 3 groups. Our disks will be in the hundreds or in the thousands. We won't have a remainder because 3 is a factor of 9.

NOTES ON MULTIPLE MEANS OF ENGAGEMENT:

Students who still need visual support to divide may be allowed to draw place value disks or to use concrete place value disks.

9 ones ÷ 3 = 3 ones   9 tens ÷ 3 = 3 tens

9 hundreds ÷ 3 = 3 hundreds   9 thousands ÷ 3 = 3 thousands

EUREKA MATH™

T: Model these expressions, using place value disks, with your partner.

S: (Draw disks and divide.)

T: What do you notice?

S: All 9 disks were split into 3 groups of 3, but they are groups of different units.

T: Write these number sentences in unit form. Turn and talk with your partner about what you notice.

S: They all look similar. → They are the same with different units. → They are all solved with 9 divided by 3; they just have different units.

Problem 2

$500 \div 5$

$350 \div 5$

$3,000 \div 5$

Display $500 \div 5$.

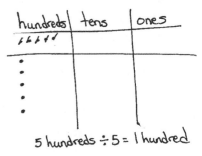

T: On your personal white board, rewrite the expression $500 \div 5$ in unit form.

S: (Write 5 hundreds ÷ 5.)

T: Why don't you need a pencil and paper to solve this problem?

S: Because 5 divided by 5 is 1, and the unit is hundreds. The answer is 1 hundred. → Five of anything divided by 5 is 1. → Yeah, 5 bananas divided by 5 is 1 banana.

Display $350 \div 5$.

T: Now, let's look at 350 divided by 5. Rewrite this expression in unit form. Talk to your partner about how representing this expression is different from the last one.

S: This time we have two units, hundreds and tens. → I can rename 3 hundreds and 5 tens as 35 tens. 35 tens divided by 5. → We didn't have to decompose 5 hundreds, but now we do have to change 3 hundreds for tens since we can't divide 3 hundreds by 5.

T: Let's use 35 tens. Say the number sentence you will use to solve in unit form.

S: 35 tens ÷ 5 = 7 tens.

T: What is the quotient of 350 divided by 5?

S: 70.

T: Let's model this on the place value chart just to be sure you really understand. Draw 3 hundreds and 5 tens and change the hundreds into smaller units.

S: It's true. When I decomposed each hundred, I got 10 more tens. 5 tens + 10 tens + 10 tens + 10 tens is 35 tens. → Each 10 tens is 1 hundred.

Display 3,000 ÷ 5.

T: Discuss with your partner a way to solve this problem.

T: (Allow one minute for students to discuss.) Solve.
     Compare your solution with a pair near you. Discuss
     the strategy you used.

T: (Allow time for sharing.) Is there a pair that would like
     to share their solution?

S: We had to decompose 3,000 into 30 hundreds because
     there weren't enough thousands to divide. → 30
     hundreds divided by 5 is easy because we know 30
     divided by 5 is 6. Then, we just had to divide
     30 hundreds by 5 and got a quotient of 6 hundreds, or
     600.

T   How is this problem related to 350 ÷ 5?

S: 3 hundreds got changed for 30 tens, and 3 thousands
     got changed for 30 hundreds. → In both problems, we
     had to change 3 larger units for 30 of the next smaller
     units. → It's like when we are subtracting and we
     don't have enough units—we have to change a larger
     unit for smaller units, too.

T: Good connections. Turn and restate the ideas of your
     peers to your partner in your own words.

T: (Allow time for talk.) Let me fire some quick problems at
     you. Tell me the first expression you would solve.
     For example, if I say 250 ÷ 2, you say 2 hundreds divided by
     2. If I say 250 ÷ 5, you say 25 tens divided by 5. Ready?

Give students a sequence of problems such as the following:
120 ÷ 2; 400 ÷ 2; 6,200 ÷ 2; 1,800 ÷ 2; 210 ÷ 3; 360 ÷ 3; 1,200 ÷ 3;
and 4,200 ÷ 3.

**NOTES ON
MULTIPLE MEANS
OF ACTION AND
EXPRESSION:**

Support English language learners and
others as they transcribe number form
to unit form. If helpful, guide students
to whisper-say the number before
writing. Depending on students'
proficiency, provide the spelling of
hundreds and *thousands*.

Help students understand how to
determine the appropriate unit form.
Say, "If the divisor is greater than the
first digit, try a smaller unit form."
Give multiple examples.

Problem 3

Display: The Hometown Hotel has a total of
480 guest rooms. That is 6 times as many rooms as
the Travelers Hotel down the street. How many
rooms are there in the Travelers Hotel?

T: Let's read this problem together. Draw a
     tape diagram to model this problem. When
     you have drawn and labeled your diagram,
     compare it with your partner's.

T: How can we determine the value of 1 unit?
     (Point to the unit representing the number
     of rooms at the Travelers Hotel.)

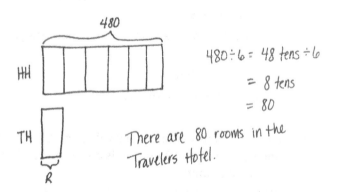

$$480 ÷ 6 = 48 \text{ tens} ÷ 6$$
$$= 8 \text{ tens}$$
$$= 80$$

There are 80 rooms in the Travelers Hotel.

Lesson 26:   Divide multiples of 10, 100, and 1,000 by single-digit numbers.

©2015 Great Minds. eureka-math.org
G4-M3-TE-B2-1.3.1-01.2016

S: We need to divide 480 by 6.

T: Yes, 480 divided by 6 units will give us the value of 1 unit. What strategy can you use to solve?

S: We can rename 4 hundreds 8 tens as 48 tens.

MP.2

T: Okay, how does that help?

S: 48 divided by 6 is 8, so 48 tens divided by 6 is 8 tens.

T: One unit is equal to …?

S: One unit equals 80.

T: So, how many rooms are there in the Travelers Hotel?

S: There are 80 rooms.

Problem Set (10 minutes)

Students should do their personal best to complete the Problem Set within the allotted 10 minutes. For some classes, it may be appropriate to modify the assignment by specifying which problems they work on first. Some problems do not specify a method for solving. Students should solve these problems using the RDW approach used for Application Problems.

Student Debrief (13 minutes)

Lesson Objective: Divide multiples of 10, 100, and 1,000 by single-digit numbers.

The Student Debrief is intended to invite reflection and active processing of the total lesson experience.

Invite students to review their solutions for the Problem Set. They should check work by comparing answers with a partner before going over answers as a class. Look for misconceptions or misunderstandings that can be addressed in the Debrief. Guide students in a conversation to debrief the Problem Set and process the lesson.

Any combination of the questions below may be used to lead the discussion.

- How is writing the number sentence in unit form helpful for solving problems like Problem 1?

- How did you rename the numbers in Problems 2(b) and 2(c) to divide?

- How are Problems 3(a) and 3(e) alike? How are they different?

> **NOTES ON MULTIPLE MEANS OF ENGAGEMENT:**
>
> Instead of moving forward into the last word problem of the Problem Set, offer students working below grade level more opportunities to determine whether or not decomposition is necessary. Have students model, on a place value chart, the suggested sequence found at the end of Problem 2. Have them do the division using the models. Finally, have them state the full number sentence using the correct unit language.

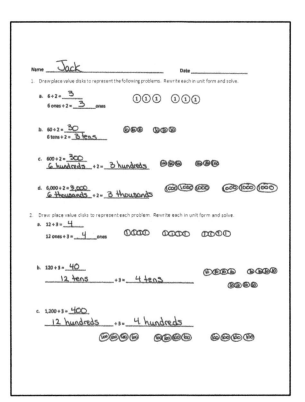

EUREKA MATH™

Lesson 26: Divide multiples of 10, 100, and 1,000 by single-digit numbers.

363

©2015 Great Minds. eureka-math.org
G4-M3-TE-B2-1.3.1-01.2016

- Explain to your partner how to solve Problem 3(g). How can you start dividing in the hundreds when there aren't enough hundreds to divide?

- How are the tape diagrams different for Problem 4 and Problem 5? How could multiplication be used to solve these problems?

- How did the Application Problem connect to today's lesson?

Exit Ticket (3 minutes)

After the Student Debrief, instruct students to complete the Exit Ticket. A review of their work will help with assessing students' understanding of the concepts that were presented in today's lesson and planning more effectively for future lessons. The questions may be read aloud to the students.

3. Solve for the quotient. Rewrite each in unit form.

a. 800 ÷ 2 = 400	b. 600 ÷ 2	c. 800 ÷ 4	d. 900 ÷ 3
8 hundreds ÷ 2 = 4 hundreds	6 hundreds ÷ 2 = 3 hundreds	8 hundreds ÷ 4 = 2 hundreds	9 hundreds ÷ 3 = 3 hundreds
e. 300 ÷ 6	f. 240 ÷ 4	g. 450 ÷ 5	h. 200 ÷ 5
30 tens ÷ 6 = _5_ tens	24 tens ÷ 4 = 6 tens	45 tens ÷ 5 = 9 tens	20 tens ÷ 5 = 4 tens
i. 3,600 ÷ 4	j. 2,400 ÷ 4	k. 2,400 ÷ 3	l. 4,000 ÷ 5
36 hundreds ÷ 4 = _9_ hundreds	24 hundreds ÷ 4 = 6 hundreds	24 hundreds ÷ 3 = 8 hundreds	40 hundreds ÷ 5 = 8 hundreds

4. Some sand weighs 2,800 kilograms. It is divided equally between 4 trucks. How many kilograms of sand are in each truck?

28 hundreds ÷ 4 = 7 hundreds
There are 700 kilograms of sand in each truck.

5. Ivy has 5 times as many stickers as Adrian has. Ivy has 350 stickers. How many stickers does Adrian have?

35 tens ÷ 5 = 7 tens
Adrian has 70 stickers.

6. An ice cream stand sold $1,600 worth of ice cream on Saturday, which was 4 times the amount sold on Friday. How much money did the ice cream stand collect on Friday?

16 hundreds ÷ 4 = 4 hundreds
The ice cream stand collected $400 on Friday.

©2015 Great Minds. eureka-math.org
G4-M3-TE-B2-1.3.1-01.2016

EUREKA MATH

Name _____   Date _____

1. Draw place value disks to represent the following problems. Rewrite each in unit form and solve.

    a. 6 ÷ 2 = _____   ① ① ①   ① ① ①

        6 ones ÷ 2 = _____ ones

    b. 60 ÷ 2 = _____

        6 tens ÷ 2 = _____

    c. 600 ÷ 2 = _____

        _____ ÷ 2 = _____

    d. 6,000 ÷ 2 = _____

        _____ ÷ 2 = _____

2. Draw place value disks to represent each problem. Rewrite each in unit form and solve.

    a. 12 ÷ 3 = _____

        12 ones ÷ 3 = _____ ones

    b. 120 ÷ 3 = _____

        _____ ÷ 3 = _____

    c. 1,200 ÷ 3 = _____

        _____ ÷ 3 = _____

EUREKA
MATH™

Lesson 26:   Divide multiples of 10, 100, and 1,000 by single-digit numbers.

365

©2015 Great Minds. eureka-math.org
G4-M3-TE-B2-1.3.1-01.2016

3. Solve for the quotient. Rewrite each in unit form.

a. $800 \div 2 = 400$ 8 hundreds ÷ 2 = 4 hundreds	b. $600 \div 2 = \underline{\hspace{1.5cm}}$	c. $800 \div 4 = \underline{\hspace{1.5cm}}$	d. $900 \div 3 = \underline{\hspace{1.5cm}}$
e. $300 \div 6 = \underline{\hspace{1.5cm}}$ 30 tens ÷ 6 = $\underline{\hspace{1cm}}$ tens	f. $240 \div 4 = \underline{\hspace{1.5cm}}$	g. $450 \div 5 = \underline{\hspace{1.5cm}}$	h. $200 \div 5 = \underline{\hspace{1.5cm}}$
i. $3{,}600 \div 4 = \underline{\hspace{1.5cm}}$ 36 hundreds ÷ 4 = $\underline{\hspace{1cm}}$ hundreds	j. $2{,}400 \div 4 = \underline{\hspace{1.5cm}}$	k. $2{,}400 \div 3 = \underline{\hspace{1.5cm}}$	l. $4{,}000 \div 5 = \underline{\hspace{1.5cm}}$

4. Some sand weighs 2,800 kilograms. It is divided equally among 4 trucks. How many kilograms of sand are in each truck?

EUREKA MATH™

5. Ivy has 5 times as many stickers as Adrian has. Ivy has 350 stickers. How many stickers does Adrian have?

6. An ice cream stand sold $1,600 worth of ice cream on Saturday, which was 4 times the amount sold on Friday. How much money did the ice cream stand collect on Friday?

Lesson 26:   Divide multiples of 10, 100, and 1,000 by single-digit numbers.

367

©2015 Great Minds. eureka-math.org
G4-M3-TE-B2-1.3.1-01.2016

Name _____   Date _____

1. Solve for the quotient. Rewrite each in unit form.

a. 600 ÷ 3 = 200 6 hundreds ÷ 3 = _____ hundreds	b. 1,200 ÷ 6 = _____	c. 2,100 ÷ 7 = _____	d. 3,200 ÷ 8 = _____

2. Hudson and 7 of his friends found a bag of pennies. There were 320 pennies, which they shared equally. How many pennies did each person get?

Divide multiples of 10, 100, and 1,000 by single-digit numbers.

EUREKA
MATH™

Name _____ Date _____

1. Draw place value disks to represent the following problems. Rewrite each in unit form and solve.

   a. 6 ÷ 3 = _____

      ① ① ① ① ① ①

      6 ones ÷ 3 = _____ones

   b. 60 ÷ 3 = _____

      6 tens ÷ 3 = _____

   c. 600 ÷ 3 = _____

      _____ ÷ 3 = _____

   d. 6,000 ÷ 3 = _____

      _____ ÷ 3 = _____

2. Draw place value disks to represent each problem. Rewrite each in unit form and solve.

   a. 12 ÷ 4 = _____

      12 ones ÷ 4 = _____ones

   b. 120 ÷ 4 = _____

      _____ ÷ 4 = _____

   c. 1,200 ÷ 4 = _____

      _____ ÷ 4 = _____

Lesson 26: Divide multiples of 10, 100, and 1,000 by single-digit numbers.

369

3. Solve for the quotient. Rewrite each in unit form.

a. 800 ÷ 4 = 200 8 hundreds ÷ 4 = 2 hundreds	b. 900 ÷ 3 = _____	c. 400 ÷ 2 = _____	d. 300 ÷ 3 = _____
e. 200 ÷ 4 = _____ 20 tens ÷ 4 = ____ tens	f. 160 ÷ 2 = _____	g. 400 ÷ 5 = _____	h. 300 ÷ 5 = _____
i. 1,200 ÷ 3 = _____ 12 hundreds ÷ 3 = ____ hundreds	j. 1,600 ÷ 4 = _____	k. 2,400 ÷ 4 = _____	l. 3,000 ÷ 5 = _____

4. A fleet of 5 fire engines carries a total of 20,000 liters of water. If each truck holds the same amount of water, how many liters of water does each truck carry?

Lesson 26: Divide multiples of 10, 100, and 1,000 by single-digit numbers.

EUREKA
MATH™

5. Jamie drank 4 times as much juice as Brodie. Jamie drank 280 milliliters of juice. How much juice did Brodie drink?

6. A diner sold $2,400 worth of French fries in June, which was 4 times as much as was sold in May. How many dollars' worth of French fries were sold at the diner in May?

ones	
tens	
hundreds	
thousands	

thousands place value chart for dividing

Lesson 26:   Divide multiples of 10, 100, and 1,000 by single-digit numbers.

Lesson 27

Objective: Represent and solve division problems with up to a three-digit dividend numerically and with place value disks requiring decomposing a remainder in the hundreds place.

Suggested Lesson Structure

■ Fluency Practice   (12 minutes)
■ Application Problem   (5 minutes)
□ Concept Development   (33 minutes)
■ Student Debrief   (10 minutes)
   Total Time   **(60 minutes)**

Fluency Practice (12 minutes)

- Sprint: Circle the Prime Number **4.OA.4**   (8 minutes)
- Divide with Place Value Disks **4.NBT.1**   (4 minutes)

Sprint: Circle the Prime Number (8 minutes)

Materials: (S) Circle the Prime Number Sprint

Note: This Sprint reviews content from Topic F.

Divide with Place Value Disks (4 minutes)

Materials: (S) Personal white board

Note: This fluency activity reviews Lesson 26's Concept Development and strengthens students' understanding of place value's role in the long division algorithm.

   T: (Display 6 ÷ 2.) On your personal white board, draw place value disks to represent the expression.
   S: (Draw 6 ones disks and divide them into 2 groups of 3.)
   T: Say the division sentence in unit form.
   S: 6 ones ÷ 2 = 3 ones.

Repeat the process using the following possible sequence: 60 ÷ 2; 600 ÷ 2; 6,000 ÷ 2; 80 ÷ 2; 1,200 ÷ 3, and 1,200 ÷ 4.

Lesson 27:   Represent and solve division problems with up to a three-digit
              dividend numerically and with place value disks requiring
              decomposing a remainder in the hundreds place.   **373**

©2015 Great Minds. eureka-math.org
G4-M3-TE-B2-1.3.1-01.2016

Application Problem (5 minutes)

Emma takes 57 stickers from her collection and divides them up equally between 4 of her friends. How many stickers will each friend receive? Emma puts the remaining stickers back in her collection. How many stickers will Emma return to her collection?

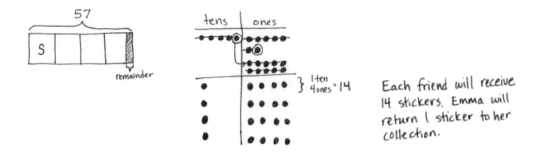

Note: This Application Problem reviews work with two-digit dividends from Lesson 17.

Concept Development (33 minutes)

Materials: (T) Thousands place value chart for dividing (Lesson 26 Template) (S) Personal white board, thousands place value chart for dividing (Lesson 26 Template)

Problem 1: Divide a three-digit number by a one-digit number using place value disks, regrouping in the hundreds.

Display 423 ÷ 3.

T: Let's find the quotient. Represent 423 on the place value chart. Tell your partner how many groups below will be needed.

S: (Draw disks on chart.) Three groups.

T: Four hundreds divided by 3. Distribute your disks and cross off what you've used. What is the quotient?

S: 1 hundred with a remainder of 1 hundred.

T: Tell me how to decompose the remaining 1 hundred.

S: Change 1 hundred for 10 tens.

T: Let's decompose 1 hundred. Turn to your partner and decide together what to do next.

S: 10 tens and 2 tens makes 12 tens. Now, we have 12 tens to divide by 3.

T: Why didn't we stop when we had a remainder of 1 hundred?

S: Because 1 hundred is just 10 tens, so you can keep dividing.

Lesson 27:   Represent and solve division problems with up to a three-digit dividend numerically and with place value disks requiring decomposing a remainder in the hundreds place.

©2015 Great Minds. eureka-math.org
G4-M3-TE-B2-1.3.1-01.2016

EUREKA MATH™

T: 12 tens divided by 3. What is the quotient? Distribute your disks and cross off what you've used.

S: 4 tens. → 4 tens distributed to each group with no remainder.

T: Does that mean we are finished?

S: No, we still have to divide the ones.

T: Do that now. Distribute and cross off your disks. 3 ones divided by 3. What is the quotient?

S: 1 one.

T: Is there any more dividing we need to do?

S: No. We have distributed all of the units from the whole.

T: Great! So, what is the quotient of 423 divided by 3? Say the whole number sentence.

S: 423 divided by 3 equals 141.

> **NOTES ON MULTIPLE MEANS OF ACTION AND EXPRESSION:**
>
> Provide learners with learning and cognitive disabilities internal scaffolds to aid their memory and organization as they draw and distribute many place value disks. Guide students to refer back to the original expression frequently (e.g., 423 ÷ 3), whisper-count as they distribute, write down any numbers they may forget, and use self-talk, such as, "Now I'll distribute 12 tens."

Problem 2

Display 783 ÷ 3.

T: Let's solve 783 ÷ 3 using a place value chart and long division side by side. Represent 783 in a place value chart and prepare for long division. (Allow time for students to draw disks and write the problem.) Starting with the largest unit, tell me what to divide.

S: We divide 7 hundreds by 3.

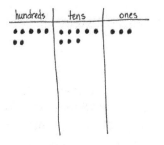

T: Do that on your chart. 7 hundreds divided by 3. What is the quotient?

S: 2 hundreds, with 1 hundred remaining.

T: (Record 2 hundreds. Point to the place value chart.) In your place value chart, you recorded 2 hundreds three times. Say a multiplication sentence that tells that.

S: 2 hundreds times 3 equals 6 hundreds.

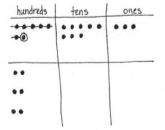

As students say the multiplication equation, refer to the algorithm, point to the 2 hundreds and the divisor, and finally, record 6 hundreds.

T: (Point to the place value chart.) We started with 7 hundreds, distributed 6 hundreds, and have 1 hundred remaining. Tell me a subtraction sentence for that.

S: 7 hundreds minus 6 hundreds equals 1 hundred.

Lesson 27:   Represent and solve division problems with up to a three-digit dividend numerically and with place value disks requiring decomposing a remainder in the hundreds place.   375

©2015 Great Minds. eureka-math.org
G4-M3-TE-B2-1.3.1-01.2016

As students say the subtraction sentence, refer to the algorithm, point to the hundreds column, record a subtraction line and symbol, and record 1 hundred.

- T: (Point to the place value chart.) How many tens remain to be divided?
- S: 8 tens.
- T: (Record an 8 next to the 1 hundred remainder.) We decompose the remaining 1 hundred for 10 tens and add on the 8 tens. Decompose the 1 hundred. Say a division sentence for how we should distribute 18 tens.
- S: 18 tens divided by 3 equals 6 tens.

As students say the division sentence, refer to the algorithm, point to the 18 tens and the divisor, and then record 6 tens in the quotient. Likewise, distribute the 18 tens in the place value chart.

- T: (Point to the place value chart.) You recorded 6 tens, three times. Say a multiplication sentence that tells that.
- S: 6 tens times 3 equals 18 tens.

As students say the multiplication equation, refer to the algorithm, point to 6 tens, then the divisor, and finally, record 18 tens.

- T: (Point to the place value chart.) We renamed 10 tens, distributed all 18 tens, and have no tens remaining. Say a subtraction sentence for that.
- S: 18 tens minus 18 tens equals 0 tens.

As students say the subtraction equation, refer to the algorithm, record a subtraction line and symbol, and 0 tens.

- T: What is left to distribute?
- S: The ones.
- T: (Point to the place value chart.) How many ones remain to be divided?
- S: 3 ones.
- T: (Record a 3 next to the 0 in the tens column.) Say a division sentence for how we should distribute 3 ones.
- S: 3 ones divided by 3 equals 1 one.

Represent and solve division problems with up to a three-digit dividend numerically and with place value disks requiring decomposing a remainder in the hundreds place.

EUREKA MATH

As students say the division sentence, refer to the algorithm, point to the 3 ones and the divisor, and then record 1 one in the quotient.

T: (Point to the place value chart.) You recorded 1 one, three times. Say a multiplication sentence that describes that.

S: 1 one times 3 equals 3 ones.

As students say the multiplication equation, refer to the algorithm, point to 1 one, then the divisor, and finally, record 3 ones.

T: (Point to the place value chart.) We have 3 ones, and we distributed 3 ones. Say a subtraction sentence for that.

S: 3 ones minus 3 ones equals 0 ones.

Have students share with a partner how the model matches the algorithm. Note that both show equal groups, as well as how both can be used to check their work using multiplication.

Problem 3

Display 546 ÷ 3.

T: Work together with a partner to solve 546 ÷ 3 using place value disks and long division. One partner solves the problem using a place value chart and disks, while the other partner uses long division. Work at the same pace, matching the action of the disks with the written method, and, of course, compare your quotients.

Circulate as students are working to offer assistance as needed.

T: How was this problem unlike the others we solved today?

S: There were more hundreds left after we distributed them. → We had to decompose 2 hundreds this time.

Lesson 27:   Represent and solve division problems with up to a three-digit dividend numerically and with place value disks requiring decomposing a remainder in the hundreds place.

©2015 Great Minds. eureka-math.org
G4-M3-TE-B2-1.3.1-01.2016

Problem Set (10 minutes)

Students should do their personal best to complete the Problem Set within the allotted 10 minutes. For some classes, it may be appropriate to modify the assignment by specifying which problems they work on first. Some problems do not specify a method for solving. Students should solve these problems using the RDW approach used for Application Problems.

NOTES ON
MULTIPLE MEANS
OF ENGAGEMENT:

Challenge students working above grade level and others to approximate estimates before they solve in order to check the reasonableness of their answers.

Student Debrief (10 minutes)

Lesson Objective: Represent and solve division problems with up to a three-digit dividend numerically and with place value disks requiring decomposing a remainder in the hundreds place.

The Student Debrief is intended to invite reflection and active processing of the total lesson experience.

Invite students to review their solutions for the Problem Set. They should check work by comparing answers with a partner before going over answers as a class. Look for misconceptions or misunderstandings that can be addressed in the Debrief. Guide students in a conversation to debrief the Problem Set and process the lesson.

Any combination of the questions below may be used to lead the discussion.

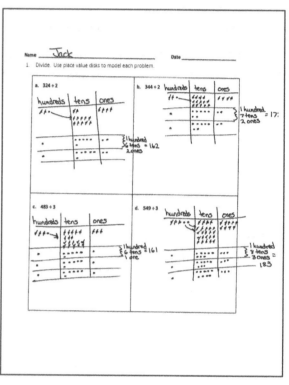

- Think about ways to connect the division Problems in 1(a) and 1(b) to word problems. What are some other ways to say *divided by two*? Try making a connection to fractions by using words like *half*.

- Problems 1(c) and 1(d) have the same divisor. Problem 1(d) has a larger whole. What conclusions can you make about quotients when the wholes are different, but the divisors are the same?

- The size of a remainder is closely connected with that of the divisor.

  - What conclusions can you make about remainders, whether they are in the hundreds, tens, or ones columns? Use Problems 2(a) and 2(b) to discuss your findings.

  - Imagine your partner found a remainder of 4 hundreds in Problem 2(b). How could you explain to him his mistake? Is there a connection with the remainder and the divisor that would help him to avoid this miscalculation in the future?

Lesson 27:   Represent and solve division problems with up to a three-digit dividend numerically and with place value disks requiring decomposing a remainder in the hundreds place.

©2015 Great Minds. eureka-math.org
G4-M3-TE-B2-1.3.1-01.2016

- In Problem 2(c), you had to decompose 2 hundreds into 20 tens. What did you find challenging about representing that using place value disks? Did it take a while to draw that many disks? Is there a model that would simplify that process? When is it more efficient to just imagine the disks and do the long division?

- What changed when we moved from dividing two-digit wholes to three-digit wholes? Would the same process we're using for three-digit wholes work for four-digit wholes? Five digits? Six digits? A million digits?

- How did the Application Problem connect to today's lesson?

Exit Ticket (3 minutes)

After the Student Debrief, instruct students to complete the Exit Ticket. A review of their work will help with assessing students' understanding of the concepts that were presented in today's lesson and planning more effectively for future lessons. The questions may be read aloud to the students.

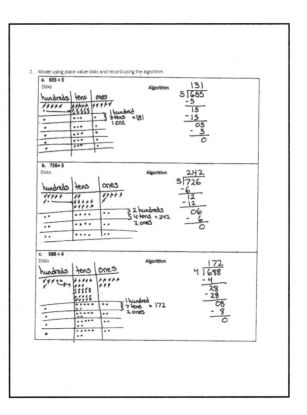

Lesson 27: Represent and solve division problems with up to a three-digit dividend numerically and with place value disks requiring decomposing a remainder in the hundreds place.

©2015 Great Minds. eureka-math.org
G4-M3-TE-B2-1.3.1-01.2016

379

A

Number Correct: _____

Circle the Prime Number

1.	4	3		23.	40	41	42
2.	6	3		24.	42	43	44
3.	8	3		25.	49	47	45
4.	5	10		26.	53	50	55
5.	5	12		27.	54	56	59
6.	5	14		28.	99	97	95
7.	8	7		29.	90	92	91
8.	9	11		30.	95	96	97
9.	11	15		31.	88	89	90
10.	15	17		32.	60	61	62
11.	19	16		33.	63	65	67
12.	14	11		34.	71	70	69
13.	13	12		35.	73	75	77
14.	18	17		36.	49	79	99
15.	19	20		37.	63	93	83
16.	21	23		38.	22	2	12
17.	25	19		39.	17	27	57
18.	29	27		40.	5	15	25
19.	31	30		41.	39	49	59
20.	33	37		42.	1	21	31
21.	9	2		43.	51	57	2
22.	51	2		44.	84	95	43

Lesson 27: Represent and solve division problems with up to a three-digit dividend numerically and with place value disks requiring decomposing a remainder in the hundreds place.

©2015 Great Minds. eureka-math.org
G4-M3-TE-B2-1.3.1-01.2016

EUREKA
MATH™

B

Number Correct: _____

Improvement: _____

Circle the Prime Number

1.	4	5
2.	6	5
3.	8	5
4.	7	10
5.	7	12
6.	7	14
7.	4	3
8.	11	10
9.	15	11
10.	17	15
11.	19	20
12.	14	13
13.	11	12
14.	16	17
15.	19	18
16.	22	23
17.	21	19
18.	29	28
19.	31	33
20.	35	37
21.	2	9
22.	57	2

23.	42	41	40
24.	44	43	42
25.	45	47	49
26.	53	55	50
27.	56	54	59
28.	95	97	99
29.	90	91	92
30.	99	98	97
31.	90	89	88
32.	67	65	63
33.	62	61	60
34.	72	71	70
35.	77	75	73
36.	27	67	77
37.	39	49	59
38.	32	2	22
39.	19	49	69
40.	5	15	55
41.	99	49	59
42.	1	21	41
43.	45	51	2
44.	48	85	67

Lesson 27:   Represent and solve division problems with up to a three-digit
dividend numerically and with place value disks requiring
decomposing a remainder in the hundreds place.

©2015 Great Minds. eureka-math.org
G4-M3-TE-B2-1.3.1-01.2016

Name _____ Date _____

1. Divide. Use place value disks to model each problem.

a. 324 ÷ 2

b. 344 ÷ 2

Lesson 27: Represent and solve division problems with up to a three-digit dividend numerically and with place value disks requiring decomposing a remainder in the hundreds place.

©2015 Great Minds. eureka-math.org
G4-M3-TE-B2-1.3.1-01.2016

EUREKA
MATH™

c. 483 ÷ 3

d. 549 ÷ 3

Lesson 27:   Represent and solve division problems with up to a three-digit
dividend numerically and with place value disks requiring
decomposing a remainder in the hundreds place.

©2015 Great Minds. eureka-math.org
G4-M3-TE-B2-1.3.1-01.2016

383

2. Model using place value disks and record using the algorithm.

a. 655 ÷ 5

Disks   Algorithm

b. 726÷ 3

Disks   Algorithm

c. 688 ÷ 4

Disks   Algorithm

Lesson 27:   Represent and solve division problems with up to a three-digit
dividend numerically and with place value disks requiring
decomposing a remainder in the hundreds place.

©2015 Great Minds. eureka-math.org
G4-M3-TE-B2-1.3.1-01.2016

**EUREKA
MATH**™

Name _____   Date _____

Divide. Use place value disks to model each problem. Then, solve using the algorithm.

1. 423 ÷ 3
   Disks   Algorithm

2. 564 ÷ 4
   Disks   Algorithm

Lesson 27:   Represent and solve division problems with up to a three-digit
dividend numerically and with place value disks requiring
decomposing a remainder in the hundreds place.

©2015 Great Minds. eureka-math.org
G4-M3-TE-B2-1.3.1-01.2016

385

Name _____ Date _____

1. Divide. Use place value disks to model each problem.

---

a. 346 ÷ 2

---

b. 528 ÷ 2

Lesson 27: Represent and solve division problems with up to a three-digit dividend numerically and with place value disks requiring decomposing a remainder in the hundreds place.

©2015 Great Minds. eureka-math.org
G4-M3-TE-B2-1.3.1-01.2016

EUREKA MATH™

c.   516 ÷ 3

d.   729 ÷ 3

Lesson 27:   Represent and solve division problems with up to a three⁻digit
dividend numerically and with place value disks requiring
decomposing a remainder in the hundreds place.

©2015 Great Minds. eureka-math.org
G4-M3-TE-B2-1.3.1-01.2016

387

2. Model using place value disks, and record using the algorithm.

---

a. 648 ÷ 4

Disks   Algorithm

---

b. 755 ÷ 5

Disks   Algorithm

---

c. 964 ÷ 4

Disks   Algorithm

Lesson 27:   Represent and solve division problems with up to a three-digit
dividend numerically and with place value disks requiring
decomposing a remainder in the hundreds place.

©2015 Great Minds. eureka-math.org
G4-M3-TE-B2-1.3.1-01.2016

**EUREKA
MATH**™

Lesson 28

Objective: Represent and solve three-digit dividend division with divisors of 2, 3, 4, and 5 numerically.

Suggested Lesson Structure

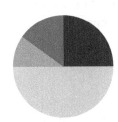

■ Fluency Practice	(15 minutes)
■ Application Problem	(6 minutes)
■ Concept Development	(30 minutes)
■ Student Debrief	(9 minutes)
Total Time	**(60 minutes)**

Fluency Practice (15 minutes)

- Multiply by Units **4.NBT.1**   (4 minutes)
- Divide Different Units **4.NBT.1**   (4 minutes)
- Group Counting **4.NBT.1**   (3 minutes)
- Divide Three-Digit Numbers by 2 **4.NBT.6**   (4 minutes)

Multiply by Units (4 minutes)

Materials: (S) Personal white board

Note: This fluency activity reviews Lesson 4.

T: (Project area model of 3 tens × 1. Beneath it, write 3 tens × 1.) Say the number sentence in unit form.

S: 3 tens × 1 = 3 tens.

T: (Write 3 tens × 1 = 3 tens.) Write the number sentence in standard form.

S: (Write 30 × 1 = 30.)

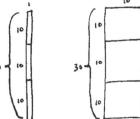
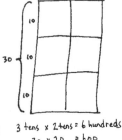

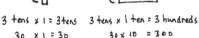

T: (Beneath 3 tens × 1 = 3 tens, write 30 × 1 = 30. Project area model of 3 tens × 1 ten. Beneath it, write 3 tens × 1 ten.) Say the number sentence in unit form.

S: (Write 3 tens × 1 ten.) 3 tens × 1 ten = 3 hundreds.

T: (Write 3 tens × 1 ten = 3 hundreds.) Write the number sentence in standard form.

S: (Write 30 × 10 = 300.)

Lesson 28:   Represent and solve three-digit dividend division with divisors of 2, 3, 4, and 5 numerically.

389

T: (Beneath 3 tens × 1 ten = 3 hundreds, write 30 × 10 = 300. Project area model of 3 tens × 2 tens.
      Beneath it, write 3 tens × 2 tens.) Say the number sentence in unit form.

S: 3 tens × 2 tens = 6 hundreds.

T: (Write 3 tens × 2 tens = 6 hundreds.) Write the number sentence in standard form.

S: (Write 30 × 20 = 600.)

T: Beneath 3 tens × 2 tens = 6 hundreds, write 30 × 20 = 600.

Continue with the following possible sequence: 3 tens × 3 tens, 3 tens × 5 tens, 2 tens × 1, 2 tens × 1 ten,
2 tens × 2 tens, 2 tens × 4 tens, and 3 tens × 4 tens.

Divide Different Units (4 minutes)

Materials: (S) Personal white board

Note: This fluency activity reviews Lesson 26's Concept Development.

$$8 \div 2 = 4 \qquad\qquad 80 \div 2 = 40 \qquad\qquad 800 \div 2 = 400 \qquad\qquad 8{,}000 \div 2 = 4{,}000$$

T: (Write 8 ÷ 2 = ___.) Say the division sentence in unit form.

S: 8 ones ÷ 2 = 4 ones.

T: (Write 8 ÷ 2 = 4. To the right, write 80 ÷ 2 = ___.) Say the division sentence in unit form.

S: 8 tens ÷ 2 = 4 tens.

T: (Write 80 ÷ 2 = 40. To the right, write 800 ÷ 2 = ___.) Say the division sentence in unit form.

S: 8 hundreds ÷ 2 = 4 hundreds.

T   (Write 800 ÷ 2 = 400. To the right, write 8,000 ÷ 2 = ___.) Say the division sentence in unit form.

S: 8 thousands ÷ 2 = 4 thousands.

T: (Write 8,000 ÷ 2 = 4,000.)

T: (Write 6 tens ÷ 2 = ___.) On your personal white board, write the division sentence in standard
      form.

S: (Write 60 ÷ 2 = 30.)

Continue with the following possible sequence: 15 tens ÷ 5, 12 hundreds ÷ 3, 28 hundreds ÷ 4, 21 tens ÷ 3,
36 tens ÷ 4, 20 tens ÷ 5, and 30 hundreds ÷ 5.

Group Counting (3 minutes)

Note: This fluency activity prepares students to divide with remainders during Lesson 30's Concept
Development.

Direct students to count forward and backward, occasionally changing the direction of the count.

- Sixes to 60
- Sevens to 70
- Eights to 80
- Nines to 90

Lesson 28:   Represent and solve three-digit dividend division with divisors
              of 2, 3, 4, and 5 numerically.

©2015 Great Minds. eureka-math.org
G4-M3-TE-B2-1.3.1-01.2016

Divide Three-Digit Numbers by 2 (4 minutes)

Materials: (S) Personal white board, thousands place value chart for dividing (Lesson 26 Template)

Note: This fluency activity reviews Lesson 27's Concept Development.

- T: (Write 546 ÷ 2.) Show 546 ÷ 2 by drawing place value disks in two different groups.
- S: (Draw place value disks.)
- T: Solve the same problem using the algorithm.
- S: (Solve.)

Repeat the process using the following possible sequence: 368 ÷ 2 and 846 ÷ 2.

Application Problem (6 minutes)

Use 846 ÷ 2 to write a word problem. Then, draw an accompanying tape diagram and solve.

Christie bought a bag of cherries weighing 846 grams. She shared half of the cherries with her neighbor. How many grams of cherries does Christie have now?

Christie has 423 grams of cherries.

Note: This Application Problem connects to Lesson 27's halving discussion in the Student Debrief. It also reinforces the use of inverse operations to check calculations. It uses the division problem from the fluency activity Divide Three-Digit Numbers. Encourage students to revise their word problems to use the word *half*.

Concept Development (30 minutes)

Materials: (T) Thousands place value chart for dividing (Lesson 26 Template) (S) Personal white board, thousands place value chart for dividing (Lesson 26 Template)

Problem 1: 297 ÷ 4

- T: (Write 297 ÷ 4.) Set up 297 ÷ 4 in your thousands place value chart, and write the problem to solve using long division.
- T: Divide 2 hundreds by 4.
- S: There aren't enough hundreds to put them into 4 groups. I need to break them apart.

Lesson 28:   Represent and solve three-digit dividend division with divisors of 2, 3, 4, and 5 numerically.

391

©2015 Great Minds. eureka-math.org
G4-M3-TE-B2-1.3.1-01.2016

T: Correct. 2 hundreds is the same as how many tens?

S: 20 tens.

T: 20 tens plus 9 tens is 29 tens. Divide 29 tens by 4. What is the quotient?

S: 7 tens.

T: Where do we record 7 tens?

S: Above the 9.

T: Why?

S: Because the 9 is in the tens place. It represents the number of tens.

T: Record 7 tens. When we distribute 29 tens into 4 groups, there are 7 tens in each group. Say the multiplication sentence that tells how many of the tens were distributed.

S: 7 tens times 4 equals 28 tens.

NOTES ON
MULTIPLE MEANS
OF ENGAGEMENT:

This vignette supports students step by step when using it in combination with Lesson 27. Consider enhancing the experience for learners who have limited executive functioning by guiding students to set appropriate individual goals. Goals may include effort, efficiency, timing, organization, and persistence. In addition, consider adjusting the numbers to challenge students working above grade level or offer alternatives such as developing a game to practice the skill.

As students are reciting the multiplication sentence, point to the 7 tens, then to the divisor, and then record the 28. Be sure students are also recording.

T: We began with 29 tens, but we distributed 28 of them. How many tens are remaining? Say the subtraction sentence that will show that.

S: 29 tens minus 28 tens equals 1 ten.

T: Continue dividing with your partner.

Allow time for students to divide.

T: What is the quotient and the remainder?

S: The quotient is 74 and the remainder is 1.

T: How can we use multiplication and addition to check if our quotient is correct?

S: We can multiply 74 by 4, and then add the remainder 1. If we get 297, then we are correct.

T: Check your quotient using multiplication.

T: What was the new complexity for this division problem?

S: We didn't have enough hundreds to divide, so we decomposed them as tens and divided by tens first.

Lesson 28:   Represent and solve three-digit dividend division with divisors of 2, 3, 4, and 5 numerically.

©2015 Great Minds. eureka-math.org
G4-M3-TE-B2-1.3.1-01.2016

Problem 2

How many weeks are there in one year?

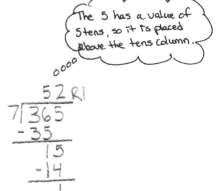

- T: What do we need to know in order to solve this problem?
- S: The number of days in one year.
- T: How many days are in one year?
- S: 365. → Sometimes 366.
- T: Good! Let's use 365 days. What other information is necessary?
- S: There are 7 days in a week.
- T: Okay, use a tape diagram to represent this problem. Show your partner how you set up your tape diagram. Solve and then check your work.

Allow students time to work independently. Circulate and offer assistance as necessary.

- T: Did you find that 365 could be divided by 7 evenly?
- S: No, there was a remainder of 1.
- T: In this problem, what does the remainder mean?
- S: It means that there is one extra day.
- T: Talk to your partner. How did you know it was an extra day?
- S: Our whole, or total, represented the number of days in a year, 365, so our remainder is days. → 365 minus 52 groups of 7 leaves 1 day remaining. → 1 one is one day. 365 ones, or days, is one year.
- T: So, what would be a good sentence to write?
- S: We can say, "There are 52 weeks and 1 day in one year."

Problem Set (10 minutes)

Students should do their personal best to complete the Problem Set within the allotted 10 minutes. For some classes, it may be appropriate to modify the assignment by specifying which problems they work on first. Some problems do not specify a method for solving. Students should solve these problems using the RDW approach used for Application Problems.

Lesson 28:   Represent and solve three-digit dividend division with divisors of 2, 3, 4, and 5 numerically.

©2015 Great Minds. eureka-math.org
G4-M3-TE-B2-1.3.1-01.2016

393

Student Debrief (9 minutes)

Lesson Objective: Represent and solve three-digit dividend division with divisors of 2, 3, 4, and 5 numerically.

The Student Debrief is intended to invite reflection and active processing of the total lesson experience.

Invite students to review their solutions for the Problem Set. They should check work by comparing answers with a partner before going over answers as a class. Look for misconceptions or misunderstandings that can be addressed in the Debrief. Guide students in a conversation to debrief the Problem Set and process the lesson.

Any combination of the questions below may be used to lead the discussion.

- Look at all of the problems with 4 as a divisor. They all have a remainder of 1, 2, or 3. If you were dividing by 4 and came up with a remainder of 4, 5, or 6, what would you know?

- Problems 1(a) and 1(b) have the same quotient. How can the same quotient come from two different whole amounts? Let's draw a tape diagram for each to show how that could be true.

- Problems 1(c) and 1(d) have the same whole. Which quotient is larger? Why?

- How did the Application Problem connect to today's lesson?

Exit Ticket (3 minutes)

After the Student Debrief, instruct students to complete the Exit Ticket. A review of their work will help with assessing students' understanding of the concepts that were presented in today's lesson and planning more effectively for future lessons. The questions may be read aloud to the students.

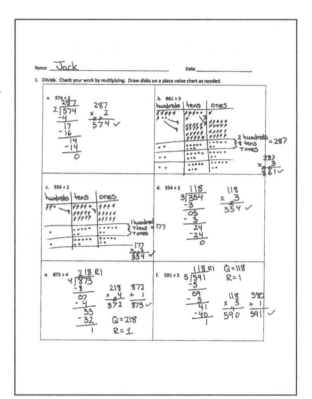

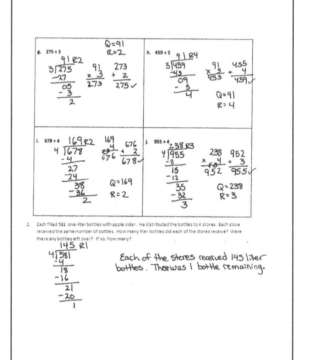

Lesson 28:   Represent and solve three-digit dividend division with divisors of 2, 3, 4, and 5 numerically.

©2015 Great Minds. eureka-math.org
G4-M3-TE-B2-1.3.1-01.2016

EUREKA MATH

Name _____   Date _____

1. Divide. Check your work by multiplying. Draw disks on a place value chart as needed.

---

a. 574 ÷ 2

---

b. 861 ÷ 3

---

c. 354 ÷ 2

Lesson 28:   Represent and solve three-digit dividend division with divisors
of 2, 3, 4, and 5 numerically.

395

©2015 Great Minds. eureka-math.org
G4-M3-TE-B2-1.3.1-01.2016

d. 354 ÷ 3

e. 873 ÷ 4

f. 591 ÷ 5

Lesson 28: Represent and solve three-digit dividend division with divisors of 2, 3, 4, and 5 numerically.

EUREKA
MATH™

g. 275 ÷ 3

h. 459 ÷ 5

i. 678 ÷ 4

Lesson 28:   Represent and solve three-digit dividend division with divisors
of 2, 3, 4, and 5 numerically.

©2015 Great Minds. eureka-math.org
G4-M3-TE-B2-1.3.1-01.2016

397

j. 955 ÷ 4

2. Zach filled 581 one-liter bottles with apple cider. He distributed the bottles to 4 stores. Each store received the same number of bottles. How many liter bottles did each of the stores receive? Were there any bottles left over? If so, how many?

Lesson 28: Represent and solve three-digit dividend division with divisors of 2, 3, 4, and 5 numerically.

©2015 Great Minds. eureka-math.org
G4-M3-TE-B2-1.3.1-01.2016

Name _____   Date _____

1. Divide. Check your work by multiplying. Draw disks on a place value chart as needed.

a. $776 \div 2$	b. $596 \div 3$

2. A carton of milk contains 128 ounces. Sara's son drinks 4 ounces of milk at each meal. How many 4-ounce servings will one carton of milk provide?

Lesson 28:   Represent and solve three-digit dividend division with divisors of 2, 3, 4, and 5 numerically.

399

©2015 Great Minds. eureka-math.org
G4-M3-TE-B2-1.3.1-01.2016

Name _____ Date _____

1. Divide. Check your work by multiplying. Draw disks on a place value chart as needed.

a. 378 ÷ 2

b. 795 ÷ 3

c. 512 ÷ 4

Lesson 28: Represent and solve three-digit dividend division with divisors of 2, 3, 4, and 5 numerically.

©2015 Great Minds. eureka-math.org
G4-M3-TE-B2-1.3.1-01.2016

EUREKA MATH™

d. 492 ÷ 4

e. 539 ÷ 3

f. 862 ÷ 5

Lesson 28:   Represent and solve three-digit dividend division with divisors
of 2, 3, 4, and 5 numerically.

401

©2015 Great Minds. eureka-math.org
G4-M3-TE-B2-1.3.1-01.2016

g. 498 ÷ 3

h. 783 ÷ 5

i. 621 ÷ 4

Lesson 28: Represent and solve three-digit dividend division with divisors of 2, 3, 4, and 5 numerically.

©2015 Great Minds. eureka-math.org
G4-M3-TE-B2-1.3.1-01.2016

EUREKA MATH

j.   531 ÷ 4

2. Selena's dog completed an obstacle course that was 932 meters long. There were 4 parts to the course, all equal in length. How long was 1 part of the course?

Lesson 28:   Represent and solve three-digit dividend division with divisors
                   of 2, 3, 4, and 5 numerically.

©2015 Great Minds. eureka-math.org
G4-M3-TE-B2-1.3.1-01.2016

403

Lesson 29

Objective: Represent numerically four-digit dividend division with divisors of 2, 3, 4, and 5, decomposing a remainder up to three times.

Suggested Lesson Structure

■ Fluency Practice   (12 minutes)

■ Application Problem   (5 minutes)

■ Concept Development   (33 minutes)

■ Student Debrief   (10 minutes)

   Total Time   **(60 minutes)**

Fluency Practice (12 minutes)

- Multiply by Units **4.NBT.1**   (4 minutes)
- Divide Different Units **4.NBT.1**   (4 minutes)
- Divide to Find Half **4.NBT.6**   (4 minutes)

Multiply by Units (4 minutes)

Materials: (S) Personal white board

Note: This fluency activity reviews Lesson 4.

 T: (Write $2 \times 4 = $ ___.) Say the multiplication sentence in unit form.

 S: 2 ones $\times$ 4 = 8 ones.

 T: Write the equation in standard form.

 S: (Write $2 \times 4 = 8$.)

 T: (Write $20 \times 4 = $ ___.) Say the multiplication sentence in unit form.

 S: 2 tens $\times$ 4 = 8 tens.

 T: Write the equation in standard form.

 S: (Write $20 \times 4 = 80$.)

 T: (Write 2 tens $\times$ 4 tens = ___.) Say the multiplication sentence in unit form.

 S: 2 tens $\times$ 4 tens = 8 hundreds.

 T: Write the equation in standard form.

 S: (Write $20 \times 40 = 800$.)

Continue with the following possible sequence: 3×3, 30×3, 30×30, 30×40, 5×3, 50×3, 50×30, 50×50, 5×8, 50×8, and 50×80.

404   Lesson 29:   Represent numerically four-digit dividend division with divisors
                             of 2, 3, 4, and 5, decomposing a remainder up to three times.

©2015 Great Minds. eureka-math.org
G4-M3-TE-B2-1.3.1-01.2016

Divide Different Units (4 minutes)

Materials: (S) Personal white board

Note: This fluency activity reviews Lesson 26's Concept Development and strengthens students' understanding of place value's role in the long division algorithm.

Repeat the process from Lesson 28 using the following possible sequence: 9 ones ÷ 3, 9 tens ÷ 3, 9 hundreds ÷ 3, 9 thousands ÷ 3, 16 tens ÷ 4, 15 hundreds ÷ 5, 27 hundreds ÷ 3, 24 tens ÷ 3, 32 tens ÷ 4, 40 tens ÷ 5, and 20 hundreds ÷ 5.

Divide to Find Half (4 minutes)

Materials: (S) Personal white board

Note: This fluency activity reviews Lesson 28's Concept Development.

- T: Find half of 38 using long division.
- S: 19.
- T: Find half of 386.
- S: 193.

Continue with the following possible sequence: half of 56, 562, 74, and 744.

Application Problem (5 minutes)

Janet uses 4 feet of ribbon to decorate each pillow. The ribbon comes in 225-foot rolls. How many pillows will she be able to decorate with one roll of ribbon? Will there be any ribbon left over?

Note: This Application Problem reviews the skill of decomposing units in order to divide and interpreting a remainder within the context of a word problem so that those skills may be applied to today's work with four-digit dividends.

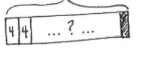

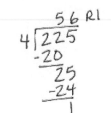

Janet can make 56 pillows from 1 roll of ribbon, and she will have 1 foot of ribbon left over.

Lesson 29:   Represent numerically four-digit dividend division with divisors of 2, 3, 4, and 5, decomposing a remainder up to three times.

405

©2015 Great Minds. eureka-math.org
G4-M3-TE-B2-1.3.1-01.2016

Concept Development (33 minutes)

Materials: (S) Personal white board

Problem 1: Divide using the standard algorithm and multiply to check the answer.

- T: (Write 4,325 ÷ 3.) Write 4,325 ÷ 3 on your personal white board.
- T: Divide 4 thousands by 3. What is the quotient?
- S: 1 thousand.
- T: Record 1 thousand. Say the multiplication sentence that tells how many of the thousands we distributed.
- S: 1 thousand times three equals 3 thousands.

NOTES ON
MULTIPLE MEANS
OF ENGAGEMENT:

In order to sustain the interest of some learners, it may be meaningful to couple the long division with premade modeling with place value disks or real objects that can be referred to throughout the vignette. Give students graph paper to ease the recording of numbers in their place value columns.

As students are reciting the multiplication sentence, point to the thousand, then to the divisor, and then record the 3 in the thousands column. Be sure students are also recording.

- T: We began with 4 thousands and distributed 3 of them. How many thousands remain? What is the subtraction sentence that will show that?
- S: 4 thousands minus 3 thousands equals 1 thousand.

As students are reciting the subtraction sentence, point to the 4 thousands and the 3 thousands, and then record the remaining 1.

- T: What do you notice about what we subtracted?
- S: We have 1 thousand left that we can decompose into 10 hundreds.
- T: How many hundreds did we already have?
- S: 3 hundreds. Now, our division sentence for the hundreds is 13 hundreds divided by 3. 13 hundreds divided by 3 is 4 hundreds.
- T: Record 4 hundreds. Continue dividing with your partner.

Allow time for students to complete the long division.

- T: Say the complete division sentence.
- S: 4,325 divided by 3 is 1,441 with a remainder of 2.
- T: Great! How can we use multiplication and addition to check if our quotient and remainder are correct?
- S: We can multiply 1,441 by 3 and then add the remainder of 2.

Repeat with 2,254 ÷ 3. Use the standard algorithm and multiply to check the answer. (Students see 22 hundreds ÷ 3 is the first step instead of 2 thousands ÷ 3.)

$$
\begin{array}{r}
1{,}441 \text{ R2} \\
3\overline{)4{,}325} \\
-3 \\
\hline
13 \\
-12 \\
\hline
12 \\
-12 \\
\hline
05 \\
-3 \\
\hline
2
\end{array}
$$

$$
\begin{array}{r}
1{,}441 \\
\times\ \ 3 \\
\hline
4{,}323
\end{array}
\qquad
\begin{array}{r}
4{,}323 \\
+\ \ \ 2 \\
\hline
4{,}325\ \checkmark
\end{array}
$$

$$
\begin{array}{r}
751 \text{ R1} \\
3\overline{)2{,}254} \\
-21 \\
\hline
15 \\
-15 \\
\hline
04 \\
-3 \\
\hline
1
\end{array}
$$

$$
\begin{array}{r}
751 \\
\times\ \ 3 \\
\hline
2{,}253
\end{array}
\qquad
\begin{array}{r}
2{,}253 \\
+\ \ \ 1 \\
\hline
2{,}254\ \checkmark
\end{array}
$$

Lesson 29:   Represent numerically four-digit dividend division with divisors
of 2, 3, 4, and 5, decomposing a remainder up to three times.

©2015 Great Minds. eureka-math.org
G4-M3-TE-B2-1.3.1-01.2016

EUREKA
MATH

Problem 2

Ellie bought two packs of beads. Altogether, she has 1,254 beads. If the number of beads in each bag is the same, how many beads are in three packs?

T: Draw something to help you solve this problem. (Pause.) What did you draw?

S: (Method A) I drew a tape diagram. I made 2 units and labeled the whole as 1,254, since we know that there are 1,254 beads in two packs. Then, I just drew a third unit. I labeled all 3 units with a question mark to represent how many beads are in three packs.

S: (Method B) Not me. After I drew two equal parts, I drew a second tape diagram below with three equal parts.

T: What conclusions did you make from your drawing?

S: We need to divide 1,254 by 2 to find out how many beads are in each bag. This helps because if we know how many beads are in one bag, we can multiply by 3 to find out how many beads are in three bags.

T: 1,254 divided by 2 is …?

S: 1,254 divided by 2 is 627.

T: Are we done?

S: No! We needed to multiply 627 by 3 to find the total number of beads in three packs.

S: 627 times 3 equals 1,881. There are 1,881 beads in three packs.

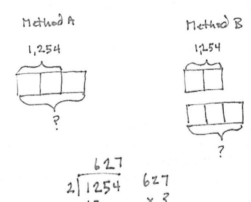

1 unit = 1,254 ÷ 2 = 627
3 units = 627 × 3 = 1,881

There are 1,881 beads in 3 packs.

Note: Clearly this is scripted to reflect a classroom where students have confidence with the tape diagram. If students need a more guided approach, it should be provided.

Problem Set (20 minutes)

Students should do their personal best to complete the Problem Set within the allotted 20 minutes. For some classes, it may be appropriate to modify the assignment by specifying which problems they work on first. Some problems do not specify a method for solving. Students should solve these problems using the RDW approach used for Application Problems.

Lesson 29: Represent numerically four-digit dividend division with divisors of 2, 3, 4, and 5, decomposing a remainder up to three times.

407

©2015 Great Minds. eureka-math.org
G4-M3-TE-B2-1.3.1-01.2016

Student Debrief (10 minutes)

Lesson Objective: Represent numerically four-digit dividend division with divisors of 2, 3, 4, and 5, decomposing a remainder up to three times.

The Student Debrief is intended to invite reflection and active processing of the total lesson experience.

Invite students to review their solutions for the Problem Set. They should check work by comparing answers with a partner before going over answers as a class. Look for misconceptions or misunderstandings that can be addressed in the Debrief. Guide students in a conversation to debrief the Problem Set and process the lesson.

Any combination of the questions below may be used to lead the discussion.

- All of the problems in the Problem Set divided a four-digit number by a one-digit number. Why do some of the quotients contain three digits while others have four?

- What did you notice about the size of the quotient in Problems 1(e) and 1(f) when the divisor increased from 2 to 3?

- Problems 1(i) and 1(j) resulted in the same quotient. Explain why that is possible.

- When is it possible for you to know, before dividing, whether or not a division problem will have a remainder?

- We have divided two-, three-, and now four-digit numbers. Explain to your partner how each time the whole became larger, another step was added. Discuss what you think would be true for dividing a number with a greater number of digits.

Exit Ticket (3 minutes)

After the Student Debrief, instruct students to complete the Exit Ticket. A review of their work will help with assessing students' understanding of the concepts that were presented in today's lesson and planning more effectively for future lessons. The questions may be read aloud to the students.

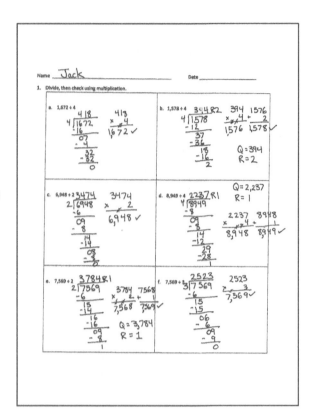

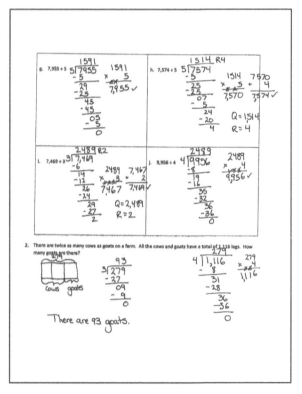

Lesson 29: Represent numerically four-digit dividend division with divisors of 2, 3, 4, and 5, decomposing a remainder up to three times.

EUREKA MATH

Name _____   Date _____

1. Divide, and then check using multiplication.

a. 1,672 ÷ 4

b. 1,578 ÷ 4

c. 6,948 ÷ 2

Lesson 29:   Represent numerically four-digit dividend division with divisors
of 2, 3, 4, and 5, decomposing a remainder up to three times.

©2015 Great Minds. eureka-math.org
G4-M3-TE-B2-1.3.1-01.2016

409

d. 8,949 ÷ 4

e. 7,569 ÷ 2

f. 7,569 ÷ 3

Lesson 29:   Represent numerically four-digit dividend division with divisors
              of 2, 3, 4, and 5, decomposing a remainder up to three times.

©2015 Great Minds. eureka-math.org
G4-M3-TE-B2-1.3.1-01.2016

EUREKA
MATH™

g. 7,955 ÷ 5

h. 7,574 ÷ 5

i. 7,469 ÷ 3

EUREKA MATH

Lesson 29: Represent numerically four-digit dividend division with divisors
of 2, 3, 4, and 5, decomposing a remainder up to three times.

411

©2015 Great Minds. eureka-math.org
G4-M3-TE-B2-1.3.1-01.2016

j.   9,956 ÷ 4

2.   There are twice as many cows as goats on a farm. All the cows and goats have a total of 1,116 legs. How many goats are there?

Name _____   Date _____

1. Divide, and then check using multiplication.

a. $1,773 \div 3$	b. $8,472 \div 5$

2. The post office had an equal number of each of 4 types of stamps. There was a total of 1,784 stamps. How many of each type of stamp did the post office have?

Lesson 29: Represent numerically four-digit dividend division with divisors of 2, 3, 4, and 5, decomposing a remainder up to three times.

413

©2015 Great Minds. eureka-math.org
G4-M3-TE-B2-1.3.1-01.2016

Name _____   Date _____

1. Divide, and then check using multiplication.

a. 2,464 ÷ 4

b. 1,848 ÷ 3

c. 9,426 ÷ 3

Lesson 29:   Represent numerically four-digit dividend division with divisors
of 2, 3, 4, and 5, decomposing a remainder up to three times.

©2015 Great Minds. eureka-math.org
G4-M3-TE-B2-1.3.1-01.2016

d. 6,587 ÷ 2

e. 5,445 ÷ 3

f. 5,425 ÷ 2

Lesson 29: Represent numerically four-digit dividend division with divisors of 2, 3, 4, and 5, decomposing a remainder up to three times.

415

©2015 Great Minds. eureka-math.org
G4-M3-TE-B2-1.3.1-01.2016

g. 8,467 ÷ 3

h. 8,456 ÷ 3

i. 4,937 ÷ 4

Lesson 29:   Represent numerically four-digit dividend division with divisors
of 2, 3, 4, and 5, decomposing a remainder up to three times.

©2015 Great Minds. eureka-math.org
G4-M3-TE-B2-1.3.1-01.2016

EUREKA
MATH™

j. 6,173 ÷ 5

2. A truck has 4 crates of apples. Each crate has an equal number of apples. Altogether, the truck is carrying 1,728 apples. How many apples are in 3 crates?

Lesson 29: Represent numerically four-digit dividend division with divisors of 2, 3, 4, and 5, decomposing a remainder up to three times.

417

©2015 Great Minds. eureka-math.org
G4-M3-TE-B2-1.3.1-01.2016

Lesson 30

Objective: Solve division problems with a zero in the dividend or with a zero in the quotient.

Suggested Lesson Structure

■ Fluency Practice   (12 minutes)
▨ Application Problem   (5 minutes)
▢ Concept Development   (33 minutes)
▨ Student Debrief   (10 minutes)

   Total Time   **(60 minutes)**

Fluency Practice (12 minutes)

- Multiply Using the Standard Algorithm **4.NBT.5**   (4 minutes)
- Divide Different Units **4.NBT.1**   (4 minutes)
- Find the Quotient and Remainder **4.NBT.6**   (4 minutes)

Multiply Using the Standard Algorithm (4 minutes)

Materials: (S) Personal white board

Note: This fluency activity reviews the Concept Development from Lessons 10 and 11, in anticipation of Topic H.

   T: (Write 773 × 2 = ___.) On your personal white board, find the product using the standard algorithm.
   S: (Solve.)

Repeat the process for the following possible sequence: 147 × 3, 1,605 × 3, and 5,741 × 5.

Divide Different Units (4 minutes)

Materials: (S) Personal white board

Note: This fluency activity reviews Lesson 26's Concept Development and strengthens students' understanding of place value's role in the long division algorithm.

Repeat the process from Lesson 28 using the following possible sequence: 15 ones ÷ 3, 15 tens ÷ 3, 25 hundreds ÷ 5, 21 hundreds ÷ 3, 28 tens ÷ 4, 30 tens ÷ 5, and 40 hundreds ÷ 5.

EUREKA
MATH™

Find the Quotient and Remainder (4 minutes)

Materials: (S) Personal white board

Note: This fluency activity reviews Lesson 29's Concept Development.

T: (Write 4,768 ÷ 2.) On your personal white board, find the quotient and remainder.

S: (Solve.)

Continue with the following possible sequence: 6,851 ÷ 5, 1,264 ÷ 4, and 1,375 ÷ 4.

Application Problem (5 minutes)

The store wanted to put 1,455 bottles of juice into packs of 4. How many complete packs can they make?
How many more bottles do they need to make another pack?

Note: This problem is a review of Lesson 29, which bridges dividing with remainders to the current lesson.

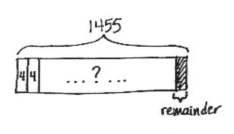

The store can make
363 complete packs.
They need 1 more
bottle to make another pack.

Concept Development (33 minutes)

Materials: (S) Personal white board

Problem 1: Divide with a zero in the dividend.

804 ÷ 4

T: What is our first step to divide 804 by 4?

S: Divide the hundreds place. → Divide the largest units
       by 4.

T: 8 hundreds divided by 4 is…?

S: 2 hundreds.

T: Say a multiplication sentence that tells how many
       hundreds have been distributed, starting with
       2 hundreds.

S: 2 hundreds times 4 equals 8 hundreds.

**NOTES ON
MULTIPLE MEANS
OF REPRESENTATION:**

Build understanding of long division by
showing 804 divided by 4 with place
value disks, base ten blocks, or real
objects such as money. If beneficial,
try the following:

- Use color to record the partial
  dividends (e.g., 8 hundreds).

- Draw arrows to the numbers that
  are brought down when remainders
  are regrouped with smaller units
  from the whole.

- Encourage students to ask questions
  for clarity as they work.

Lesson 30:   Solve division problems with a zero in the dividend or with a zero in
                   the quotient.

©2015 Great Minds. eureka-math.org
G4-M3-TE-B2-1.3.1-01.2016

419

T: Tell your partner how to find how many hundreds remain.

S: 8 hundreds minus 8 hundreds is 0 hundreds. Zero hundreds remain.

T: Zero hundreds remain. If zero hundreds remain, we can't decompose hundreds into tens to keep dividing. Are we finished?

S: If there are no more hundreds to regroup as tens, I guess we are finished. → Even if we had hundreds to regroup, there aren't any tens to regroup with. → There are still 4 ones. We have to divide those.

T: Can we move straight to dividing in the ones column? Discuss with your partner what happens if we just pass by the tens since there are zero tens.

S: We have to divide all of the units in the whole, so yeah, let's divide 4 ones by 4. → If we do that, we record 1 one in the ones column, but then we have nothing to record in the tens column because we skipped it. → Our answer could be 21. But if I multiply 21 times 4, that's 84, and the whole is 804. → We have to keep dividing in the tens, even if there are zero tens to divide, otherwise our answer will be wrong.

T: Yes, we must keep dividing unit by unit, even if there is a zero in a unit. Zero hundreds renamed as tens is zero tens. Zero tens plus zero tens is zero tens. What is zero tens divided by 4?

MP.8

S: Zero tens.

T: We continue recording even if we have zero tens to regroup. Zero tens times 4 is…?

S: Zero tens.

T: Zero tens minus zero tens is zero tens. 4 ones remain. Work with your partner to find the quotient.

S: (Continue dividing until they reach the quotient of 201.)

T: Say the complete equation.

S: 804 divided by 4 equals 201.

T: Check your work using multiplication.

S: 201 times 4 equals 804.

T: Tell your partner how you know when to stop dividing.

S: When there are no more remainders, you are finished. → You must keep dividing in each place value, even if there are zero remainders or a zero in the whole. → Keep dividing until each place value has been divided. Once you divide the ones, you have a quotient and possibly a remainder. → You must keep dividing the smaller units even if you don't have any larger units to divide.

EUREKA MATH™

Problem 2: Divide with a zero in the quotient.

$4,218 \div 3$

T: Work with your partner to divide the thousands and the hundreds. As I circulate around the room, let me hear you using the language of units as you divide.

Allow students one to two minutes to divide. Have two students come to the board to show their work.

T: I see that these students have found the quotient contains 1 thousand and 4 hundreds. When they subtracted the distributed hundreds, there was no remainder. We don't need to rename zero hundreds as tens, but we do have 1 ten to divide. Discuss with your partner your next steps.

S: 1 ten cannot be divided by 3. I'm not sure what to do. → But 10 divided by 3 would give me a quotient of 3. → But that's 3 ones, not 3 tens. → If I divided 1 ten into 3 groups, I would distribute zero tens if I was using disks, so the answer is zero tens. We should record zero tens in our quotient.

T: Right! If we distribute zero tens we record zero in the quotient and still have 1 ten and 8 ones remaining. Talk with your partner about your next steps.

S: We can change 1 ten for 10 ones. Now we have 18 ones divided by 3 is 6 ones. Our quotient is 1,406.

T: Talk with your partner about the importance of the zero in your quotient.

S: If I didn't record the zero, my answer would be wrong. → The zero is a placeholder of the tens. I can't leave that place empty. Or, what if I tried recording the 6 ones in the tens place? Then, my answer would really be wrong! → I can always use multiplication or estimation to check my work in case I may have recorded wrong.

Problem Set (20 minutes)

Students should do their personal best to complete the Problem Set within the allotted 20 minutes. For some classes, it may be appropriate to modify the assignment by specifying which problems they work on first. Some problems do not specify a method for solving. Students should solve these problems using the RDW approach used for Application Problems.

NOTES ON MULTIPLE MEANS OF ENGAGEMENT:

Students working above grade level will enjoy the challenge of Problem 11(b) on the Problem Set. Extend the problem further by asking, "How could you change the whole so that there is a zero in the quotient in a different place (than the hundreds place)?"

Lesson 30:   Solve division problems with a zero in the dividend or with a zero in the quotient.

©2015 Great Minds. eureka-math.org
G4-M3-TE-B2-1.3.1-01.2016

421

Student Debrief (10 minutes)

Lesson Objective: Solve division problems with a zero in the dividend or with a zero in the quotient.

The Student Debrief is intended to invite reflection and active processing of the total lesson experience.

Invite students to review their solutions for the Problem Set. They should check work by comparing answers with a partner before going over answers as a class. Look for misconceptions or misunderstandings that can be addressed in the Debrief. Guide students in a conversation to debrief the Problem Set and process the lesson.

Any combination of the questions below may be used to lead the discussion.

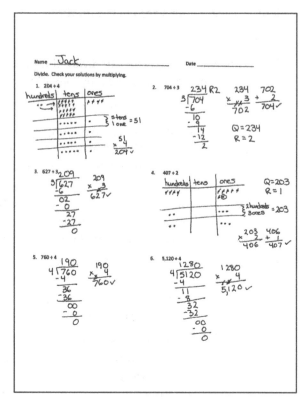

- In Problem 6, did anyone get 128? How did you know that was wrong?

- In Problem 10, the whole had consecutive zeros. How does your place value knowledge help you to keep track of where you are dividing?

- How does multiplication help you check your division?

- For what reason might there be a zero in the quotient?

- We divide, starting with the largest unit, and see if there is a remainder. What do we do with the remaining unit or units? How is that different than what we do in the ones place?

- Normally, we stop dividing at the ones place, and if there's a remainder, we give the remainder with the quotient. What if we were dividing up money? If we got down to the ones place, using dollars, what could we do?

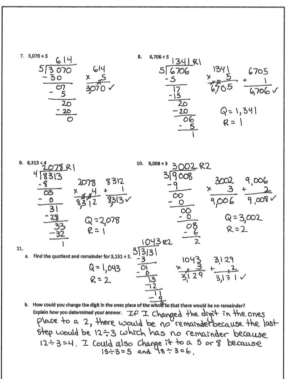

Exit Ticket (3 minutes)

After the Student Debrief, instruct students to complete the Exit Ticket. A review of their work will help with assessing students' understanding of the concepts that were presented in today's lesson and planning more effectively for future lessons. The questions may be read aloud to the students.

EUREKA
MATH™

Name _____ Date _____

Divide. Check your solutions by multiplying.

1. 204 ÷ 4

2. 704 ÷ 3

3. 627 ÷ 3

4. 407 ÷ 2

EUREKA
MATH™

Lesson 30: Solve division problems with a zero in the dividend or with a zero in the quotient.

©2015 Great Minds. eureka-math.org
G4-M3-TE-B2-1.3.1-01.2016

423

5. $760 \div 4$

6. $5,120 \div 4$

7. $3,070 \div 5$

8. $6,706 \div 5$

Lesson 30: Solve division problems with a zero in the dividend or with a zero in the quotient.

©2015 Great Minds. eureka-math.org
G4-M3-TE-B2-1.3.1-01.2016

EUREKA
MATH™

9. 8,313 ÷ 4

10. 9,008 ÷ 3

11. a. Find the quotient and remainder for 3,131 ÷ 3.

b. How could you change the digit in the ones place of the whole so that there would be no remainder? Explain how you determined your answer.

Lesson 30: Solve division problems with a zero in the dividend or with a zero in the quotient.

©2015 Great Minds. eureka-math.org
G4-M3-TE-B2-1.3.1-01.2016

425

Name _____   Date _____

Divide. Check your solutions by multiplying.

1. 380 ÷ 4

2. 7,040 ÷ 3

Lesson 30:   Solve division problems with a zero in the dividend or with a zero in
                the quotient.

©2015 Great Minds. eureka-math.org
G4-M3-TE-B2-1.3.1-01.2016

EUREKA
MATH™

Name _____   Date _____

Divide. Check your solutions by multiplying.

1. 409 ÷ 5

2. 503 ÷ 2

3. 831 ÷ 4

4. 602 ÷ 3

Lesson 30:   Solve division problems with a zero in the dividend or with a zero in
                 the quotient.

©2015 Great Minds. eureka-math.org
G4-M3-TE-B2-1.3.1-01.2016

427

5. $720 \div 3$

6. $6,250 \div 5$

7. $2,060 \div 5$

8. $9,031 \div 2$

Lesson 30:   Solve division problems with a zero in the dividend or with a zero in the quotient.

EUREKA
MATH™

9. 6,218 ÷ 4

10. 8,000 ÷ 4

Lesson 30: Solve division problems with a zero in the dividend or with a zero in the quotient.

©2015 Great Minds. eureka-math.org
G4-M3-TE-B2-1.3.1-01.2016

429

Lesson 31

Objective: Interpret division word problems as either *number of groups unknown* or *group size unknown*.

Suggested Lesson Structure

■ Fluency Practice   (11 minutes)
▨ Application Problem   (5 minutes)
▨ Concept Development   (34 minutes)
■ Student Debrief   (10 minutes)

   Total Time   **(60 minutes)**

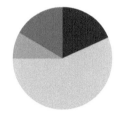

Fluency Practice (11 minutes)

▪ Sprint: Divide Different Units **4.NBT.1**   (9 minutes)
▪ Group Size or Number of Groups Unknown **4.OA.1**   (2 minutes)

Sprint: Divide Different Units (9 minutes)

Materials: (S) Divide Different Units Sprint

Note: This Sprint reviews Lesson 26's Concept Development and strengthens students' understanding of place value's role in the long division algorithm.

Group Size or Number of Groups Unknown (2 minutes)

Note: This fluency activity prepares students for today's Concept Development.

T: (Draw or project the 8 ÷ 2 = 4 tape diagrams shown on the right.) Here are two tape diagrams representing 8 ÷ 2 = 4. (Point to the model on the left.) What does the 2 represent, the size of the group or the number of groups?

S: The size of the group!

T: (Point to the second model.) In the model to the right?

S: The number of groups.

Repeat with 12 ÷ 3 = 4.

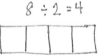
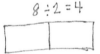
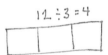

Lesson 31:   Interpret division word problems as either *number of groups unknown*
                          or *group size unknown*.

**EUREKA
MATH**™

Application Problem (5 minutes)

1,624 shirts need to be sorted into 4 equal groups. How many shirts will be in each group?

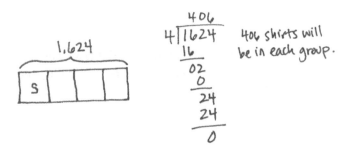

406 shirts will be in each group.

Note: This Application Problem is a review of Lesson 30, practicing with a zero in the quotient. In Problem 1 of the Concept Development, students discuss whether the unknown in this problem is the group size or the number of groups.

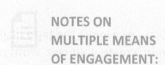

NOTES ON MULTIPLE MEANS OF ENGAGEMENT:

Differentiate the difficulty of the Application Problem by adjusting the numbers.

Extend for students working above grade level with these questions:

- How or why might the shirts be sorted?
- Were you able to predict that a zero would be in the quotient? How?

Concept Development (34 minutes)

Materials: (S) Personal white board

Problem 1

Dr. Casey has 1,868 milliliters of Medicine T. She pours equal amounts of the medicine into 4 containers. How many milliliters of medicine are in each container?

T: Can you draw something to help you solve this problem? What can you draw? Go ahead and do so.

S: (Draw.)

T: What did you draw?

S: I drew a tape diagram with the whole labeled as 1,868 milliliters. → I made the whole into 4 equal parts because she poured the medicine into four containers.

MP.5 T: What are we trying to find out?

S: We need to find out how many milliliters are in each container. → We need to find the size of the group.

T: Right, we are finding the size of the group. We already know how many groups there are, four.

T: Let's label the unknown with *t* for Medicine T.

T: Solve for how much medicine will be in each container. (Allow time for students to work.)

S: There will be 467 milliliters in each container.

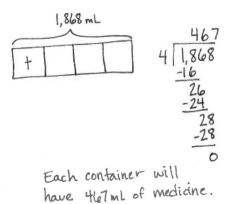

Each container will have 467 mL of medicine.

T: Compare this tape diagram to the one you drew in the Application Problem. Discuss the similarities. Were you solving for the number of groups or the size of the group?

S: Both tape diagrams are broken into four groups. → Both show we were solving for the size of each group.

Problem 2

T: (Draw or project the tape diagram shown below.) With your partner, discuss the tape diagram. Then, create your own word problem to match. Remember to determine if you are finding the size of the group or the number of groups. (We might also express this choice as the number of measurements or the size of the measurements.)

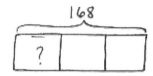

Guide students to see that the equal partitioned parts of the tape diagram tell how many groups there are. Students need to write a problem that asks for the number in each group or the size of the measurement. Suggest the context of 168 liters of cleaning solution to be poured equally into 3 containers. Have a few sets of partners share their word problems to verify students are writing to solve for group size unknown.

Problem 3

Two hundred thirty-two people are driving to a conference. If each car holds 4 people, including the driver, how many cars will be needed?

T: Can you draw something to help you solve this problem? Go ahead. (Pause while students draw.) What did you draw?

S: I drew a tape diagram with the whole labeled as 232 people.

T: Tell your partner how you partitioned the tape diagram. Are you finding the size of each group or the number of groups?

S: We made 4 equal parts because each car has 4 people in it. → We know the size of the group. Each car has 4 people. We don't know how many groups or how many cars. → We showed that 4 are in each car, but we don't know the number of cars. → Each unit of the tape diagram shows there are 4 people in each car, but we didn't know how many cars to draw.

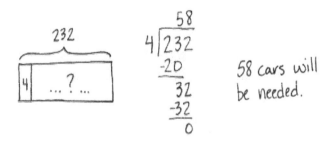

T: We labeled the tape diagram to show 4 people in each car and used a question mark to show we didn't know how many cars were needed. Solve.

S: (Solve.)

Interpret division word problems as either *number of groups unknown* or *group size unknown*.

©2015 Great Minds. eureka-math.org
G4-M3-TE-B2-1.3.1-01.2016

T: Tell your partner how you solved.

S: I divided 232 by 4. The quotient is 58.

Problem 4

T: (Draw or project the tape diagram shown below.)
With your partner, discuss the parts of the tape
diagram. Then, write your own word problem to
match. Remember to determine if you are solving for
the size of the group or the number of groups.
(We might also express this choice as the number of
measurements or the size of the measurements.)

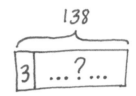

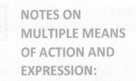

NOTES ON
MULTIPLE MEANS
OF ACTION AND
EXPRESSION:

Give extra time and opportunities for
discussion to English language learners
and others as they write their own
word problem. If time is an issue, use
the suggestion mentioned or provide
the following frame:

There are 138 _____.

*If we put 3 _____ in each group, how
many groups can be made?*

Guide students to see the first partitioned part of the tape diagram tells how many are in each group.
Students need to write a problem that asks for the number of groups and account for a remainder.
Suggest the context of 138 feet of rope cut into 3-foot segments, solving for the number of ropes, or groups
(measurements). Have a few sets of partners share their word problems to verify students are writing to find
the unknown number of groups. Have students compare and contrast the tape diagrams and word problems
for this problem and Problem 2 of the Concept Development.

Problem Set (10 minutes)

Students should do their personal best to complete the
Problem Set within the allotted 10 minutes. For some
classes, it may be appropriate to modify the assignment by
specifying which problems they work on first.
Some problems do not specify a method for solving.
Students should solve these problems using the RDW
approach used for Application Problems.

Student Debrief (10 minutes)

Lesson Objective: Interpret division word problems as
either *number of groups unknown* or *group size unknown.*

The Student Debrief is intended to invite reflection and
active processing of the total lesson experience.

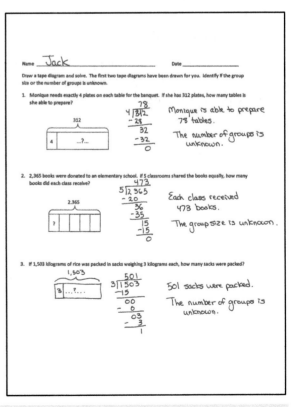

Invite students to review their solutions for the Problem Set. They should check work by comparing answers with a partner before going over answers as a class. Look for misconceptions or misunderstandings that can be addressed in the Debrief. Guide students in a conversation to debrief the Problem Set and process the lesson.

Any combination of the questions below may be used to lead the discussion .

- How and why are the tape diagrams in Problems 1 and 2 different?

- Share your tape diagram for Problem 3. What led you to draw a tape diagram to solve for the number of groups?

- For Problem 3, if our tape diagram shows the whole divided into 3 equal groups instead, would we get the wrong quotient?

- Compare your tape diagrams for Problem 2 and Problem 4. Describe how your tape diagrams differ between one- and two-step problems. If there are two unknowns, how do you determine which one to solve first?

- If, for Problem 5, the tape diagram was drawn to show groups of 5, instead of 5 equal groups, how might that lead to challenges when solving the second part of the problem?

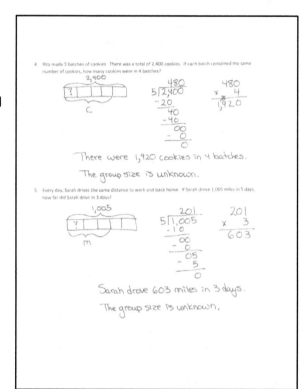

Exit Ticket (3 minutes)

After the Student Debrief, instruct students to complete the Exit Ticket. A review of their work will help with assessing students' understanding of the concepts that were presented in today's lesson and planning more effectively for future lessons. The questions may be read aloud to the students.

Lesson 31:   Interpret division word problems as either *number of groups unknown* or *group size unknown.*

EUREKA
MATH

A

Number Correct: _____

Divide.

1.	$6 \div 2 =$		23.	$300 \div 5 =$	
2.	$60 \div 2 =$		24.	$3,000 \div 5 =$	
3.	$600 \div 2 =$		25.	$16 \div 4 =$	
4.	$6,000 \div 2 =$		26.	$160 \div 4 =$	
5.	$9 \div 3 =$		27.	$18 \div 6 =$	
6.	$90 \div 3 =$		28.	$1,800 \div 6 =$	
7.	$900 \div 3 =$		29.	$28 \div 7 =$	
8.	$9,000 \div 3 =$		30.	$280 \div 7 =$	
9.	$10 \div 5 =$		31.	$48 \div 8 =$	
10.	$15 \div 5 =$		32.	$4,800 \div 8 =$	
11.	$150 \div 5 =$		33.	$6,300 \div 9 =$	
12.	$1,500 \div 5 =$		34.	$200 \div 5 =$	
13.	$2,500 \div 5 =$		35.	$560 \div 7 =$	
14.	$3,500 \div 5 =$		36.	$7,200 \div 9 =$	
15.	$4,500 \div 5 =$		37.	$480 \div 6 =$	
16.	$450 \div 5 =$		38.	$5,600 \div 8 =$	
17.	$8 \div 4 =$		39.	$400 \div 5 =$	
18.	$12 \div 4 =$		40.	$6,300 \div 7 =$	
19.	$120 \div 4 =$		41.	$810 \div 9 =$	
20.	$1,200 \div 4 =$		42.	$640 \div 8 =$	
21.	$25 \div 5 =$		43.	$5,400 \div 6 =$	
22.	$30 \div 5 =$		44.	$4,000 \div 5 =$	

Lesson 31: Interpret division word problems as either *number of groups unknown* or *group size unknown*.

435

B

Divide.

1.	4 ÷ 2 =	
2.	40 ÷ 2 =	
3.	400 ÷ 2 =	
4.	4,000 ÷ 2 =	
5.	6 ÷ 3 =	
6.	60 ÷ 3 =	
7.	600 ÷ 3 =	
8.	6,000 ÷ 3 =	
9.	10 ÷ 5 =	
10.	15 ÷ 5 =	
11.	150 ÷ 5 =	
12.	250 ÷ 5 =	
13.	350 ÷ 5 =	
14.	3,500 ÷ 5 =	
15.	4,500 ÷ 5 =	
16.	450 ÷ 5 =	
17.	9 ÷ 3 =	
18.	12 ÷ 3 =	
19.	120 ÷ 3 =	
20.	1,200 ÷ 3 =	
21.	25 ÷ 5 =	
22.	20 ÷ 5 =	

23.	200 ÷ 5 =	
24.	2,000 ÷ 5 =	
25.	12 ÷ 4 =	
26.	120 ÷ 4 =	
27.	21 ÷ 7 =	
28.	2,100 ÷ 7 =	
29.	18 ÷ 6 =	
30.	180 ÷ 6 =	
31.	54 ÷ 9 =	
32.	5,400 ÷ 9 =	
33.	5,600 ÷ 8 =	
34.	300 ÷ 5 =	
35.	490 ÷ 7 =	
36.	6,300 ÷ 9 =	
37.	420 ÷ 6 =	
38.	4,800 ÷ 8 =	
39.	4,000 ÷ 5 =	
40.	560 ÷ 8 =	
41.	6,400 ÷ 8 =	
42.	720 ÷ 8 =	
43.	4,800 ÷ 6 =	
44.	400 ÷ 5 =	

Lesson 31: Interpret division word problems as either *number of groups unknown* or *group size unknown*.

©2015 Great Minds. eureka-math.org
G4-M3-TE-B2-1.3.1-01.2016

EUREKA
MATH™

Name _____   Date _____

Draw a tape diagram and solve. The first two tape diagrams have been drawn for you. Identify if the group size or the number of groups is unknown.

1. Monique needs exactly 4 plates on each table for the banquet. If she has 312 plates, how many tables is she able to prepare?

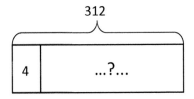

2. 2,365 books were donated to an elementary school. If 5 classrooms shared the books equally, how many books did each class receive?

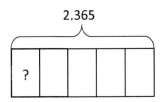

3. If 1,503 kilograms of rice was packed in sacks weighing 3 kilograms each, how many sacks were packed?

Lesson 31:   Interpret division word problems as either *number of groups unknown* or *group size unknown*.

437

©2015 Great Minds. eureka-math.org
G4-M3-TE-B2-1.3.1-01.2016

4. Rita made 5 batches of cookies. There was a total of 2,400 cookies. If each batch contained the same number of cookies, how many cookies were in 4 batches?

5. Every day, Sarah drives the same distance to work and back home. If Sarah drove 1,005 miles in 5 days, how far did Sarah drive in 3 days?

Lesson 31:   Interpret division word problems as either *number of groups unknown* or *group size unknown*.

©2015 Great Minds. eureka-math.org
G4-M3-TE-B2-1.3.1-01.2016

Name _____ Date _____

Solve the following problems. Draw tape diagrams to help you solve. Identify if the group size or the number of groups is unknown.

1. 572 cars were parked in a parking garage. The same number of cars was parked on each floor. If there were 4 floors, how many cars were parked on each floor?

2. 356 kilograms of flour were packed into sacks holding 2 kilograms each. How many sacks were packed?

Lesson 31: Interpret division word problems as either *number of groups unknown* or *group size unknown*.

©2015 Great Minds. eureka-math.org
G4-M3-TE-B2-1.3.1-01.2016

439

Name _____   Date _____

Solve the following problems. Draw tape diagrams to help you solve. Identify if the group size or the number of groups is unknown.

1. 500 milliliters of juice was shared equally by 4 children. How many milliliters of juice did each child get?

2. Kelly separated 618 cookies into baggies. Each baggie contained 3 cookies. How many baggies of cookies did Kelly make?

3. Jeff biked the same distance each day for 5 days. If he traveled 350 miles altogether, how many miles did he travel each day?

Lesson 31:   Interpret division word problems as either *number of groups unknown*
                        or *group size unknown*.

                    ©2015 Great Minds. eureka-math.org
                    G4-M3-TE-B2-1.3.1-01.2016

4. A piece of ribbon 876 inches long was cut by a machine into 4-inch long strips to be made into bows. How many strips were cut?

5. Five Martians equally share 1,940 Groblarx fruits. How many Groblarx fruits will 3 of the Martians receive?

EUREKA
MATH™

Lesson 31:   Interpret division word problems as either *number of groups unknown* or *group size unknown.*

©2015 Great Minds. eureka-math.org
G4-M3-TE-B2-1.3.1-01.2016

441

Lesson 32

Objective: Interpret and find whole number quotients and remainders to solve one-step division word problems with larger divisors of 6, 7, 8, and 9.

Suggested Lesson Structure

■ Fluency Practice   (12 minutes)
▨ Application Problem   (7 minutes)
▢ Concept Development   (31 minutes)
▨ Student Debrief   (10 minutes)
  Total Time   **(60 minutes)**

Fluency Practice (12 minutes)

- Quadrilaterals **3.G.1**   (4 minutes)
- Multiply Units **4.NBT.1**   (4 minutes)
- Group Counting **4.OA.1**   (4 minutes)

Quadrilaterals (4 minutes)

Materials: (T) Shapes (Fluency Template)

Note: This fluency activity reviews Grade 3 geometry concepts in anticipation of Module 4 content. The sheet can be duplicated for students, if you prefer.

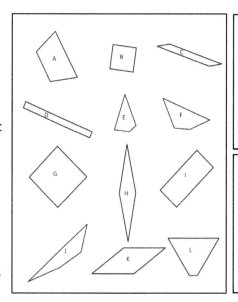

Attributes
Number of Sides
Length of Sides
Size of Angle
Right Angle

Shapes
Quadrilateral
Rhombus
Square
Rectangle
Parallelogram
Trapezoid

T: (Project the shapes template and the list of attributes.) Take one minute to discuss the attributes of the shapes you see. You can use the list to help.

S: Some have right angles. → All have straight sides. → They all have 4 sides. → B and G and maybe H and K have all equal sides. I'm not really sure.

T: If we wanted to verify whether the sides are equal, what would we do?

S: Measure!

T: What about the angles? How could you verify that they're right angles?

S: I could compare it to something that I know is a right angle.

Lesson 32:   Interpret and find whole number quotients and remainders to solve
                                one-step division word problems with larger divisors of 6, 7, 8, and 9.

©2015 Great Minds. eureka-math.org
G4-M3-TE-B2-1.3.1-01.2016

T: (Post the shape names.) Now, look at the shape names. Determine, to the best of your ability, which shapes might fall into each category.

S: B and G might be squares. → All of them are quadrilaterals. → H and K might be rhombuses. It's hard to know if their sides are equal. → D and I are rectangles. Oh yeah, and B and G are, too. → L and A look like trapezoids.

T: Which are quadrilaterals?

S: All of them.

T: Which shapes appear to be rectangles?

S: B, D, G, and I.

T: Which appear to have opposite sides of equal length but are not rectangles?

S: C, H, K. → A and L have one pair of opposite sides that look the same.

T: Squares are rhombuses with right angles. Do you see any other shapes that might have four equal sides without right angles?

S: H and K.

Multiply Units (4 minutes)

Materials: (S) Personal white board

Note: This fluency activity reviews Lesson 4's content.

T: (Write $2 \times 4 =$ ___.) Say the multiplication sentence in unit form.

S: 2 ones × 4 = 8 ones.

T: Write the answer in standard form.

S: (Write 8.)

T: (Write $20 \times 4 =$ ___.) Say the multiplication sentence in unit form.

S: 2 tens × 4 = 8 tens.

T: Write the answer in standard form.

S: (Write 80.)

Continue with the following possible sequence: 2 hundreds × 4, 2 thousands × 4, 3 ones × 5, 3 tens × 5, 3 thousands × 5, 3 thousands × 4, 5 tens × 6, 5 ones × 4, 5 thousands × 8, and 9 tens × 6.

Group Counting (4 minutes)

Note: This fluency activity prepares students for this lesson's Concept Development.

Direct students to count forward and backward, occasionally changing the direction of the count.

- Sixes to 60
- Sevens to 70
- Eights to 80
- Nines to 90

Application Problem (7 minutes)

Use the tape diagram to create a division word problem that solves for the unknown, the total number of threes in 4,194. Switch word problems with a partner and solve.

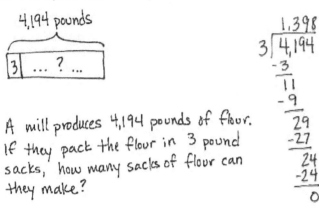

A mill produces 4,194 pounds of flour. If they pack the flour in 3 pound sacks, how many sacks of flour can they make?

They can make 1,398 sacks of flour.

Note: This problem extends understanding from Lesson 31 about solving for an unknown number of groups. Extend this problem in the Student Debrief using a divisor of 6, which connects to this lesson's Concept Development.

Concept Development (31 minutes)

Materials: (S) Personal white board

Problem 1

We all know there are 7 days in a week. How many weeks are in 259 days?

    T: Draw what we know and what we need to know on a tape diagram.

    S: I labeled the whole as 259 days. Then, I put a 7 in one part because there are 7 days in each week. We don't know how many groups of 7 days there are.

    T: How did you represent the number of weeks that are unknown?

    S: I labeled the rest of the tape diagram with a question mark.

    T: Solve for how many weeks there are in 259 days.

    S: There are 37 weeks in 259 days.

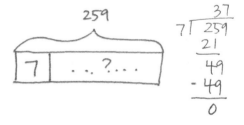

There are 37 weeks in 259 days.

444   Lesson 32:   Interpret and find whole number quotients and remainders to solve
                                one-step division word problems with larger divisors of 6, 7, 8, and 9.

©2015 Great Minds. eureka-math.org
G4-M3-TE-B2-1.3.1-01.2016

EUREKA MATH™

T: The divisor in this problem is larger than in many division problems we have solved. Tell your partner a strategy you can use to find the quotient when dividing by 7.

S: 25 tens divided by 7 is easy. It's 3 tens with 4 tens left over. → I counted by sevens, 10 at a time: 10 sevens is 70, 20 sevens is 140, 30 sevens is 210, and 40 sevens would be too big. So, I got 30 sevens with 49 left over. → That still means you get 3 tens in the quotient. One way is like we did with place value disks. The other is like we did with the area model. But they'll both give the same answer.

T: Either way of thinking will work for finding the quotient. When our divisor is large, how do I check to see if my quotient and remainder are correct?

S: The same way we always do! → It's no different for big divisors than for small divisors—multiply the number of groups times the size of each group. → And, don't forget to add the remainder. → Multiply the divisor by the quotient, and add the remainder.

T: So, what we learned about small divisors still helps us now!

Problem 2

Everyone is given the same number of colored pencils in art class. If there are 249 colored pencils and 8 students, how many pencils does each student receive?

T: Draw a tape diagram to represent the problem. Describe the parts of your tape diagram to your partner.

S: I recorded and labeled the total of 249 pencils. Then, I made 8 equal parts because there are 8 students. I need to solve for how many in each group, so I put a question mark in one part to show that I need to solve for how many pencils each student will get.

T: Solve for how many pencils each student will receive. (Allow students time to work.)

S: Each student will receive 31 colored pencils. There will be 1 pencil left over.

T: Does your drawing of the tape diagram account for the remaining pencil? Let's revise our tape diagram to show the remainder.

S: I can shade a small portion at the end of the tape diagram to represent the remaining pencil. I will have to resize each of the eight parts to make them equal.

T: Discuss a strategy you might have used when dividing by a larger divisor, like 8.

S: I counted by 8 tens. 8 tens, 16 tens, 24 tens. → I know there are 2 fours in each eight. There are 6 fours in 24. So, half of 6 is 3. There are 3 eights in 24. → I used my facts. I know 8 times 3 tens is 24 tens.

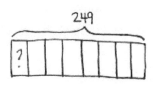

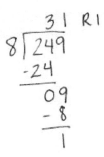

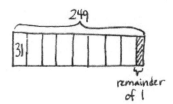

Each student receives 31 pencils. There is 1 pencil remaining.

Lesson 32: Interpret and find whole number quotients and remainders to solve one-step division word problems with larger divisors of 6, 7, 8, and 9.

445

©2015 Great Minds. eureka-math.org
G4-M3-TE-B2-1.3.1-01.2016

Problem 3

Mr. Hughes has 155 meters of volleyball netting. How many nets can he make if each court requires 9 meters of netting?

NOTES ON
MULTIPLE MEANS
OF REPRESENTATION:

English language learners and others may benefit from a brief explanation of the terms *volleyball*, *netting*, and *court*.

T: Draw a tape diagram to represent the problem. Describe the parts of your tape diagram to your partner.

S: My tape diagram shows a total of 155. I partitioned one section for 9 meters. I don't know how many nets he can make, but I do know the length of each.

T: Solve for how many nets can be made using long division.

S: Seventeen nets can be made, but 2 meters of netting will be left over.

T: Does your drawing of the tape diagram account for the remaining netting? Let's revise our tape diagram to show the remainder.

S: I can shade a small portion at the end of the tape diagram to represent the remaining 2 meters.

T: What strategy did you use for dividing with the divisor of 9?

S: I counted by 9 tens. 9 tens, 18 tens. One hundred eighty was too big. → I used a special strategy. I made 10 nets, which meant I used 90 meters of netting. That left 65 meters. Nine times 7 is 63 so that meant 7 more nets and 2 meters left over. → I used my nines facts.

Problem Set (15 minutes)

Students should do their personal best to complete the Problem Set within the allotted 15 minutes. For some classes, it may be appropriate to modify the assignment by specifying which problems they work on first. Some problems do not specify a method for solving. Students should solve these problems using the RDW approach used for Application Problems.

EUREKA
MATH

Student Debrief (10 minutes)

Lesson Objective: Interpret and find whole number quotients and remainders to solve one-step division word problems with larger divisors of 6, 7, 8, and 9.

The Student Debrief is intended to invite reflection and active processing of the total lesson experience.

Invite students to review their solutions for the Problem Set. They should check work by comparing answers with a partner before going over answers as a class. Look for misconceptions or misunderstandings that can be addressed in the Debrief. Guide students in a conversation to debrief the Problem Set and process the lesson.

Any combination of the questions below may be used to lead the discussion.

- In Problem 2, are you solving for the quotient, the remainder, or both? Why?
- Did you have to revise your tape diagram for any of the problems? If so, which one(s), and why?
- In Problem 4, did anyone get 15 teams? Why would that be an easy mistake to make?
- How could a special strategy be used to solve Problem 1?
- How did yesterday's lesson prepare you for today's lesson?
- Revisit the Application Problem. Revise the word problems using a divisor of 6 and solve. Compare the quotients. Do you see a relationship between the quotients? Did you need to divide 4,194 by 6, or could you have gotten the new quotient directly from the previous quotient (1,398)?

Exit Ticket (3 minutes)

After the Student Debrief, instruct students to complete the Exit Ticket. A review of their work will help with assessing students' understanding of the concepts that were presented in today's lesson and planning more effectively for future lessons. The questions may be read aloud to the students.

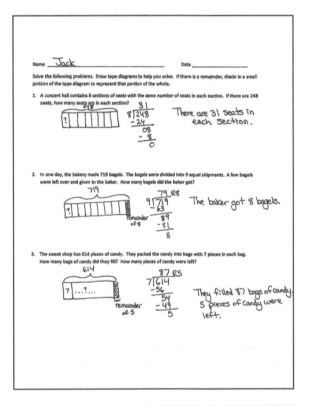

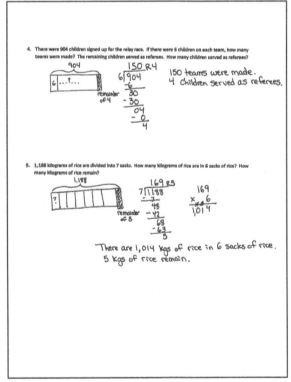

Lesson 32: Interpret and find whole number quotients and remainders to solve one-step division word problems with larger divisors of 6, 7, 8, and 9.

447

©2015 Great Minds. eureka-math.org
G4-M3-TE-B2-1.3.1-01.2016

Name _____ Date _____

Solve the following problems. Draw tape diagrams to help you solve. If there is a remainder, shade in a small portion of the tape diagram to represent that portion of the whole.

1. A concert hall contains 8 sections of seats with the same number of seats in each section. If there are 248 seats, how many seats are in each section?

2. In one day, the bakery made 719 bagels. The bagels were divided into 9 equal shipments. A few bagels were left over and given to the baker. How many bagels did the baker get?

3. The sweet shop has 614 pieces of candy. They packed the candy into bags with 7 pieces in each bag. How many bags of candy did they fill? How many pieces of candy were left?

Lesson 32: Interpret and find whole number quotients and remainders to solve one-step division word problems with larger divisors of 6, 7, 8, and 9.

©2015 Great Minds. eureka-math.org
G4-M3-TE-B2-1.3.1-01.2016

EUREKA
MATH™

4. There were 904 children signed up for the relay race. If there were 6 children on each team, how many teams were made? The remaining children served as referees. How many children served as referees?

5. 1,188 kilograms of rice are divided into 7 sacks. How many kilograms of rice are in 6 sacks of rice? How many kilograms of rice remain?

Lesson 32: Interpret and find whole number quotients and remainders to solve one-step division word problems with larger divisors of 6, 7, 8, and 9.

©2015 Great Minds. eureka-math.org
G4-M3-TE-B2-1.3.1-01.2016

449

Name _____ Date _____

Solve the following problems. Draw tape diagrams to help you solve. If there is a remainder, shade in a small portion of the tape diagram to represent that portion of the whole.

1. Mr. Foote needs exactly 6 folders for each fourth-grade student at Hoover Elementary School. If he bought 726 folders, to how many students can he supply folders?

2. Mrs. Terrance has a large bin of 236 crayons. She divides them equally among four containers. How many crayons does Mrs. Terrance have in each container?

Lesson 32: Interpret and find whole number quotients and remainders to solve one-step division word problems with larger divisors of 6, 7, 8, and 9.

©2015 Great Minds. eureka-math.org
G4-M3-TE-B2-1.3.1-01.2016

Name _____   Date _____

Solve the following problems. Draw tape diagrams to help you solve. If there is a remainder, shade in a small portion of the tape diagram to represent that portion of the whole.

1. Meneca bought a package of 435 party favors to give to the guests at her birthday party. She calculated that she could give 9 party favors to each guest. How many guests is she expecting?

2. 4,000 pencils were donated to an elementary school. If 8 classrooms shared the pencils equally, how many pencils did each class receive?

3. 2,008 kilograms of potatoes were packed into sacks weighing 8 kilograms each. How many sacks were packed?

EUREKA
MATH™

Lesson 32:   Interpret and find whole number quotients and remainders to solve
              one-step division word problems with larger divisors of 6, 7, 8, and 9.

©2015 Great Minds. eureka-math.org
G4-M3-TE-B2-1.3.1-01.2016

451

4. A baker made 7 batches of muffins. There was a total of 252 muffins. If there was the same number of muffins in each batch, how many muffins were in a batch?

5. Samantha ran 3,003 meters in 7 days. If she ran the same distance each day, how far did Samantha run in 3 days?

Lesson 32:   Interpret and find whole number quotients and remainders to solve one-step division word problems with larger divisors of 6, 7, 8, and 9.

©2015 Great Minds. eureka-math.org
G4-M3-TE-B2-1.3.1-01.2016

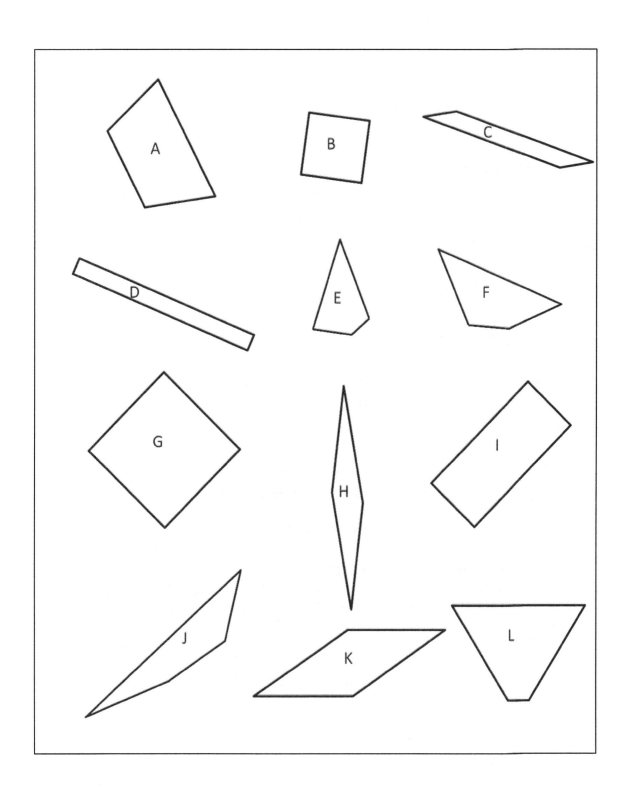

shapes

EUREKA
MATH™

Lesson 32: Interpret and find whole number quotients and remainders to solve
one-step division word problems with larger divisors of 6, 7, 8, and 9.

453

©2015 Great Minds. eureka-math.org
G4-M3-TE-B2-1.3.1-01.2016

Lesson 33

Objective: Explain the connection of the area model of division to the long division algorithm for three- and four-digit dividends.

Suggested Lesson Structure

■ Fluency Practice	(12 minutes)
▨ Application Problem	(5 minutes)
▨ Concept Development	(33 minutes)
▨ Student Debrief	(10 minutes)
Total Time	**(60 minutes)**

Fluency Practice (12 minutes)

- Quadrilaterals **3.G.1**   (4 minutes)
- Group Counting **4.OA.1**   (4 minutes)
- Multiply Units **4.NBT.1**   (4 minutes)

Quadrilaterals (4 minutes)

Materials: (T) Shapes (Lesson 32 Fluency Template) (S) Personal white board

Note: This fluency activity reviews Grade 3 geometry concepts in anticipation of Module 4 content.

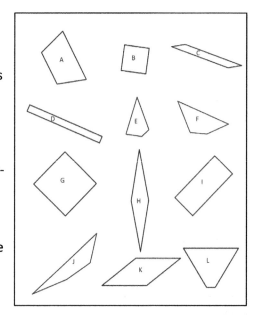

> T: (Project the shapes template which includes the following: a square; a rhombus that is not a square; a rectangle that is not a square; and several quadrilaterals that are not squares, rhombuses, or rectangles.) How many sides does each polygon have?
>
> S: 4.
>
> T: On your personal white board, write the name for any four-sided polygon.
>
> S: (Write *quadrilateral*.)
>
> T: (Point to the square.) This quadrilateral has four equal sides and four right angles. On your board, write what type of quadrilateral it is.
>
> S: (Write *square*.)

Lesson 33: Explain the connection of the area model of division to the long division algorithm for three- and four-digit dividends.

©2015 Great Minds. eureka-math.org
G4-M3-TE-B2-1.3.1-01.2016

**EUREKA
MATH™**

T: Rhombuses are quadrilaterals with four equal sides. Is this polygon a rhombus?

S: Yes.

T: Is it a rectangle?

S: Yes.

T: (Point to the rhombus that is not a square.) This polygon has four equal sides, but the angles are not the same. Write the name of this quadrilateral.

S: (Write *rhombus*.)

T: Is the square also a rhombus?

S: Yes!

T: (Point to the rectangle that is not a square.) This polygon has four equal angles, but the sides are not equal. Write the name of this quadrilateral.

S: (Write *rectangle*.)

T: Draw a quadrilateral that is not a square, rhombus, or rectangle.

Group Counting (4 minutes)

Note: This fluency activity prepares students to divide with remainders.

Direct students to count forward and backward, occasionally changing the direction of the count.

- Sixes to 60
- Sevens to 70
- Eights to 80
- Nines to 90

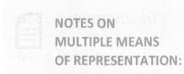

NOTES ON MULTIPLE MEANS OF REPRESENTATION:

Allow those students who consistently struggle with group counting at the pace of the majority of the class to count by the given multiple on a personal white board. Monitor their progress from one session to the next.

Multiply Units (4 minutes)

Materials: (S) Personal white board

Note: This fluency activity reviews Lesson 4's content.

T: (Write 3 × 3 = ___.) Say the multiplication sentence in unit form.

S: 3 ones × 3 = 9 ones.

T: Write the answer in standard form.

S: (Write 9.)

T: (Write 30 × 3 = ___.) Say the multiplication sentence in unit form.

S: 3 tens × 3 = 9 tens.

T: Write the answer in standard form.

S: (Write 90.)

Continue with the following possible sequence: 3 hundreds × 3, 3 thousands × 3, 4 ones × 3, 4 tens × 3, 4 thousands × 3, 5 thousands × 2, 5 tens × 4, 5 hundreds × 8, and 8 tens × 6.

EUREKA
MATH™

Lesson 33:   Explain the connection of the area model of division to the long
                  division algorithm for three- and four-digit dividends.

©2015 Great Minds. eureka-math.org
G4-M3-TE-B2-1.3.1-01.2016

Application Problem (5 minutes)

Write an equation to find the unknown length of each rectangle. Then, find the sum of the two unknown lengths.

| 3 m | 600 square m | 3 m | 72 square m |

The sum of the two unknown
lengths is 224 meters.

$$\left(600 \div 3\right) + \left(72 \div 3\right)$$
$$= 200 \quad + \quad 24$$
$$= 224$$

$$
\begin{array}{r}
24 \\
3\overline{\smash{)}72} \\
-6 \\
\hline
12 \\
-12 \\
\hline
0
\end{array}
$$

Note: This Application Problem serves as an introduction to today's Concept Development, in which students find the total unknown length of a rectangle with an area of 672 square meters.

Concept Development (33 minutes)

Materials: (S) Personal white board

Problem 1

672 ÷ 3 and 1,344 ÷ 6

T: Draw a rectangle with an area of 672 square inches and a width of 3 inches.

S: (Draw.)

T: Draw a new rectangle with the same area directly below, but partitioned to make it easy for you to divide each part using mental math and your knowledge of place value. (Allow time for students to work.)

T: Share with a partner how you partitioned your new rectangle.

S: I made one part 6 hundred, two parts of 3 tens, and one part 12 ones. → I made two parts of 3 hundreds, one part of 6 tens, and one part 12 ones. → I made mine one part 6 hundred and two parts 36.

T: Draw a number bond to match the whole and parts of your rectangles.

S: (Draw bonds as pictured to the right.)

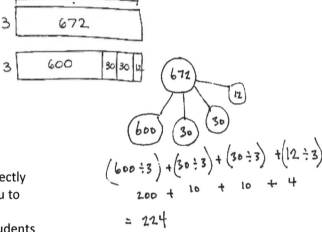

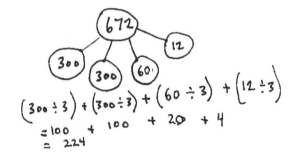

Lesson 33:   Explain the connection of the area model of division to the long
division algorithm for three- and four-digit dividends.

EUREKA
MATH™

T: Find the unknown side lengths of the smaller rectangles, and add them to find the length of the largest rectangle.

T: Take a moment to record the number sentences, reviewing with your partner the connection to both the number bond and the area model.

Those who finish early can find other ways to decompose the rectangle or work with 1,344 ÷ 6.

T: (Allow students to work for about four minutes.)

T: What were some ways you found to partition 1,344 to divide it easily by 6?

S: We chopped it into 12 hundreds, 12 tens, and 24 ones. → We decomposed it as 2 six hundreds, 2 sixties, and 24. → I realized 1,344 is double 672. But, 6 is double 3 and that's like the associative property 224 × 2 × 3, so 1,344 ÷ 6 equals 672 ÷ 3.

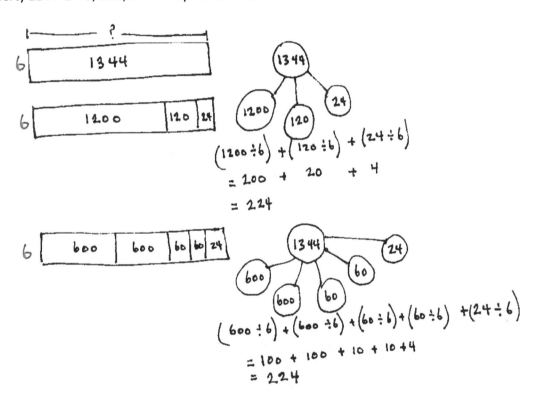

T: How can we see from our bonds that 1,344 is double 672?

S: When we chopped up the rectangles, I saw 600, 60, and 12 made 672, and the chopped up rectangle for 1,344 had two of all those!

T: Explain to your partner why different ways of partitioning give us the same correct side length.

S: You are starting with the same amount of area but just chopping it up differently. → The sum of the lengths is the same as the whole length. → You can take a total, break it into two or more parts, and divide each of them separately.

Lesson 33:   Explain the connection of the area model of division to the long division algorithm for three- and four-digit dividends.

©2015 Great Minds. eureka-math.org
G4-M3-TE-B2-1.3.1-01.2016

457

Problem 2

672 ÷ 3

T: (Write 672 ÷ 3.) This expression can describe a rectangle with an area of 672 square units. We are trying to find out the length of the unknown side.

T: What is the known side length?

S: 3.

T: (Draw a rectangle with a width of 3.) Three times how many hundreds gets us as close as possible to an area of 6 hundred square units? (Point to the 6 hundreds of the dividend.)

S: 2 hundreds.

T: Let's give 2 hundreds to the length. (Label 2 lengths of hundreds.) Let's record the 2 hundreds in the hundreds place.

T: What is 3 times 2 hundreds?

S: 6 hundreds. (Record 6 below the 6 hundreds.)

T: How many square units is that?

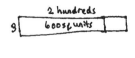

S: 600 square units. (Record 600 square units in the rectangle.)

T: How many hundreds remain?

S: Zero.

T: (Record 0 hundreds below the 6 hundreds.) 0 hundreds and 7 tens is…? (Record the 7 tens to the right of the 0 hundreds.)

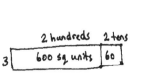 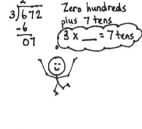

S: 7 tens.

T: We have 70 square units left with a width of 3. (Point to the 7 tens in the algorithm.) Three times how many tens gets us as close as possible to 7 tens?

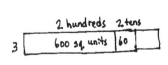

S: 2 tens.

T: Let's give 2 tens to the length.

T: 3 times 2 tens is?

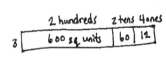 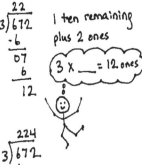

S: 6 tens.

T: How many square units?

S: 60 square units.

T: 7 tens minus 6 tens is?

S: 1 ten.

Lesson 33: Explain the connection of the area model of division to the long division algorithm for three- and four-digit dividends.

©2015 Great Minds. eureka-math.org
G4-M3-TE-B2-1.3.1-01.2016

EUREKA
MATH™

T: That is 10 square units of area to add to 2 square units. The remaining area is…?

S: 12 square units!

T: Three times how many ones gets us as close as possible to 12 ones?

S: 4 ones.

T: Let's give 4 ones to the length.

T: Three times 4 ones is…?

S: 12 ones.

T: Do we have any remaining area?

S: No!

T: What is the length of the unknown side?

S: 224 length units.

T: Review our drawings and our process with your partner. Try to reconstruct what we did step by step before we try another one. (Allow students time to review.)

T: We solved 672 divided by 3 in two very different ways using the area model. First we started with the whole rectangle and partitioned it. The second way was to go one place value at a time and make the whole rectangle from parts.

Give students the chance to try the following problems in partners, in a small group with the teacher, or independently, as they are able.

539 ÷ 2

This first practice problem has an easy divisor and a remainder in the ones. Guide students to determine the greatest length possible first for the remaining area at each place value.

438 ÷ 5

This next practice problem involves seeing the first area as 40 tens and having a remainder of 3 in the ones.

1,216 ÷ 4

The final practice problem involves a four-digit number. Like the previous example, students must see the first area as 12 hundreds and the next area as 16 ones.

Problem Set (13 minutes)

Students should do their personal best to complete the Problem Set within the allotted 13 minutes. For some classes, it may be appropriate to modify the assignment by specifying which problems they work on first. Some problems do not specify a method for solving. Students should solve these problems using the RDW approach used for Application Problems.

NOTES ON MULTIPLE MEANS OF ACTION AND EXPRESSION:

Guide English language learners and students working below grade level who may not complete the Problem Set in the allotted 13 minutes to set specific goals for their work. After briefly considering their progress, strengths, and weaknesses, have students choose the problems they will solve strategically. For example, a learner who is perfecting sequencing his written explanations might choose Problem 2. Connect this short-term goal to long-term goals.

EUREKA MATH™   Lesson 33:   Explain the connection of the area model of division to the long   **459**
                                                    division algorithm for three- and four-digit dividends.

©2015 Great Minds. eureka-math.org
G4-M3-TE-B2-1.3.1-01.2016

Student Debrief (10 minutes)

Lesson Objective: Explain the connection of the area model of division to the long division algorithm for three- and four-digit dividends.

The Student Debrief is intended to invite reflection and active processing of the total lesson experience.

Invite students to review their solutions for the Problem Set. They should check work by comparing answers with a partner before going over answers as a class. Look for misconceptions or misunderstandings that can be addressed in the Debrief. Guide students in a conversation to debrief the Problem Set and process the lesson.

Any combination of the questions below may be used to lead the discussion.

- In Problem 1, is there another way Ursula could have represented the division problem with an area model? Would your number bond in 1(b) need revision if the area model changed?

- Compare your area model in Problem 2(a) to your partner's. Is it easier to solve the area model separating it into 2 parts, 3 parts, 4 parts, etc.?

- How do you decide how many parts are needed when building the area model for division?

- How are area models, number bonds, and the long division algorithm connected? Is there a correct order in which to use them to solve division problems?

Exit Ticket (3 minutes)

After the Student Debrief, instruct students to complete the Exit Ticket. A review of their work will help with assessing students' understanding of the concepts that were presented in today's lesson and planning more effectively for future lessons. The questions may be read aloud to the students.

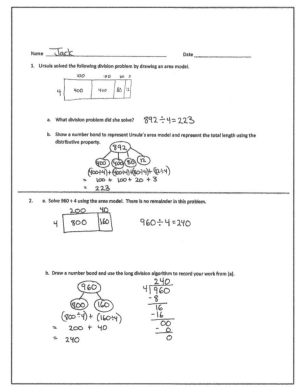

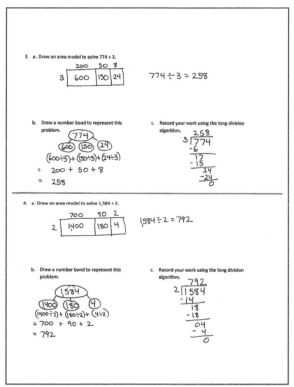

Lesson 33:   Explain the connection of the area model of division to the long division algorithm for three- and four-digit dividends.

EUREKA
MATH™

Name _____   Date _____

1. Ursula solved the following division problem by drawing an area model.

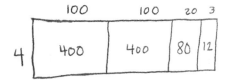

    a. What division problem did she solve?

    b. Show a number bond to represent Ursula's area model, and represent the total length using the distributive property.

2. a. Solve 960 ÷ 4 using the area model. There is no remainder in this problem.

    b. Draw a number bond and use the long division algorithm to record your work from Part (a).

Lesson 33:   Explain the connection of the area model of division to the long
              division algorithm for three- and four-digit dividends.

©2015 Great Minds. eureka-math.org
G4-M3-TE-B2-1.3.1-01.2016

461

3. a. Draw an area model to solve 774 ÷ 3.

    b. Draw a number bond to represent this
        problem.

    c. Record your work using the long division
        algorithm.

---

4. a. Draw an area model to solve 1,584 ÷ 2.

    b. Draw a number bond to represent this
        problem.

    c. Record your work using the long division
        algorithm.

Lesson 33:   Explain the connection of the area model of division to the long
             division algorithm for three- and four-digit dividends.

©2015 Great Minds. eureka-math.org
G4-M3-TE-B2-1.3.1-01.2016

Name _____   Date _____

1. Anna solved the following division problem by drawing an area model.

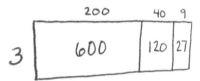

   a. What division problem did she solve?

   b. Show a number bond to represent Anna's area model, and represent the total length using the distributive property.

_____

2. a. Draw an area model to solve 1,368 ÷ 2.

   b. Draw a number bond to represent this problem.

   c. Record your work using the long division algorithm.

Lesson 33:   Explain the connection of the area model of division to the long division algorithm for three- and four-digit dividends.

©2015 Great Minds. eureka-math.org
G4-M3-TE-B2-1.3.1-01.2016

463

Name _____   Date _____

1. Arabelle solved the following division problem by drawing an area model.

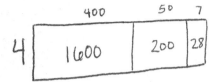

    a. What division problem did she solve?

    b. Show a number bond to represent Arabelle's area model, and represent the total length using the distributive property.

---

2. a. Solve 816 ÷ 4 using the area model. There is no remainder in this problem.

    b. Draw a number bond and use a written method to record your work from Part (a).

Explain the connection of the area model of division to the long
         division algorithm for three- and four-digit dividends.

©2015 Great Minds. eureka-math.org
G4-M3-TE-B2-1.3.1-01.2016

EUREKA
MATH™

3. a. Draw an area model to solve 549 ÷ 3.

    b. Draw a number bond to represent this problem.

    c. Record your work using the long division algorithm.

---

4. a. Draw an area model to solve 2,762 ÷ 2.

    b. Draw a number bond to represent this problem.

    c. Record your work using the long division algorithm.

Lesson 33: Explain the connection of the area model of division to the long division algorithm for three- and four-digit dividends.

©2015 Great Minds. eureka-math.org
G4-M3-TE-B2-1.3.1-01.2016

465

Mathematics Curriculum

4 GRADE

Topic H

Multiplication of Two-Digit by Two-Digit Numbers

4.NBT.5, 4.OA.3, 4.MD.3

Focus Standard:	4.NBT.5	Multiply a whole number of up to four digits by a one-digit whole number, and multiply two two-digit numbers, using strategies based on place value and the properties of operations. Illustrate and explain the calculation by using equations, rectangular arrays, and/or area models.
Instructional Days:	5	
Coherence -Links from:	G3–M1	Properties of Multiplication and Division and Solving Problems with Units of 2–5 and 10
	G3–M3	Multiplication and Division with Units of 0, 1, 6–9, and Multiples of 10
-Links to:	G5–M2	Multi-Digit Whole Number and Decimal Fraction Operations

Module 3 closes with Topic H as students multiply two-digit by two-digit numbers.

Lesson 34 begins this topic by having students use the area model to represent and solve the multiplication of two-digit multiples of 10 by two-digit numbers using a place value chart. Practice with this model helps to prepare students for two-digit by two-digit multiplication and builds the understanding of multiplying units of 10. In Lesson 35, students extend their learning to represent and solve the same type of problems using area models and partial products.

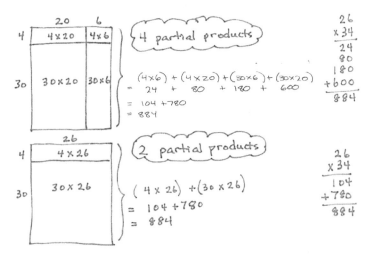

In Lesson 36, students make connections to the distributive property and use both the area model and four partial products to solve problems. Lesson 37 deepens students' understanding of multi-digit multiplication by transitioning from four partial products with representation of the area model to two partial products with representation of the area model and finally to two partial products without representation of the area model.

EUREKA
MATH™

Topic H culminates at the most abstract level with Lesson 38 as students are introduced to the multiplication algorithm for two-digit by two-digit numbers. Knowledge from Lessons 34–37 provides a firm foundation for understanding the process of the algorithm as students make connections from the area model to partial products to the standard algorithm (**4.NBT.5**). Students see that partial products written vertically are the same as those obtained via the distributive property: 4 twenty-sixes + 30 twenty-sixes = 104 + 780 = 884.

A Teaching Sequence Toward Mastery of Multiplication of Two-Digit by Two-Digit Numbers
Objective 1: Multiply two-digit multiples of 10 by two-digit numbers using a place value chart. (Lesson 34)
Objective 2: Multiply two-digit multiples of 10 by two-digit numbers using the area model. (Lesson 35)
Objective 3: Multiply two-digit by two-digit numbers using four partial products. (Lesson 36)
Objective 4: Transition from four partial products to the standard algorithm for two-digit by two-digit multiplication. (Lessons 37–38)

Lesson 34

Objective: Multiply two-digit multiples of 10 by two-digit numbers using a place value chart.

Suggested Lesson Structure

■ Fluency Practice   (12 minutes)

▨ Application Problem   (5 minutes)

▢ Concept Development   (33 minutes)

■ Student Debrief   (10 minutes)

   Total Time   **(60 minutes)**

Fluency Practice (12 minutes)

- Draw a Unit Fraction **3.G.2**   (4 minutes)
- Divide Three Different Ways **4.NBT.6**   (4 minutes)
- Multiply Units **4.NBT.1**   (4 minutes)

Draw a Unit Fraction (4 minutes)

Materials: (S) Personal white board

Note: This fluency activity reviews Grade 3 geometry and fraction concepts in anticipation of Modules 4 and 5. Accept reasonable drawings. Using rulers and protractors is not necessary to review the concept and takes too long.

   T: On your personal white boards, draw a quadrilateral with 4 equal sides and 4 right angles.

   S: (Draw.)

   T: What's the name of a quadrilateral with 4 equal sides and 4 right angles?

   S: Square.

   T: Partition the square into 3 equal parts.

   S: (Partition.)

   T: Shade in 1 part of 3.

   S: (Shade.)

   T: Write the fraction of the square that's shaded.

   S: (Write $\frac{1}{3}$.)

Repeat the process, partitioning a rhombus into fourths, a rectangle into fifths, and a rectangle into eighths.

Lesson 34:   Multiply two-digit multiples of 10 by two-digit numbers using a place
                                       value chart.

©2015 Great Minds. eureka-math.org
G4-M3-TE-B2-1.3.1-01.2016

Divide Three Different Ways (4 minutes)

Materials: (S) Personal white board

Note: This fluency activity reviews content from Lessons 32 and 33.

   T: (Write 732 ÷ 6.) Solve this problem by drawing place value disks.
   S: (Solve.)
   T: Solve 732 ÷ 6 using the area model.
   S: (Solve.)
   T: Solve 732 ÷ 6 using the standard algorithm.
   S: (Solve.)

Continue with this possible suggestion: 970 ÷ 8.

Multiply Units (4 minutes)

Materials: (S) Personal white board

Note: This fluency activity reviews Lesson 4.

   T: (Write 4 ones × 3.) Solve. Say the multiplication sentence in unit form.
   S: 4 ones × 3 = 12 ones.
   T: Write the equation in standard form.
   S: (Write 4 × 3 = 12.)
   T: (Write 4 tens × 3.) Solve. Write the equation in standard form.
   S: (Write 40 × 3 = 120.)
   T: (Write 4 tens × 3 tens.) Solve. Write the equation in standard form.
   S: (Write 40 × 30 = 1,200.)
   T: (Write 3 × 2.) Solve. Say the multiplication sentence.
   S: 3 × 2 = 6.
   T: Write the equation in unit form.
   S: (Write 3 ones × 2 = 6 ones.)
   T: (Write 30 × 2.) Solve. Write the equation in unit form.
   S: (Write 3 tens × 2 = 6 tens.)
   T: (Write 30 × 20.) Solve. Write the equation in unit form.
   S: (Write 3 tens × 2 tens = 6 hundreds.)

Continue with the following possible sequence: 30 × 5, 30 × 50, 3 tens × 6, 3 tens × 6 tens, 50 × 4, 5 tens × 8 tens, and 60 × 50.

Lesson 34:   Multiply two-digit multiples of 10 by two-digit numbers using a place value chart.

469

Application Problem (5 minutes)

Mr. Goggins planted 10 rows of beans, 10 rows of squash, 10 rows of tomatoes, and 10 rows of cucumbers in his garden. He put 22 plants in each row. Draw an area model, label each part, and then write an expression that represents the total number of plants in the garden.

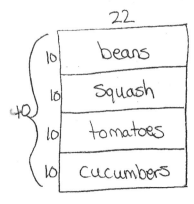

$(4 \times 10) \times 22$

Note: This Application Problem builds on Topic B, where students learned to multiply by multiples of 10, and Topic C, where students learned to multiply two-digit by one-digit numbers using an area model. This Application Problem helps bridge to today's lesson as students learn to multiply multiples of 10 by two-digit numbers.

Concept Development (33 minutes)

Materials: (S) Personal white board, thousands place value chart (Lesson 4 Template)

Problem 1: Discover that 4 × 10 × 22 and 40 × 22 represent the same amount.

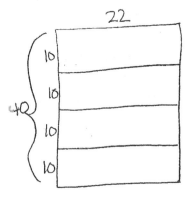

- T: Look at the area model that we drew for the Application Problem. (Erase the names of the plants.)
- T: How many 10 × 22 rectangles are there in the model?
- S: 4.
- T: Write an expression to show the entire length of the rectangle. (Indicate the vertical side length).
- S: 4 × 10.
- T: What is the area formula?
- S: Length times width.
- T: Discuss with your partner an expression to show the total area of the largest rectangle.
- S: 40 times 22. → (4 × 10) × 22.
- T: What can we say about the expressions (4 × 10) × 22 and 40 × 22?
- S: They represent the same amount.

EUREKA MATH™

T: How can you tell? Turn and talk to your partner.

S: The total length is 4 tens. → We can write 4 tens as 4 times 10 or 40. → You can either find the area of the smallest rectangle and multiply it by four or just multiply 40 times 22.

T: We can say that 40 × 22 = 4 × 10 × 22 or 10 × 4 × 22.

S: Yes.

T: That's good because we can solve 4 times 10 times 22, but 40 times 22 is new territory.

Problem 2: Multiply 40 × 22 using a place value chart.

Write:

$$40 × 22 = (4 × 10) × 22$$
$$40 × 22 = 4 × (10 × 22)$$
$$40 × 22 = 10 × (4 × 22)$$

T: Show 22 on your place value chart.

T: Show 10 times as many. 10 × 22 is?

S: (Draw disks to show 22, and then draw arrows to show 10 times that amount.)

T: How many hundreds? How many tens?

S: 2 hundreds and 2 tens.

T: Show 4 times as many.

S: (Draw disks to show 3 more groups of 2 hundreds 2 tens.)

T: Tell how many you have now.

S: 8 hundreds and 8 tens.

T: What number does that represent? Say the number sentence.

S: 4 × (10 × 22) = 880. → 40 × 22 = 880.

Repeat the process, this time beginning by multiplying 22 by 4 as in the model above and to the right. (Write 40 × 22 = (10 × 4) × 22 = 10 × (4 × 22).)

©2015 Great Minds. eureka-math.org
G4-M3-TE-B2-1.3.1-01.2016

Next, have students see that they can conceive of the problem as 40 times 22, as pictured below, without breaking the process into the two steps of multiplying by 4 and 10 in whatever order.

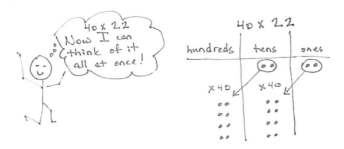

Problem 3: Multiply 50 × 31 using a place value chart.

T: What is another way to express 50 × 31?

S: 10 × (5 × 31). → 5 × (10 × 31).

T: Tell your partner why you chose to represent 50 using the numbers 5 and 10.

S: 50 = 5 × 10. I know how to multiply by 10 and by 5, but I don't know how to multiply by 50.

T: Yes, you are using the associative property, which allows us to use the factors of a number to help us multiply. What factors did we use for 50?

S: 5 and 10.

T: Show 31 on your place value chart.

T: Show 10 times as many.

S: (Draw disks to show 31, and then draw arrows to show 10 times that amount.)

T: How many hundreds? How many tens?

S: 3 hundreds and 1 ten.

T: Show 5 times as many.

S: (Draw disks to show 4 more groups of 3 hundreds 1 ten.)

T: Tell how many you have now.

S: 15 hundreds and 5 tens. I change 10 hundreds for one thousand. I have 1 thousand, 5 hundreds, and 5 tens.

T: What number does that represent?

S: 1,550.

> **NOTES ON**
> **MULTIPLE MEANS**
> **OF REPRESENTATION:**
>
> You may present the following scaffolds to assist students in organizing and keeping track of arrays of place value disks:
>
> ▪ Alternate colors as they draw 5 rows of 3 hundreds.
>
> ▪ Give extra time to model.
>
> ▪ Couple disks with words (e.g., 3 hundreds × 5).
>
> ▪ Use manipulatives at first, and then transition to drawings.

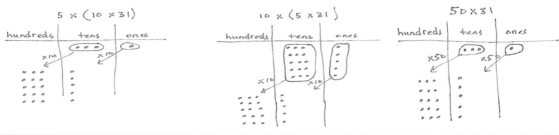

Problem 4: Multiply 50 × 31 without using a place value chart.

T: 50 × 31 is the same 50 × (30 + 1). Discuss with your partner why this is true.

S: We drew 31 as 3 tens and 1 one on the place value chart and multiplied each unit by 50. → 50 groups of 31 is the same as 50 groups of 30 and 50 groups of 1. → It's the break apart and distribute property! → It's the distributive property!

T: 50 × (30 + 1) = 50 × 30 + 50 × 1. Can you see that on our place value chart? (Show that on the place value chart.) At first, we broke apart 50 into 10 × 5 or 5 × 10, but, in the end, we just thought of it as 50 × 31.

T: Let's say 50 × 30 + 50 × 1 in unit language.

S: 5 tens × 3 tens + 5 tens × 1 one.

T: 5 tens times 3 tens is…?

S: 15 hundreds.

T: 5 tens times 1 one is…?

S: 5 tens.

T: 15 hundreds + 5 tens is…?

S: 1,550.

T: 50 × 31 is…?

S: 1,550.

T: Did we get the same product just by multiplying that we did when we used the chart?

S: Yes.

Problem Set (10 minutes)

Students should do their personal best to complete the Problem Set within the allotted 10 minutes. For some classes, it may be appropriate to modify the assignment by specifying which problems they work on first. Some problems do not specify a method for solving. Students should solve these problems using the RDW approach used for Application Problems.

NOTES ON MULTIPLE MEANS OF ENGAGEMENT:

Challenge students working above grade level to do mental computations. For example, students can use the distributive property to think of 6 × 560 as (6 × 500) + (6 × 60) and then solve using what they know about multiplying multiples of 10.

Students who are not ready for the mental computations may continue to draw the area model used in previous lessons to confirm their final product.

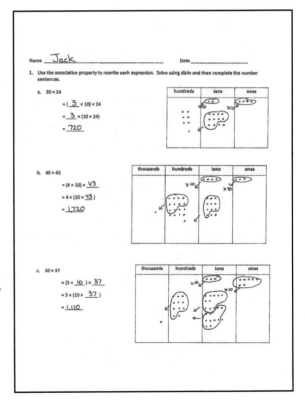

Lesson 34:   Multiply two-digit multiples of 10 by two-digit numbers using a place value chart.

©2015 Great Minds. eureka-math.org
G4-M3-TE-B2-1.3.1-01.2016

473

Student Debrief (10 minutes)

Lesson Objective: Multiply two-digit multiples of 10 by two-digit numbers using a place value chart.

The Student Debrief is intended to invite reflection and active processing of the total lesson experience.

Invite students to review their solutions for the Problem Set. They should check work by comparing answers with a partner before going over answers as a class. Look for misconceptions or misunderstandings that can be addressed in the Debrief. Guide students in a conversation to debrief the Problem Set and process the lesson.

Any combination of the questions below may be used to lead the discussion.

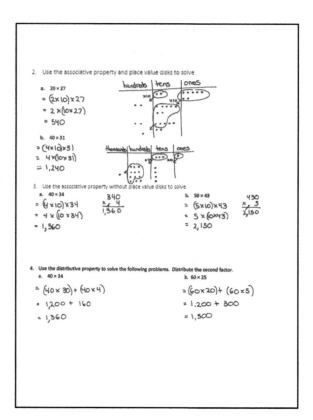

- In Problem 1(a), is it best to model 30 or 24 on the chart initially? Why?

- Tell your partner how you used the associative property in Problem 3(a). Is there an order you find easier for multiplying the three factors like when multiplying using the place value chart?

- Why was it helpful to break the multiple of 10 into two factors before solving?

- How did distributing the second factor in Problem 4 of the Concept Development make it easier to solve?

- Compare Problems 3(a) and 4(a). Why did you get the same answer by using two different methods? What does this tell you about the associative and distributive property? Compare their processes. How are they different?

- How did representing the multiplication with disks help you solve and understand the multiplication?

- How did the Application Problem connect to today's lesson?

Exit Ticket (3 minutes)

After the Student Debrief, instruct students to complete the Exit Ticket. A review of their work will help with assessing students' understanding of the concepts that were presented in today's lesson and planning more effectively for future lessons. The questions may be read aloud to the students.

Name _____ Date _____

1. Use the associative property to rewrite each expression. Solve using disks, and then complete the number sentences.

a. 30 × 24

    = (_____ × 10) × 24

    = _____ × (10 × 24)

    = _____

hundreds	tens	ones

b. 40 × 43

    = (4 × 10) × _____

    = 4 × (10 × ___)

    = _____

thousands	hundreds	tens	ones

c. 30 × 37

    = (3 × _____) × _____

    = 3 × (10 × _____)

    = _____

thousands	hundreds	tens	ones

Lesson 34:   Multiply two-digit multiples of 10 by two-digit numbers using a place value chart.

475

©2015 Great Minds. eureka-math.org
G4-M3-TE-B2-1.3.1-01.2016

2. Use the associative property and place value disks to solve.

   a. 20 × 27

   b. 40 × 31

3. Use the associative property without place value disks to solve.

   a. 40 × 34   b. 50 × 43

4. Use the distributive property to solve the following problems. Distribute the second factor.

   a. 40 × 34   b. 60 × 25

Lesson 34:   Multiply two-digit multiples of 10 by two-digit numbers using a place
value chart.

©2015 Great Minds. eureka-math.org
G4-M3-TE-B2-1.3.1-01.2016

Name _____ Date _____

1. Use the associative property to rewrite each expression. Solve using disks, and then complete the number sentences.

    20 × 41

    _____ × _____ × _____ = _____

hundreds	tens	ones

2. Distribute 32 as 30 + 2 and solve.

    60 × 32

EUREKA
MATH™

Lesson 34:   Multiply two-digit multiples of 10 by two-digit numbers using a place value chart.

©2015 Great Minds. eureka-math.org
G4-M3-TE-B2-1.3.1-01.2016

477

Name _____   Date _____

1. Use the associative property to rewrite each expression. Solve using disks, and then complete the number sentences.

a. 20 × 34

$= (\_\_\_\_ × 10) × 34$

$= \_\_\_\_ × (10 × 34)$

$= \_\_\_\_\_$

hundreds	tens	ones

b. 30 × 34

$= (3 × 10) × \_\_\_\_\_$

$= 3 × (10 × \_\_\_)$

$= \_\_\_\_\_$

thousands	hundreds	tens	ones

c. 30 × 42

$= (3 × \_\_\_\_) × \_\_\_\_\_$

$= 3 × (10 × \_\_\_\_\_)$

$= \_\_\_\_\_$

thousands	hundreds	tens	ones

Lesson 34:   Multiply two-digit multiples of 10 by two-digit numbers using a place value chart.

©2015 Great Minds. eureka-math.org
G4-M3-TE-B2-1.3.1-01.2016

EUREKA MATH

2. Use the associative property and place value disks to solve.

   a. 20×16

   b. 40×32

3. Use the associative property without place value disks to solve.

   a. 30×21

   b. 60×42

4. Use the distributive property to solve the following. Distribute the second factor.

   a. 40×43

   b. 70×23

Lesson 34: Multiply two-digit multiples of 10 by two-digit numbers using a place value chart.

©2015 Great Minds. eureka-math.org
G4-M3-TE-B2-1.3.1-01.2016

479

Lesson 35

Objective: Multiply two-digit multiples of 10 by two-digit numbers using the area model.

Suggested Lesson Structure

■ Fluency Practice   (12 minutes)
■ Application Problem   (6 minutes)
■ Concept Development   (32 minutes)
■ Student Debrief   (10 minutes)

   Total Time   **(60 minutes)**

Fluency Practice (12 minutes)

- Draw and Label Unit Fractions **3.G.2**   (4 minutes)
- Divide Three Different Ways **4.NBT.6**   (4 minutes)
- Multiply by Multiples of 10 **4.NBT.1**   (4 minutes)

Draw and Label Unit Fractions (4 minutes)

Materials: (S) Personal white board

Notes: This fluency activity reviews Grade 3 geometry and fraction concepts in anticipation of Modules 4 and 5. Accept reasonable drawings. Using rulers and protractors is not necessary to review the concept and takes too long.

   T: On your personal white boards, write the name for any four-sided figure.
   S: (Write *quadrilateral*.)
   T: Draw a quadrilateral that has 4 right angles but not 4 equal sides.
   S: (Draw a rectangle that is not a square.)
   T: Partition the rectangle into 3 equal parts.
   S: (Partition.)
   T: Label the whole rectangle as 1. Write the unit fraction in each part.

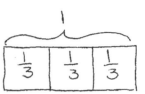

Continue partitioning and labeling with the following possible sequence: a square as 4 fourths, a rhombus as 2 halves, a square as 5 fifths, and a rectangle as 6 sixths.

EUREKA
MATH™

Divide Three Different Ways (4 minutes)

Materials: (S) Personal white board

Note: This fluency activity reviews content from Lessons 32 and 33.

- T: (Write 348 ÷ 6.) Find the quotient using place value disks.
- S: (Solve.)
- T: Find the quotient using the area model.
- S: (Solve.)
- T: Find the quotient using the standard algorithm.
- S: (Solve.)

Continue for 2,816 ÷ 8.

Multiply by Multiples of 10 (4 minutes)

Materials: (S) Personal white board

Note: This fluency activity reviews Lesson 34's content.

- T: (Write 40 × 22 = 22 × 10 × ___.) On your personal white boards, fill in the unknown factor to create a multiplication sentence.
- S: (Write 40 × 22 = 22 × 10 × 4.)
- T: What's 22 × 10?
- S: 22 × 10 = 220.
- T: (Write 220 × 4 = ___.) On your boards, write the answer.
- S: (Write 220 × 4 = 880.)

$$40 \times 22 = 22 \times 10 \times 4$$
$$40 \times 22 = 220 \times 4$$
$$40 \times 22 = 880$$

Continue with the following possible sequence: 30 × 21, 30 × 43, and 50 × 39.

Application Problem (6 minutes)

Materials: (S) Thousands place value chart (Lesson 4 Template)

For 30 days out of one month, Katie exercised for 25 minutes a day. What is the total number of minutes that Katie exercised? Solve using a place value chart.

Note: This Application Problem builds on the content of Lesson 34 by using a place value chart to represent and then multiply a multiple of 10 by a two-digit number. Although some students may easily solve this problem using mental math, encourage them to see that the model verifies their mental math skills. Students can use their mental math and place value chart solution to verify their answer in Problem 1 of the Concept Development.

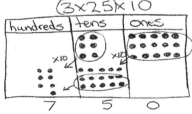

Lesson 35:   Multiply two-digit multiples of 10 by two-digit numbers using the area model.

©2015 Great Minds. eureka-math.org
G4-M3-TE-B2-1.3.1-01.2016

481

Concept Development (32 minutes)

Materials: (S) Personal white board

Problem 1: Find the product of 30 and 25 using an area model to solve.

T: Aside from the place value chart, what is another way that we have represented multiplication?

S: Arrays. → Equal groups. → The area model.

T: Let's use an area model to show 30 × 25.
Since 30 × 25 = 10 × (3 × 25), let's represent 3 × 25 first since we already know how to draw area models for one-digit by two-digit multiplication. (Draw an area model to represent 3 × 25.) We've decomposed 3 × 25 into what two products? Give me an expression for each in unit form.

S: 3 × 2 tens and 3 × 5 ones.

T: 3 × 2 tens is?

S: 6 tens.

T: And, 3 × 5 ones?

S: 15 ones.

T: So, 3 × 25 is?

S: 75.

T: What unit does this 3 have right now?

S: Ones.

T: Let's change that unit. Let's make it tens. (Draw the new area model.) What new multiplication problem is represented?

S: 30 × 25.

T: Let's find the total area by finding partial products again. (Point to the 30 by 5 rectangle.) In unit form, give me a multiplication sentence to find the area of this portion.

S: 3 tens × 5 = 15 tens.

T: Do we need to put a unit on the 5?

S: It would be ones. → We don't always have to say the unit when it's just ones.

T: (Record as shown. Then, point to the 30 by 20 rectangle.) In unit form, give me a multiplication sentence to find the area of this rectangle.

S: 3 tens × 2 tens = 6 hundreds.

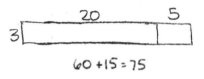

60 + 15 = 75

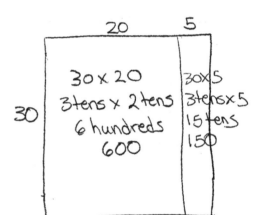

600 + 150 = 750

NOTES ON
MULTIPLE MEANS
OF REPRESENTATION:

Help students understand that multiplying tens, unlike adding, results in a larger unit. Here, 3 tens times 2 tens is 6 hundreds, not 6 tens. To clarify, refer back to the magnifying arrows on the place value chart, the number form, or place value blocks (cubes, longs, and flats).

EUREKA
MATH™

T: I noticed this time you gave me the units of both factors. Why?

S: They were both tens. → This way, I can just think of 3 × 2, and all I have to do is figure out what the new unit will be. → Tens times tens gives me hundreds.

T: Find the product for 30 × 25, and discuss with your partner how the two products, (3 × 25) and (30 × 25), are related.

S: One was 75 and the other was 750. That's 10 times as much. → The first was 6 tens plus 15 ones. The other was 6 hundreds plus 15 tens. → For the first one, we did 3 × 5 and 3 × 20. On the second, we just multiplied the 3 by 10 and got 30 × 5 and 30 × 20. That's 150 + 600, or 750. → The only difference was the unit on the 3. 3 ones were changed to 3 tens.

Problem 2: Find the product of 60 and 34 using an area model. Record the partial products to solve.

T: Draw an area model to represent 60 × 34, and then write the expressions that solve for the area of each rectangle.

S: (Draw area model and write expressions.)

T: Write 60 × 34 vertically next to the area model, and then record the partial products beginning with the area of the smaller rectangle.

S: (Record partial products as 240 and 1,800.)

T: What does the partial product of 240 represent?

S: The area of the small rectangle. → 6 tens times 4.

T: What does the partial product of 1,800 represent?

S: The area of the larger part. → 6 tens times 3 tens.

T: How do we find the product for 60 × 34?

S: We need to add the partial products.
     240 + 1,800 = 2,040. → 60 × 34 = 2,040.

**NOTES ON
MULTIPLE MEANS
OF ACTION AND
EXPRESSION:**

Some learners may benefit from graph paper or lines outlining the place values to assist their accurate recording of the partial products.

Problem 3: Find the product of 90 and 34 without using an area model. Record the partial products to solve.

T: Write 90 × 34 vertically. If we were to create an area model to solve 90 × 34, what would it look like?

S: It would be 90 units by 34 units. The 34 would be split into two parts: 30 and 4.

MP.8

T: Imagine the area model, and use it to record the two partial products using the vertical written method. Then, use unit language to explain to your partner how you solved the problem.

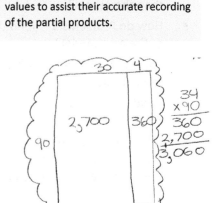

Circulate and listen for phrases such as 9 tens times 4 and 9 tens × 3 tens. Ensure students are accurately lining up digits in the appropriate place value columns.

Repeat with 30 × 34.

©2015 Great Minds. eureka-math.org
G4-M3-TE-B2-1.3.1-01.2016

Problem Set (10 minutes)

Students should do their personal best to complete the
Problem Set within the allotted 10 minutes. For some
classes, it may be appropriate to modify the assignment by
specifying which problems they work on first. Some
problems do not specify a method for solving. Students
should solve these problems using the RDW approach used
for Application Problems.

Student Debrief (10 minutes)

Lesson Objective: Multiply two-digit multiples of 10 by
two-digit numbers using the area model.

The Student Debrief is intended to invite reflection and
active processing of the total lesson experience.

Invite students to review their solutions for the Problem
Set. They should check work by comparing answers with a
partner before going over answers as a class. Look for
misconceptions or misunderstandings that can be
addressed in the Debrief. Guide students in a conversation
to debrief the Problem Set and process the lesson.

Any combination of the questions below may be used to
lead the discussion.

- How is Problem 1 of the Problem Set less complex
  than the others?

- How do Problems 3–7 lend themselves to the use
  of the area model?

- Can you explain why Problems 6 and 7 have the
  same product?

- What can you say about area models for Problems
  8 and 9?

- When we record partial products, do we have to
  start with the one with the smallest place value?
  Will we get a different result if we start with the
  tens?

- When we multiply by a multiple of 10, why is there
  always a 0 in the ones place?

- What significant math vocabulary did we use today
  to communicate precisely?

- How did the Application Problem connect to today's lesson?

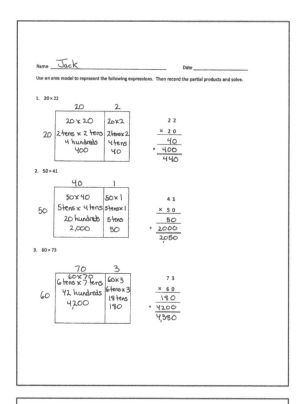

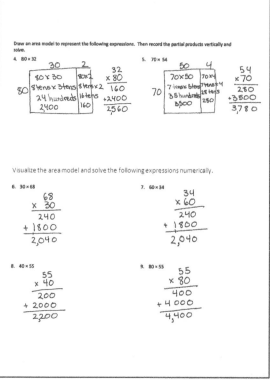

EUREKA
MATH™

Exit Ticket (3 minutes)

After the Student Debrief, instruct students to complete the Exit Ticket. A review of their work will help with assessing students' understanding of the concepts that were presented in today's lesson and planning more effectively for future lessons. The questions may be read aloud to the students.

Lesson 35:   Multiply two-digit multiples of 10 by two-digit numbers using the area model.

©2015 Great Minds. eureka-math.org
G4-M3-TE-B2-1.3.1-01.2016

485

Name _____ Date _____

Use an area model to represent the following expressions. Then, record the partial products and solve.

1. 20 × 22

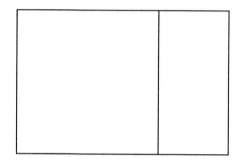

```
     2 2
  ×  2 0
  _____

+ _____
  =======
```

2. 50 × 41

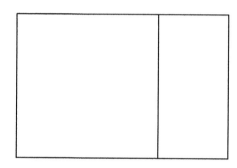

```
     4 1
  ×  5 0
  _____

+ _____
  =======
```

3. 60 × 73

```
     7 3
  ×  6 0
  _____

+ _____
  =======
```

Lesson 35: Multiply two-digit multiples of 10 by two-digit numbers using the area model.

EUREKA MATH

Draw an area model to represent the following expressions. Then, record the partial products vertically and solve.

4. 80×32

5. 70×54

Visualize the area model, and solve the following expressions numerically.

6. 30×68

7. 60×34

8. 40×55

9. 80×55

Lesson 35:   Multiply two-digit multiples of 10 by two-digit numbers using the area model.

487

©2015 Great Minds. eureka-math.org
G4-M3-TE-B2-1.3.1-01.2016

Name _____   Date _____

Use an area model to represent the following expressions. Then, record the partial products and solve.

1. 30 × 93

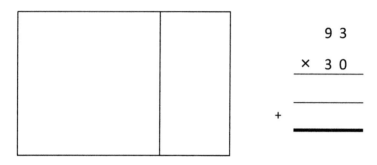

```
      9 3
  ×   3 0
  _____

+ _____
  ═══════
```

2. 40 × 76

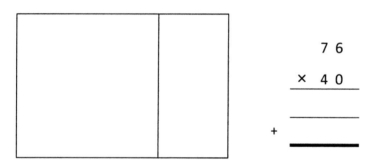

```
      7 6
  ×   4 0
  _____

+ _____
  ═══════
```

EUREKA MATH™

©2015 Great Minds. eureka-math.org
G4-M3-TE-B2-1.3.1-01.2016

Name _____ Date _____

Use an area model to represent the following expressions. Then, record the partial products and solve.

1. 30 × 17

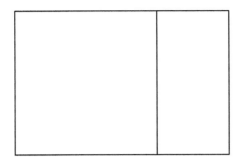

```
      1 7
   ×  3 0
   _____

 + _____
   ========
```

2. 40 × 58

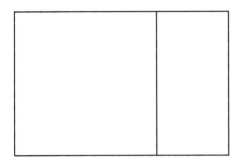

```
      5 8
   ×  4 0
   _____

 + _____
   ========
```

3. 50 × 38

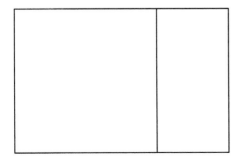

```
      3 8
   ×  5 0
   _____

 + _____
   ========
```

EUREKA MATH™

Lesson 35:   Multiply two-digit multiples of 10 by two-digit numbers using the area model.

©2015 Great Minds. eureka-math.org
G4-M3-TE-B2-1.3.1-01.2016

489

Draw an area model to represent the following expressions. Then, record the partial products vertically and solve.

4. 60 × 19

5. 20 × 44

Visualize the area model, and solve the following expressions numerically.

6. 20 × 88

7. 30 × 88

8. 70 × 47

9. 80 × 65

Lesson 35:   Multiply two-digit multiples of 10 by two-digit numbers using the area model.

©2015 Great Minds. eureka-math.org
G4-M3-TE-B2-1.3.1-01.2016

Lesson 36

Objective: Multiply two-digit by two-digit numbers using four partial products.

Suggested Lesson Structure

- ■ Fluency Practice   (12 minutes)
- ▨ Application Problem   (6 minutes)
- ▢ Concept Development   (32 minutes)
- ■ Student Debrief   (10 minutes)

Total Time   **(60 minutes)**

Fluency Practice (12 minutes)

- Draw a Unit Fraction **3.G.2**   (4 minutes)
- Divide Three Different Ways **4.NBT.6**   (4 minutes)
- Multiply by Multiples of 10 Written Vertically **4.NBT.5**   (4 minutes)

Draw a Unit Fraction (4 minutes)

Materials: (S) Personal white board

Note: This fluency activity reviews Grade 3 geometry and fraction concepts in anticipation of Modules 4 and 5. Accept reasonable drawings. Using rulers is not necessary to review the concept and takes too long.

- T: On your personal white boards, write the name for any four-sided figure.
- S: (Write *quadrilateral*.)
- T: Draw a quadrilateral that has 4 right angles and 4 equal sides.
- S: (Draw a square.)
- T: Partition the square into 4 equal parts.
- S: (Partition.)
- T: Shade in 1 of the parts.
- S: (Shade.)
- T: Write the fraction of the square that you shaded.
- S: (Write $\frac{1}{4}$.)

Continue with the following possible sequence: Partition a rectangle into 5 equal parts, shading $\frac{1}{5}$; partition a rhombus into 2 equal parts, shading $\frac{1}{2}$; partition a square into 12 equal parts, shading $\frac{1}{12}$; and partition a rectangle into 8 equal parts, shading $\frac{1}{8}$.

Lesson 36:   Multiply two-digit by two-digit numbers using four partial products.   **491**

Divide Three Different Ways (4 minutes)

Materials: (S) Personal white board

Note: This fluency activity reviews Lessons 32 and 33.

- T: (Write 406 ÷ 7.) Find the quotient using place value disks.
- T: Find the quotient using the area model.
- T: Find the quotient using the standard algorithm.

Repeat using 3,168 ÷ 9.

Multiply by Multiples of 10 Written Vertically (4 minutes)

Materials: (S) Personal white board

Note: This fluency activity reviews Lesson 35's content.

- T: (Write 30 × 23 vertically.) When I write 30 × 23, you say "3 tens times 3 ones plus 3 tens times 2 tens." (Point to the corresponding expressions as students speak.)
- S: 3 tens times 3 ones + 3 tens times 2 tens.
- T: Write and solve the entire equation vertically.
- T: What is 30 times 23?
- S: 690.

Continue with the following possible sequence: 30 × 29, 40 × 34, and 50 × 45.

Application Problem (6 minutes)

Mr. Goggins set up 30 rows of chairs in the gymnasium. If each row had 35 chairs, how many chairs did Mr. Goggins set up? Draw an area model to represent and to help solve this problem. Discuss with a partner how the area model can help you solve 30 × 35.

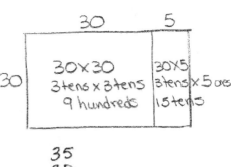

Note: This Application Problem builds on prior learning from Lesson 35 where students used an area model and partial products to multiply a two-digit multiple of 10 by a two-digit number using an area model. This Application Problem also helps bridge to today's lesson in that students apply prior knowledge of the area model and partial products to represent and solve two-digit by two-digit multiplication.

EUREKA
MATH™

Concept Development (32 minutes)

Materials: (S) Personal white board

Problem 1: Use the distributive property to represent and solve two-digit by two-digit multiplication.

NOTES ON
MULTIPLE MEANS
OF ENGAGEMENT:

Lead a discussion with students in order to deepen their understanding of representing expressions in numerical form and unit form. Be sure that students understand that there are different ways to express numbers in both written and oral form.

T: (Use the context of the Application Problem to continue with today's lesson.) Mr. Goggins set up an additional 4 rows of chairs with 35 chairs in each row. Let's change our area model to represent the additional rows. (Revise the area model.)

T: What is the length of this entire side? (Point to the vertical length.)

S: 34.

T: And the length of this side? (Point to the horizontal length.)

S: 35.

T: Use the area formula. What expression is shown by the area model now?

S: 34 × 35.

T: We can use the area model to help us represent two-digit times two-digit multiplication. Write the expressions that represent the areas of the two smaller rectangles that we just created.

S: 4 × 5 and 4 × 30.

T: Let's say the expressions in unit form to help us understand their value. Using the units for each factor, say 4 × 5 and 4 × 30 in unit form.

S: 4 ones × 5 ones and 4 ones × 3 tens.

T: Write those unit expressions in each rectangle. How can we use these expressions and the expressions of the other two rectangles to find the area of the whole rectangle?

MP.4

S: We can find the sum of all of the smaller areas.

T: Let's represent this using the distributive property. We are going to move from top to bottom, right to left to represent the areas of the smaller rectangles. You tell me the numerical expressions as I point to each of the smaller rectangles. I will write what you say. 34 × 35 equals…?

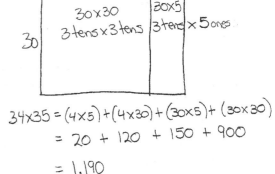

S: 34 × 35 = (4 × 5) + (4 × 30) + (30 × 5) + (30 × 30).

T: Now, express this same number sentence in unit form (without rewriting).

S: 34 × 35 = (4 ones × 5 ones) + (4 ones × 3 tens) + (3 tens × 5 ones) + (3 tens × 3 tens).

T: Now, we are ready to solve! First, let's find each of the four partial products. Then, we can add the four partial products to find 34 × 35.

S: 20 ones + 12 tens + 15 tens + 9 hundreds = 20 + 120 + 150 + 900 = 1,190.

Problem 2: Find the product of 23 and 31 using an area model and partial products to solve.

T: Let's solve 23 × 31 using area to model the product.

T: (Draw a rectangle.) Break down the length and width according to place value units.

S: 2 tens 3 ones and 3 tens 1 one. → 20 and 3. 30 and 1.

T: (Draw one vertical and one horizontal line subdividing the rectangle.) Turn and tell your partner the length and width of each of the 4 smaller rectangles we just created.

S: 3 and 1, 3 and 30, 20 and 1, and 20 and 30.

T: Using the area model that you just drew, write an equation that represents the product of 23 and 31 as the sum of those four areas.

S: 23 × 31 = (3 × 1) + (3 × 30) + (20 × 1) + (20 × 30).

T: Now, we are ready to solve!

T: Let's look at a way to record the partial products. (Write 23 × 31 vertically.) Recall that when we multiplied a one-digit number by a two-, three-, or four-digit number, we recorded the partial products. We also recorded partial products when we multiplied a two-digit number by a multiple of 10. Let's put it all together and do precisely the same thing here.

T: (Point to the area model and the expression showing the distributive property.) What is the product of 3 ones and 1 one?

S: 3 ones.

T: Record the product below. Draw an arrow connecting the rectangle with the corresponding partial product. How about 3 ones times 3 tens?

S: 9 tens.

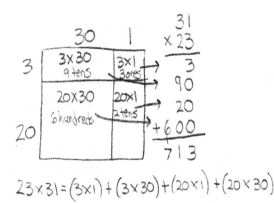

NOTES ON MULTIPLE MEANS OF REPRESENTATION:

Students working below grade level may benefit from continuing to write out the expressions used to find each of the partial products. Students may write the expressions in numerical form or in unit form.

To help solidify place value, it might also be helpful to have students shade, in different colors, the rectangles that represent the ones, tens, and hundreds.

Students working above grade level may be ready to use the four partial product algorithm and can be encouraged to do so.

T: Record the product below the first partial product. Draw an arrow connecting the rectangle with the corresponding partial product. What is 2 tens times 1 one?

S: 2 tens or 20.

T: As before, record the partial product below the other two and do the same with 2 tens times 3 tens.

T: Draw arrows to connect the new partial products with the corresponding rectangles. Now, let's add the partial products together. What is the sum?

S: The sum is 713. That means that 23 × 31 = 713.

Problem 3: Find the product of 26 and 34 using partial products. Verify partial products using the area model.

- T: Draw an area model to represent 26 × 34.
- T: How do I find the area of the smallest rectangle?
- S: Multiply 6 ones times 4 ones.
- T: Point to 6 ones times 4 ones in the algorithm. What is 6 ones times 4 ones?
- S: 24 ones.
- T: Record 24 beneath the expression and in the corresponding area.
- T: Point to the next area to solve for. Tell me the expression.
- S: 6 ones times 3 tens.
- T: Locate those numbers in the algorithm. Solve for 6 ones times 3 tens.
- S: 18 tens.
- T: Record 18 tens under the expression.
- S: We can also record 18 tens in this rectangle.

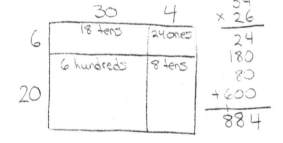

Continue connecting the width and length of each rectangle in the model to the location of those units in the algorithm. Record the partial products first under the expression and then inside the area.

- T: What is the last step?
- S: Add together all of the partial products. 24 + 180 + 80 + 600 = 884. → 26 × 34 = 884.

Problem 4: Find the product of 26 and 34 without using an area model. Record the partial products to solve.

- T: Take a mental picture of your area model before you erase it, the partial products, and the final product.
- T: When we multiplied these numbers before, with what did we start?
- S: 6 ones × 4 ones.
- T: Do you see 6 ones × 4 ones?
- S: Yes.

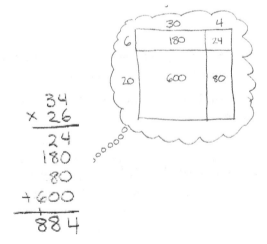

Students point to 6 ones × 4 ones. You might model on the board as students also record.

- T: What is 6 ones × 4 ones?
- S: 24 ones.
- T: Record 24 ones as a partial product.
- T: What did we multiply next?
- S: 6 ones × 3 tens. That's 18 tens or 180.
- T: Where do we record 180?
- S: Below the 24.

T: Now what?

S: We multiply the tens. 2 tens × 4 ones and then 2 tens × 3 tens.

T: What are 2 tens × 4 ones and 2 tens × 3 tens?

S: 8 tens and 6 hundreds.

T: Let's record these as partial products. Notice that we have four partial products. Let's again identify from where they came. (Point to each part of the algorithm as students chorally read the expressions used to solve the two-digit by two-digit multiplication.)

S: 6 ones × 4 ones = 24 ones. 6 ones × 3 tens = 18 tens. 2 tens × 4 ones = 8 tens.
     2 tens × 3 tens = 6 hundreds.

T: What is their sum?

S: 24 + 180 + 80 + 600 = 884. → 26 × 34 = 884.

T: Visualize to relate this back to the area model that we drew earlier.

Repeat for 38 × 43. You might first draw the area model (without multiplying out the partial products) and then erase it so that students again visualize the connection.

Problem Set (10 minutes)

Students should do their personal best to complete the Problem Set within the allotted 10 minutes. For some classes, it may be appropriate to modify the assignment by specifying which problems they work on first. Some problems do not specify a method for solving. Students should solve these problems using the RDW approach used for Application Problems.

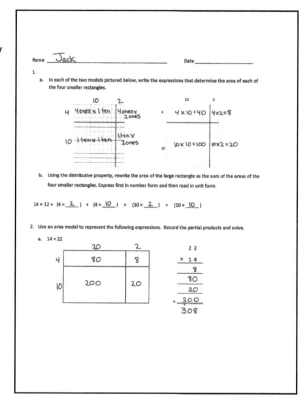

Student Debrief (10 minutes)

Lesson Objective: Multiply two-digit by two-digit numbers using four partial products.

The Student Debrief is intended to invite reflection and active processing of the total lesson experience.

Invite students to review their solutions for the Problem Set. They should check work by comparing answers with a partner before going over answers as a class. Look for misconceptions or misunderstandings that can be addressed in the Debrief. Guide students in a conversation to debrief the Problem Set and process the lesson.

Any combination of the questions below may be used to lead the discussion.

- How does Problem 1(a) support your understanding of the distributive property and partial products?

©2015 Great Minds. eureka-math.org
G4-M3-TE-B2-1.3.1-01.2016

- How do Problems 1 and 2 help to prepare you to solve Problems 3, 4, 5, and 6?

- How did our previous work with area models and partial products help us to be ready to solve two-digit by two-digit multiplication problems using partial products?

- How is it helpful to think about the areas of each rectangle in terms of *units*?

- How could you explain to someone that *ones × tens* equals *tens* but *tens × tens* equals *hundreds*?

- What significant math vocabulary did we use today to communicate precisely?

- How did the Application Problem connect to today's lesson?

Exit Ticket (3 minutes)

After the Student Debrief, instruct students to complete the Exit Ticket. A review of their work will help with assessing students' understanding of the concepts that were presented in today's lesson and planning more effectively for future lessons. The questions may be read aloud to the students.

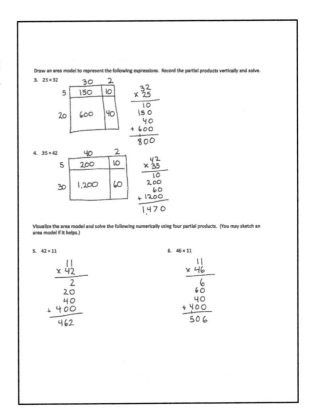

EUREKA
MATH™

Lesson 36:   Multiply two-digit by two-digit numbers using four partial products.

497

©2015 Great Minds. eureka-math.org
G4-M3-TE-B2-1.3.1-01.2016

Name _____   Date _____

1. a. In each of the two models pictured below, write the expressions that determine the area of each of the four smaller rectangles.

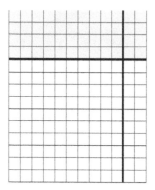 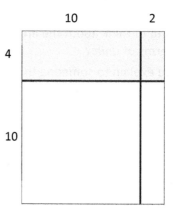

    b. Using the distributive property, rewrite the area of the large rectangle as the sum of the areas of the four smaller rectangles. Express first in number form, and then read in unit form.

     $14 \times 12 = (4 \times$ _____ $) + (4 \times$ _____ $) + (10 \times$ _____ $) + (10 \times$ _____ $)$

2. Use an area model to represent the following expression. Record the partial products and solve.

    14×22

$$\begin{array}{r} 2\,2 \\ \times\ 1\,4 \\ \hline \\ \hline \\ \hline \\ +\ \rule{2cm}{0.4pt} \end{array}$$

     Lesson 36:   Multiply two-digit by two-digit numbers using four partial products.

EUREKA
MATH™

Draw an area model to represent the following expressions. Record the partial products vertically and solve.

3. 25 × 32

4. 35 × 42

Visualize the area model and solve the following numerically using four partial products. (You may sketch an area model if it helps.)

5. 42 × 11

6. 46 × 11

EUREKA
MATH™

Lesson 36:   Multiply two-digit by two-digit numbers using four partial products.

499

©2015 Great Minds. eureka-math.org
G4-M3-TE-B2-1.3.1-01.2016

Name _____ Date _____

Record the partial products to solve.

Draw an area model first to support your work, or draw the area model last to check your work.

1. 26×43

2. 17×55

Lesson 36: Multiply two-digit by two-digit numbers using four partial products.

Name _____ Date _____

1. a. In each of the two models pictured below, write the expressions that determine the area of each of the four smaller rectangles.

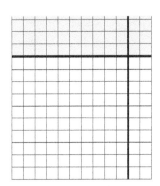 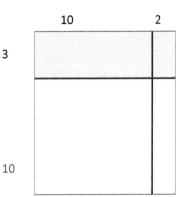

   b. Using the distributive property, rewrite the area of the large rectangle as the sum of the areas of the four smaller rectangles. Express first in number form, and then read in unit form.

   13 × 12 = (3 × _____) + (3 × _____) + (10 × _____) + (10 × _____)

Use an area model to represent the following expression. Record the partial products and solve.

2. 17 × 34

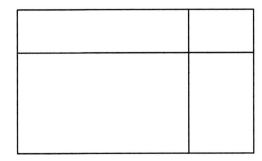

```
      3 4
  ×   1 7
  _____
  _____
+ _____
  _____
```

EUREKA
MATH™

Lesson 36:   Multiply two-digit by two-digit numbers using four partial products.

501

©2015 Great Minds. eureka-math.org
G4-M3-TE-B2-1.3.1-01.2016

Draw an area model to represent the following expressions. Record the partial products vertically and solve.

3. 45 × 18

4. 45 × 19

Visualize the area model and solve the following numerically using four partial products. (You may sketch an area model if it helps.)

5. 12 × 47

6. 23 × 93

7. 23 × 11

8. 23 × 22

EUREKA
MATH

Lesson 37

Objective: Transition from four partial products to the standard algorithm for two-digit by two-digit multiplication.

Suggested Lesson Structure

■ Fluency Practice   (10 minutes)

░ Application Problem   (5 minutes)

░ Concept Development   (35 minutes)

■ Student Debrief   (10 minutes)

  Total Time   **(60 minutes)**

Fluency Practice (10 minutes)

- Decompose 90 and 180 **4.MD.7**   (4 minutes)
- Multiply by Multiples of 10 Written Vertically **4.NBT.5**   (6 minutes)

Decompose 90 and 180 (4 minutes)

Materials: (S) Personal white board

Note: This fluency activity prepares students for composing and decomposing benchmark angles of 90 and 180 degrees in Module 4.

  T: (Project a number bond with a whole of 90 and a part of 10.) On your personal white boards, fill in the unknown part in the number bond.

  S: (Fill in 80.)

  T: (Write 90 – 10 = ____.) Say the subtraction sentence.

  S: 90 – 10 = 80.

Continue decomposing 90, taking away the following possible suggested parts: 20, 30, 85, 40, 45, 25, 35, and 15.

Using the same process, take away the following possible suggested parts from 180: 10, 100, 90, 70, 150, 60, 5, 15, 75, 65, and 45.

Lesson 37:   Transition from four partial products to the standard algorithm for two-digit by two-digit multiplication.

503

©2015 Great Minds. eureka-math.org
G4-M3-TE-B2-1.3.1-01.2016

Multiply by Multiples of 10 Written Vertically (6 minutes)

Materials: (S) Personal white board

Note: This fluency activity reviews Lesson 35's content.

- T: Solve 30×23 vertically as you say the unit form: 3 tens times 3 ones plus 3 tens times 2 tens. You have one minute. If you finish early, go on to 40×23.
- T: (Allow students a minute to work.) 3 tens times 3 ones is…?
- S: 9 tens. (Write 90.)
- T: 3 tens times 2 tens is…?
- S: 6 hundreds. (Write 600.)
- T: The sum of 90 and 600 is…?
- S: 690.
- T: 30 groups of 23 is…?
- S: 690.

Continue with the following possible sequence: 40×23, 40×34, 50×45, and 60×39.

Application Problem (5 minutes)

Sylvie's teacher challenged the class to draw an area model to represent the expression 24×56 and then to solve using partial products. Sylvie solved the expression as seen to the right. Is her answer correct? Why or why not?

Note: This Application Problem builds on the content of Lessons 34, 35, and 36. Students now have a solid foundation upon which to build understanding of two-digit by two-digit multiplication. They move from pictorial representations to abstract representations. This Application Problem guides such movement and builds to the content of today's lesson where students see how all of the work that they have done fits together and prepares them to solve using the standard algorithm (Lesson 38).

```
    56
  × 24
  ────
    24
   200
    12
  +100
  ─────
   336
```

Sylvie's answer is not correct. She drew the area model correctly, but she made 2 mistakes when she multiplied. Sylvie wrote that $20 \times 6 = 12$. It should be 120 since 2 tens $\times 6 = 12$ tens = 120. She also wrote that $20 \times 50 = 100$. It should be 1,000 since 2 tens $\times$ 5 tens = 10 hundreds. 10 hundreds = 1 thousand.

EUREKA
MATH™

Concept Development (35 minutes)

Materials: (S) Paper, pencil

Problem 1: Solve 26 × 35 using four partial products and two partial products.

T: Work with a partner:

1.   Draw an area model for 26 × 35.
2.   Record the partial products within each of four smaller rectangles.
3.   Write the expression 26 × 35 vertically.
4.   Write the four partial products under the expression.
5.   Find their sum.
6.   Connect the rectangles in the area model to the partial products using arrows.

S: (Draw area model and solve.) 26 × 35 = 910.

T: Shade the top half of the area model with the side of your pencil. Shade the corresponding partial products as well.

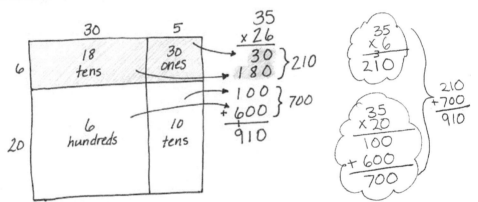

T: Use mental math to add the two partial products that you just shaded.

S: 30 + 180 = 210.

T: What multiplication expression can be used to represent the entire shaded area?

S: 6 × 35.

T: Find the total for 6 thirty-fives.

S: (Solve.)

S: 6 × 35 = 210. Hey, that's the same as when we added the two partial products that are shaded.

T: Explain why they are the same.

S: The two smaller rectangles in the shaded portion take up the same amount of space as the larger rectangle in the shaded portion.

T: Use mental math to add the two partial products that are not shaded.

S: 100 + 600 = 700.

T: What expression can be used to represent the area of the larger rectangle that is not shaded?

Lesson 37:   Transition from four partial products to the standard algorithm for
two-digit by two-digit multiplication.

©2015 Great Minds. eureka-math.org
G4-M3-TE-B2-1.3.1-01.2016

505

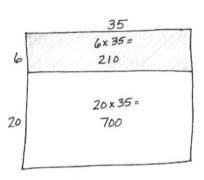

S: 20 × 35.

T: Solve for 20 thirty-fives.

S: (Solve.)

S: 700. It's the same!

T: (Draw an area model to show two partial products.) Say an addition sentence for the sum of the two parts.

S: 210 + 700 = 910. That's the same answer as when we added the four partial products.

T: We can solve by finding two partial products instead of four!

Problem 2: Solve 43 × 67 using four partial products and two partial products.

T: Work with a partner to draw and label an area model for 43 × 67 and solve.

T: Draw arrows to show how the parts of the area model relate to the partial products.

T: Draw and label another area model, as we did in Problem 1, which shows how we can combine the rectangles in the top portion and the rectangles in the bottom portion. (Guide students as they draw and label.) What expressions do the rectangles represent? Write the expressions in the rectangles. Solve for each expression.

MP.4

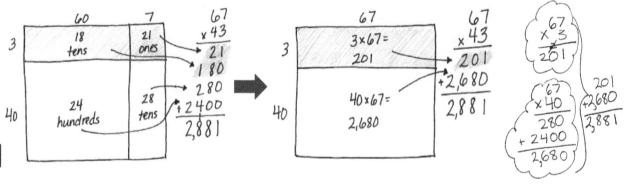

S: (3 × 67) and (40 × 67). 3 sixty-sevens is 201. 40 sixty-sevens is 2,680.

T: Write the two partial products within their corresponding rectangles. Write 43 × 67 vertically, and then write the partial products. Draw arrows to show how the parts of the area model relate to the partial products. (Guide students as they make the connections.)

T: What is the sum of the two partial products?

S: 201 + 2,680 = 2,881. Again, it's the same as when we solved using four partial products.

T: We found the value of 3 sixty-sevens and then added the value of 40 sixty-sevens.

NOTES ON MULTIPLE MEANS OF REPRESENTATION:

If students are not ready to complete the transition away from the area model, encourage them to quickly sketch an area model so that they can visually see the partial products.

Lesson 37:   Transition from four partial products to the standard algorithm for two-digit by two-digit multiplication.

EUREKA MATH™

Problem 3: Solve 24 × 36 using two partial products and an area model.

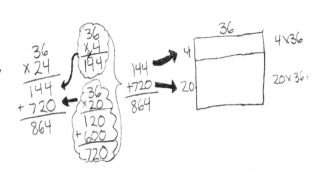

T: Write 24 × 36 vertically, and then represent it by drawing an area model. Discuss with a partner how to solve with two partial products.

S: One rectangle represents 4 thirty-sixes, and the other represents 20 thirty-sixes. We can find the area of each rectangle and then find their sum.

T: (Draw arrows next to where the partial products will be written.) Let's write the expressions for each partial product. (Write expressions next to where the partial products will be written as students do the same.) Find each partial product, and then determine their sum.

S: 144 + 720 = 864.

T: Look at the area model that you drew. Connect the partial products in the area model to the partial products in the vertical expression. Close your eyes and create a picture in your mind of how the partial products relate to the area model.

Problem 4: Solve 37 × 49 using two partial products without an area model.

T: Write 37 × 49 vertically on your personal white board. How can we solve?

S: I can think about what the area model would look like. I know that the expressions for the partial products are 7 × 49 and 30 × 49.

T: Find each partial product. (Allow time for students to calculate answers.)

S: 7 forty-nines is 343; 30 forty-nines is 1,470.

T: How did you solve for the partial products?

S: I multiplied the numbers off to the side because I know how to multiply one-digit numbers by two-digit numbers and multiples of 10 by two-digit numbers.

T: Write the partial products beneath the expression. What is their sum?

S: 343 + 1,470 = 1,813. → 37 × 49 = 1,813.

> **NOTES ON MULTIPLE MEANS OF ACTION AND EXPRESSION:**
>
> Lead students through steps that help them to create a picture in their mind of the area model. Ask questions such as the following to support the visualization.
> - Can you see the rectangle?
> - How many parts does it have?
> - What are the two lengths of the vertical side?
> - What is the length of the horizontal side?
> - What expressions give us the area of each smaller rectangle?
> - Look at the vertical expression that we have written. Do you see the expressions for the area of each smaller rectangle?

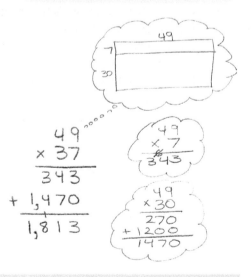

 Lesson 37:　Transition from four partial products to the standard algorithm for two-digit by two-digit multiplication.

©2015 Great Minds. eureka-math.org
G4-M3-TE-B2-1.3.1-01.2016

507

Problem Set (10 minutes)

Students should do their personal best to complete the Problem Set within the allotted 10 minutes. For some classes, it may be appropriate to modify the assignment by specifying which problems they work on first. Some problems do not specify a method for solving. Students should solve these problems using the RDW approach used for Application Problems.

Student Debrief (10 minutes)

Lesson Objective: Transition from four partial products to the standard algorithm for two-digit by two-digit multiplication.

The Student Debrief is intended to invite reflection and active processing of the total lesson experience.

Invite students to review their solutions for the Problem Set. They should check work by comparing answers with a partner before going over answers as a class. Look for misconceptions or misunderstandings that can be addressed in the Debrief. Guide students in a conversation to debrief the Problem Set and process the lesson.

Any combination of the questions below may be used to lead the discussion.

- Did you record the 15 or 57 as the width of the rectangle in Problem 3? Does it matter the order? Which number as the width is easiest for you to solve the rest of the problem? Explain.

- Imagine the area models for Problems 4(c) and (d). Notice how the rectangle in Problem 4(d) is half as wide and double the length of the rectangle in Problem 4(c). What might the areas look like? Why does that result in the same product?

- How does the shading on the area models help you understand the movement from four partial products to two partial products?

- Why would we want to represent the area model using two partial products instead of four?

- How did the Application Problem connect to today's lesson?

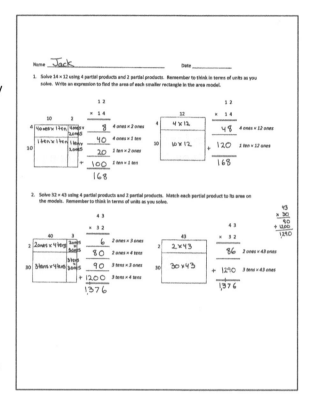

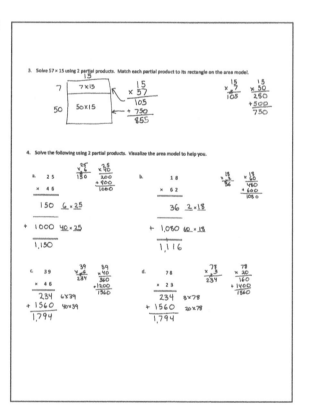

EUREKA
MATH™

Exit Ticket (3 minutes)

After the Student Debrief, instruct students to complete the Exit Ticket. A review of their work will help with assessing students' understanding of the concepts that were presented in today's lesson and planning more effectively for future lessons. The questions may be read aloud to the students.

Lesson 37:   Transition from four partial products to the standard algorithm for two-digit by two-digit multiplication.

©2015 Great Minds. eureka-math.org
G4-M3-TE-B2-1.3.1-01.2016

509

Name _____ Date _____

1. Solve 14 × 12 using 4 partial products and 2 partial products. Remember to think in terms of units as you solve. Write an expression to find the area of each smaller rectangle in the area model.

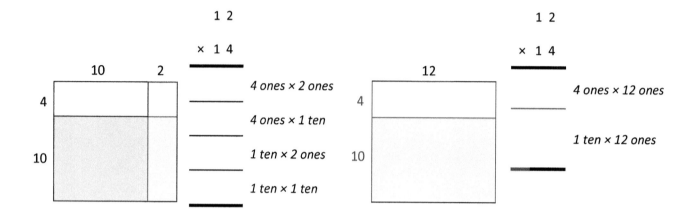

```
        1 2
      × 1 4
      ───────
      ───────   4 ones × 2 ones
      ───────   4 ones × 1 ten
      ───────   1 ten × 2 ones
      ───────   1 ten × 1 ten
      ═══════
```

```
        1 2
      × 1 4
      ───────
      ───────   4 ones × 12 ones
      ───────   1 ten × 12 ones
      ═══════
```

2. Solve 32 × 43 using 4 partial products and 2 partial products. Match each partial product to its area on the models. Remember to think in terms of units as you solve.

```
        4 3
      × 3 2
      ───────
      ───────   2 ones × 3 ones
      ───────   2 ones × 4 tens
      ───────   3 tens × 3 ones
      ───────   3 tens × 4 tens
      ═══════
```

```
        4 3
      × 3 2
      ═══════
      ───────   2 ones × 43 ones
      ───────   3 tens × 43 ones
      ═══════
```

Lesson 37: Transition from four partial products to the standard algorithm for two-digit by two-digit multiplication.

©2015 Great Minds. eureka-math.org
G4-M3-TE-B2-1.3.1-01.2016

EUREKA MATH

3. Solve 57 × 15 using 2 partial products. Match each partial product to its rectangle on the area model.

4. Solve the following using 2 partial products. Visualize the area model to help you.

a.
```
    2 5
  × 4 6
  ───────

        ____ × ____
  _____
        ____ × ____
  ━━━━━━━
```

b.
```
    1 8
  × 6 2
  ───────

        ____ × ____
  _____
        ____ × ____
  ━━━━━━━
```

c.
```
    3 9
  × 4 6
  ━━━━━━━
```

d.
```
    7 8
  × 2 3
  ━━━━━━━
```

EUREKA MATH **Lesson 37:** Transition from four partial products to the standard algorithm for two-digit by two-digit multiplication.

©2015 Great Minds. eureka-math.org
G4-M3-TE-B2-1.3.1-01.2016

511

Name _____ Date _____

1. Solve 43 × 22 using 4 partial products and 2 partial products. Remember to think in terms of units as you solve. Write an expression to find the area of each smaller rectangle in the area model.

```
          20        2            2 2
                              ×  4 3
    3                         _____
                              _____      3 ones × 2 ones
                              _____      3 ones × 2 tens
   40                         _____      4 tens × 2 ones
                                            4 tens × 2 tens
                              _____
```

```
              22                 2 2
                              ×  4 3
    3                         _____
                                            3 ones × 22 ones
                              _____
   40                                       4 tens × 22 ones

                              _____
```

2. Solve the following using 2 partial products.

```
                 6 4
              ×    1 5
              _____
                            5 ones × 64 ones
              _____
                            1 ten × 64 ones

              _____
```

EUREKA
MATH™

Name _____   Date _____

1. Solve 26 × 34 using 4 partial products and 2 partial products. Remember to think in terms of units as you solve. Write an expression to find the area of each smaller rectangle in the area model.

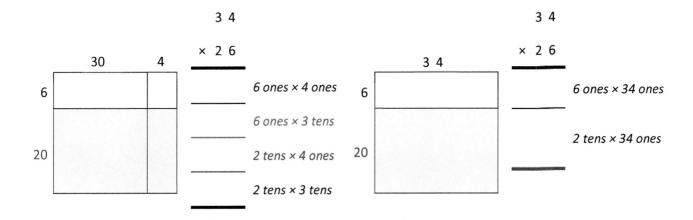

2. Solve using 4 partial products and 2 partial products. Remember to think in terms of units as you solve. Write an expression to find the area of each smaller rectangle in the area model.

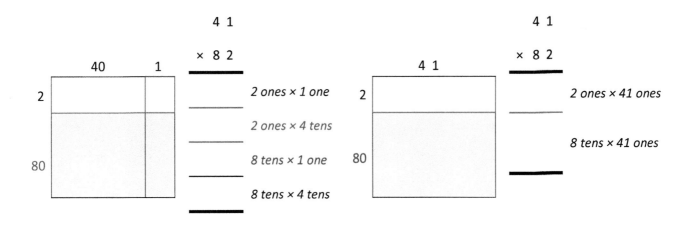

EUREKA MATH™   **Lesson 37:**   Transition from four partial products to the standard algorithm for two-digit by two-digit multiplication.   **513**

©2015 Great Minds. eureka-math.org
G4-M3-TE-B2-1.3.1-01.2016

3. Solve 52 × 26 using 2 partial products and an area model. Match each partial product to its area on the model.

4. Solve the following using 2 partial products. Visualize the area model to help you.

a.

    6 8

× 2 3
_____

_____ × _____

_____

_____ × _____

_____

b.

    4 9

× 3 3
_____

_____ × _____

_____

_____ × _____

_____

c.

    1 6

× 2 5
_____

d.

    5 4

× 7 1
_____

©2015 Great Minds. eureka-math.org
G4-M3-TE-B2-1.3.1-01.2016

EUREKA
MATH

Lesson 38

Objective: Transition from four partial products to the standard algorithm for two-digit by two-digit multiplication.

Suggested Lesson Structure

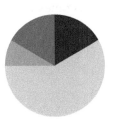

■ Fluency Practice   (10 minutes)
▨ Application Problem   (5 minutes)
▢ Concept Development   (35 minutes)
■ Student Debrief   (10 minutes)

   Total Time   **(60 minutes)**

Fluency Practice (10 minutes)

- Decompose 90 and 180 **4.MD.7**   (4 minutes)
- Multiply by Multiples of 10 Written Vertically **4.NBT.5**   (6 minutes)

Decompose 90 and 180 (4 minutes)

Materials: (S) Personal white board

Note: This fluency activity prepares students for composing and decomposing benchmark angles of 90 and 180 degrees in Module 4.

   T: (Project a number bond with a whole of 90 and a part of 10.) On your personal white boards, fill in the unknown part in the number bond.

   S: (Fill in 80.)

   T: (Write 90 – 10 = ____.) Say the subtraction sentence.

   S: 90 – 10 = 80.

Continue decomposing 90, taking away the following possible suggested parts:
20, 30, 85, 40, 45, 25, 35, and 15.

Repeat the process, taking away the following possible suggested parts from 180:
10, 100, 90, 70, 150, 60, 5, 15, 75, 65, and 45.

Lesson 38:   Transition from four partial products to the standard algorithm for
                two-digit by two-digit multiplication.   **515**

©2015 Great Minds. eureka-math.org
G4-M3-TE-B2-1.3.1-01.2016

Multiply by Multiples of 10 Written Vertically (6 minutes)

Materials: (S) Personal white board

Note: This fluency activity reviews Lesson 35's content.

  T: Solve 20 × 67 vertically as you say the unit form: 2 tens times 7 ones plus 2 tens times 6 tens. You
        have one minute. If you finish early, go on to 20 × 78.

  T: (Allow students a minute to work.) 2 tens times 7 ones is…?

  S: 14 tens. (Write 140.)

  T: 2 tens times 6 tens is…?

  S: 12 hundreds. (Write 1,200.)

  T: The sum of 140 and 1,200 is…?

  S: 1,340.

  T: 20 groups of 67 is…?

  S: 1,340.

Continue with the following possible sequence: 20 × 78, 30 × 45, 30 × 67, and 40 × 75.

Application Problem (5 minutes)

Sandy's garden has 42 plants in each row. She has 2 rows of
yellow corn and 20 rows of white corn.

Draw an area model (representing two partial products) to show
how much yellow corn and white corn has been planted in the
garden.

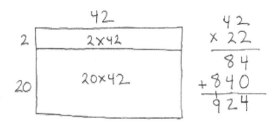

Note: This problem revisits the area model that focuses on two
partial products in preparation for work with the standard
algorithm. The area model used in the Application Problem is
used in Problem 1 of the Concept Development.

Concept Development (35 minutes)

Materials: (S) Personal white boards

**Problem 1: Represent 22 × 42 with the distributive property,
and connect the two partial products to the standard algorithm.**

  T: Look at the model you drew in the Application
        Problem. We found the total for 22 rows of 42, or 22
        forty-twos. What multiplication expression is that?

  S: 22 × 42.

**NOTES ON
MULTIPLE MEANS
OF ACTION AND
EXPRESSION:**

When multiplying two-digit by two-
digit numbers, use place value cards
(e.g., Hide Zero cards) to represent the
factors. The cards provide a concrete
representation of the place value of
each digit within the factors and are
another way to promote
understanding of the multiplication
algorithm.

Lesson 38:   Transition from four partial products to the standard algorithm for
                      two-digit by two-digit multiplication.

EUREKA
MATH™

T: Write 22 × 42 vertically. 22 units of 42.

T: Which expression represents the first of the two partial products that we recorded?

S: 2 × 42.

T: 2 ones times 2 ones equals…?

S: 4 ones.

T: Let's record the 4 ones in the ones place.

T: 2 ones times 4 tens equals…?

S: 8 tens.

T: Let's record the 8 tens in the tens place. What's the first partial product?

S: 84.

T: Draw an arrow to the area model to show where the partial product is represented.

T: In unit form, which expression represents the second of the two partial products that we recorded?

S: 2 tens × 4 tens 2 ones.

T: Let's solve.

T: What is 2 tens times 2 ones?

S: 4 tens.

T: Let's record 4 tens as 40 to start the second partial product. (Model.)

T: 2 tens times 4 tens equals how many hundreds?

S: 8 hundreds.

T: Record 8 hundreds in the hundreds place. Draw an arrow to the area model to show where the partial product is represented.

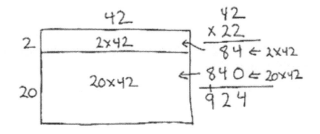

T: What's the second partial product?

S: 840.

T: Find the sum of the two partial products.

T: What is 22 × 42? Say the equation.

S: 22 × 42 = 924.

Problem 2: Represent 29 × 62 involving a regrouping in the first partial product.

T: We want to find the value of 29 sixty-twos using the algorithm.

T: What multiplication expression will I use?

S: 29 × 62.

T: First, let's find the value of 9 sixty-twos.

T: 9 ones times 2 ones is…?

S: 18 ones.

T: Let's record the new groups below just as we have done in the past. (Write the 1 on the line under the tens place first and the 8 in the ones place second.)

T: 9 ones times 6 tens is…?

Lesson 38:   Transition from four partial products to the standard algorithm for
             two-digit by two-digit multiplication.   **517**

©2015 Great Minds. eureka-math.org
G4-M3-TE-B2-1.3.1-01.2016

S: 54 tens.

T: (Point to the regrouped ten.) 54 tens plus 1 ten is…?

S: 55 tens. Now we need to cross off the 1 ten that we regrouped.

T: What is 9 × 62?

S: 558.

T: Now let's find the value of the second partial product, 20 sixty-twos.

T: 2 tens times 2 ones is…?

S: 4 tens.

T: Record the 4 tens as 40 ones. 2 tens times 6 tens is…?

S: 12 hundreds.

T: Record 12 hundreds in the second partial product. What is our second partial product?

S: 1,240.

T: What is the sum of our partial products?

S: 1,798.

T: What is 29 × 62? Say the complete equation.

S: 29 × 62 = 1,798.

T: Yes, 9 sixty-twos plus 20 sixty-twos is 29 sixty-twos. The product is 1,798.

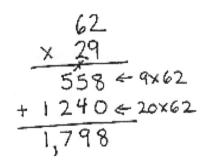

Problem 3: Solve 46 x 63 involving a regrouping in the second partial product.

T: Let's find the value of 46 sixty-threes. Write the multiplication expression.

S: (Write 46 × 63.)

T: Which partial product do we find first?

S: 6 × 63.

T: 6 ones times 3 ones is…?

S: 18 ones.

T: Let's record. (Write the 1 on the line under the tens place first and the 8 in the ones place second.)

T: What do we multiply next?

S: 6 ones times 6 tens. That's 36 tens. When I add the 1 ten, I get 37 tens.

T: Record 37 tens. Did you remember to cross off the 1 ten? The value of 6 sixty-threes is…?

S: 378.

T: Now, let's find the value of 40 sixty-threes. What do we do first?

MP.8

518   **Lesson 38:**   Transition from four partial products to the standard algorithm for two-digit by two-digit multiplication.

©2015 Great Minds. eureka-math.org
G4-M3-TE-B2-1.3.1-01.2016

EUREKA
MATH

S: 4 tens times 3 ones equals 12 tens.

T: 12 tens is 1 hundred 2 tens. Record the 1 hundred in the hundreds column of the second partial product. Record 2 tens as 20.

T: What do we multiply next?

S: 4 tens times 6 tens. That's 24 hundreds.

T: The total number of hundreds is…?

S: We had 24 hundreds, plus one more hundred is 25 hundreds.

MP.8

T: Cross out the 1 hundred and record 25 hundreds.

T: What is the second partial product?

S: 2,520.

T: Turn and tell your partner what the next step is.

S: We add the partial products.

T: What is 46 sixty-threes?

S: 46 × 63 = 2,898.

Problem Set (10 minutes)

Students should do their personal best to complete the Problem Set within the allotted 10 minutes. For some classes, it may be appropriate to modify the assignment by specifying which problems they work on first. Some problems do not specify a method for solving. Students should solve these problems using the RDW approach used for Application Problems.

Student Debrief (10 minutes)

Lesson Objective: Transition from four partial products to the standard algorithm for two-digit by two-digit multiplication.

The Student Debrief is intended to invite reflection and active processing of the total lesson experience.

Invite students to review their solutions for the Problem Set. They should check work by comparing answers with a partner before going over answers as a class. Look for misconceptions or misunderstandings that can be addressed in the Debrief. Guide students in a conversation to debrief the Problem Set and process the lesson.

Any combination of the questions below may be used to lead the discussion.

- What is the relationship between the product for Problem 1 and Problem 2 of the Problem Set?

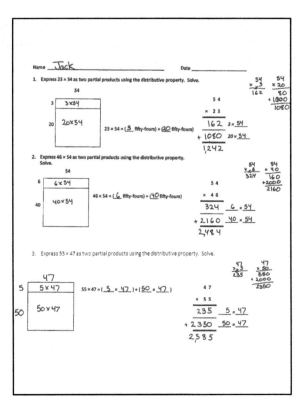

Lesson 38:   Transition from four partial products to the standard algorithm for two-digit by two-digit multiplication.   **519**

©2015 Great Minds. eureka-math.org
G4-M3-TE-B2-1.3.1-01.2016

- How does the structure of determining the answers to Problems 1 and 2 help you to solve Problem 3?

- How is recording multiplication using the multiplication algorithm the same as when we solved using two partial products? How is it different?

- How did your understanding of two partial products help you to learn the multiplication algorithm?

- How is the multiplication algorithm similar to the algorithm for addition? How is it different?

- What might be an advantage of using the multiplication algorithm to multiply?

- Explain to your partner how to multiply using the multiplication algorithm.

- What new (or significant) math vocabulary did we use today to communicate precisely?

- How did the Application Problem connect to today's lesson?

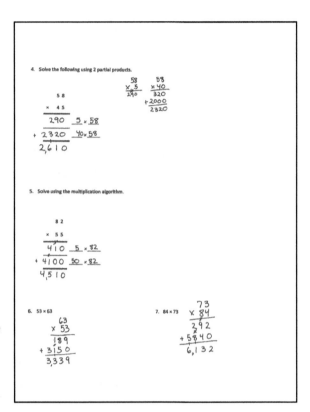

Exit Ticket (3 minutes)

After the Student Debrief, instruct students to complete the Exit Ticket. A review of their work will help with assessing students' understanding of the concepts that were presented in today's lesson and planning more effectively for future lessons. The questions may be read aloud to the students.

©2015 Great Minds. eureka-math.org
G4-M3-TE-B2-1.3.1-01.2016

EUREKA
MATH™

Name _____   Date _____

1. Express 23 × 54 as two partial products using the distributive property. Solve.

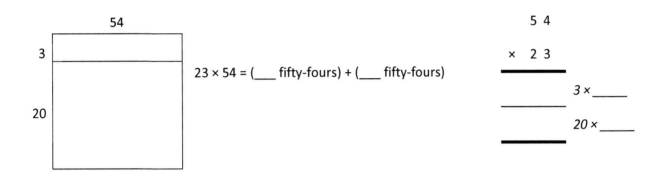

54

3

20

23 × 54 = (____ fifty-fours) + (____ fifty-fours)

      5 4
×   2 3
_____

_____   3 × _____
_____
          20 × _____
_____

2. Express 46 × 54 as two partial products using the distributive property. Solve.

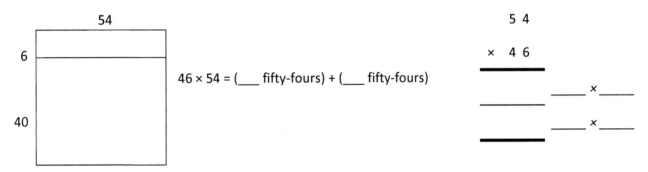

54

6

40

46 × 54 = (____ fifty-fours) + (____ fifty-fours)

      5 4
×   4 6
_____

_____   _____ × _____
_____
          _____ × _____
_____

3. Express 55 × 47 as two partial products using the distributive property. Solve.

55 × 47 = (_____ × _____) + (_____ × _____)

      4 7
×   5 5
_____

_____   _____ × _____
_____
          _____ × _____
_____

EUREKA
MATH™

Lesson 38:   Transition from four partial products to the standard algorithm for
two-digit by two-digit multiplication.

521

©2015 Great Minds. eureka-math.org
G4-M3-TE-B2-1.3.1-01.2016

4. Solve the following using 2 partial products.

```
       5 8
   ×   4 5
   _____
   _____   ____ × ____
   _____   ____ × ____
```

5. Solve using the multiplication algorithm.

```
       8 2
   ×   5 5
   _____
   _____   ____ × ____
   _____   ____ × ____
```

6. 53×63

7. 84×73

Lesson 38:   Transition from four partial products to the standard algorithm for two-digit by two-digit multiplication.

©2015 Great Minds. eureka-math.org
G4-M3-TE-B2-1.3.1-01.2016

EUREKA
MATH

Name _____   Date _____

Solve using the multiplication algorithm.

1.

```
        7 2
    ×   4 3
    ─────────
    _____   ____ × ____
    _____
    _____   ____ × ____
    ─────────
```

2. 35 × 53

Lesson 38:   Transition from four partial products to the standard algorithm for two-digit by two-digit multiplication.

©2015 Great Minds. eureka-math.org
G4-M3-TE-B2-1.3.1-01.2016

523

Name _____ Date _____

1. Express 26 × 43 as two partial products using the distributive property. Solve.

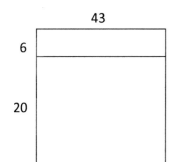

26 × 43 = (_____ forty-threes) + (_____ forty-threes)

```
      4 3
   ×  2 6
  _____
              6 × _____
  _____
            20 × _____
  _____
```

2. Express 47 × 63 as two partial products using the distributive property. Solve.

47 × 63 = (_____ sixty-threes) + (_____ sixty-threes)

```
      6 3
   ×  4 7
  _____
            _____ × _____
  _____
            _____ × _____
  _____
```

3. Express 54 × 67 as two partial products using the distributive property. Solve.

54 × 67 = (___ × _____) + (___ × _____)

```
      6 7
   ×  5 4
  _____
            _____ × _____
  _____
            _____ × _____
  _____
```

Lesson 38:   Transition from four partial products to the standard algorithm for two-digit by two-digit multiplication.

©2015 Great Minds. eureka-math.org
G4-M3-TE-B2-1.3.1-01.2016

EUREKA MATH™

4. Solve the following using two partial products.

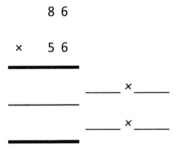

```
        5 2
  ×     3 4
  _____      ____ × _____
  _____
  _____      ____ × _____
  _____
```

5. Solve using the multiplication algorithm.

```
        8 6
  ×     5 6
  _____      _____ × _____
  _____
  _____      _____ × _____
  _____
```

6. 54×52

7. 44×76

EUREKA
MATH

Lesson 38: Transition from four partial products to the standard algorithm for two-digit by two-digit multiplication.

©2015 Great Minds. eureka-math.org
G4-M3-TE-B2-1.3.1-01.2016

525

8. 63×63

9. 68×79

Lesson 38: Transition from four partial products to the standard algorithm for two-digit by two-digit multiplication.

©2015 Great Minds. eureka-math.org
G4-M3-TE-B2-1.3.1-01.2016

EUREKA
MATH™

Name _____ Date _____

1. What is the greatest multiple of 7 that is less than 60?

2. Identify each number as prime or composite. Then, list all of its factors.

    a.   3   _____   _____

    b.   6   _____   _____

    c.   15 _____   _____

    d.   24 _____   _____

    e.   29 _____   _____

3. Use any place value strategy to divide.

    a.   3,600 ÷ 9

    b.   96 pencils come in a box. If 4 teachers share 3 boxes equally, how many pencils does each teacher receive?

EUREKA
MATH™

Module 3:   Multi-Digit Multiplication and Division

527

©2015 Great Minds. eureka-math.org
G4-M3-TE-B2-1.3.1-01.2016

4. $427 \div 3$

    a. Solve by drawing place value disks.   b. Solve numerically.

5. Use any place value strategy to multiply or divide.

                                      b. $3,809 \div 5$

    a. $5,316 \div 3$

    c. 29×56 d. 17×43

©2015 Great Minds. eureka-math.org
G4-M3-TE-B2-1.3.1-01.2016

EUREKA
MATH™

Solve using a model or equation. Show your work, and write your answer as a statement.

6. A new grocery store is opening next week.

   a. The store's rectangular floor is 42 meters long and 39 meters wide. How many square meters of flooring do they need? Use estimation to assess the reasonableness of your answer.

   b. The store ordered small posters and large posters to promote their opening. 12 times as many small posters were ordered as large posters. If there were 48 large posters, how many more small posters were ordered than large posters?

c. Uniforms are sold in packages of 8. The store's 127 employees will each be given 3 uniforms. How many packages will the store need to order?

d. There are three numbers for the combination to the store's safe. The first number is 17. The other two numbers can be multiplied together to give a product of 28. What are all of the possibilities for the other two numbers? Write your answers as multiplication equations, and then write all of the possible combinations to the safe.

End-of-Module Assessment Task   **Topics A–H**
Standards Addressed

Use the four operations with whole numbers to solve problems.

4.OA.1   Interpret a multiplication equation as a comparison, e.g., interpret $35 = 5 \times 7$ as a statement that 35 is 5 times as many as 7 and 7 times as many as 5. Represent verbal statements of multiplicative comparisons as multiplication equations.

4.OA.2   Multiply or divide to solve word problems involving multiplicative comparison, e.g., by using drawings and equations with a symbol for the unknown number to represent the problem, distinguishing multiplicative comparison from additive comparison.

4.OA.3   Solve multistep word problems posed with whole numbers and having whole-number answers using the four operations, including problems in which remainders must be interpreted. Represent these problems using equations with a letter standing for the unknown quantity. Assess the reasonableness of answers using mental computation and estimation strategies including rounding.

Gain familiarity with factors and multiples.

4.OA.4   Find all factor pairs for a whole number in the range 1–100. Recognize that a whole number is a multiple of each of its factors. Determine whether a given whole number in the range 1–100 is a multiple of a given one-digit number. Determine whether a given whole number in the range 1–100 is prime or composite.

Use place value understanding and properties of operations to perform multi-digit arithmetic.

4.NBT.5   Multiply a whole number of up to four digits by a one-digit whole number, and multiply two two-digit numbers, using strategies based on place value and the properties of operations. Illustrate and explain the calculation by using equations, rectangular arrays, and/or area models.

4.NBT.6   Find whole-number quotients and remainders with up to four-digit dividends and one-digit divisors, using strategies based on place value, the properties of operations, and/or the relationship between multiplication and division. Illustrate and explain the calculation by using equations, rectangular arrays, and/or area models.

Solve problems involving measurement and conversion of measurements from a larger unit to a smaller unit.

4.MD.3   Apply the area and perimeter formulas for rectangles in real world and mathematical problems. *For example, find the width of a rectangular room given the area of the flooring and the length, by viewing the area formula as a multiplication equation with an unknown factor.*

©2015 Great Minds. eureka-math.org
G4-M3-TE-B2-1.3.1-01.2016

Evaluating Student Learning Outcomes

A Progression Toward Mastery is provided to describe steps that illuminate the gradually increasing understandings that students develop *on their way to proficiency.* In this chart, this progress is presented from left (Step 1) to right (Step 4). The learning goal for students is to achieve Step 4 mastery. These steps are meant to help teachers and students identify and celebrate what the students CAN do now and what they need to work on next.

A Progression Toward Mastery				
Assessment Task Item	**STEP 1** Little evidence of reasoning without a correct answer. **(1 Point)**	**STEP 2** Evidence of some reasoning without a correct answer. **(2 Points)**	**STEP 3** Evidence of some reasoning with a correct answer or evidence of solid reasoning with an incorrect answer. **(3 Points)**	**STEP 4** Evidence of solid reasoning with a correct answer. **(4 Points)**
1 **4.OA.4**	The student answers incorrectly with a number that is not a multiple of 7.	The student answers incorrectly with a number that is a multiple of 7 but greater than 60.	The student answers with a multiple of 7 that is less than 60 but not 56.	The student correctly answers: The greatest multiple of 7 that is less than 60 is 56.
2 **4.OA.4**	The student is unable to complete the majority of Parts (a)–(e).	The student correctly answers prime or composite for three parts and misses more than a total of three factors.	The student correctly answers prime or composite for four of the five parts and misses three or fewer factors.	The student correctly answers: a. Prime; 1, 3 b. Composite; 1, 2, 3, 6 c. Composite; 1, 3, 5, 15 d. Composite; 1, 2, 3, 4, 6, 8, 12, 24 e. Prime; 1, 29

Module 3:   Multi-Digit Multiplication and Division

EUREKA MATH™

©2015 Great Minds. eureka-math.org
G4-M3-TE-B2-1.3.1-01.2016

A Progression Toward Mastery

3 **4.OA.3** **4.NBT.5** **4.NBT.6**	The student incorrectly answers both parts and shows no reasoning.	The student correctly answers one part and shows little reasoning.	The student answers one part correctly but shows solid reasoning in both problems, or the student shows some reasoning with correct answers for both parts.	The student correctly answers using any place value strategy: a. 400 b. Each teacher received 72 pencils.
4 **4.NBT.6**	The student incorrectly represents division using place value disks and incorrectly solves numerically.	The student incorrectly solves the numeric equation but shows some understanding of the place value chart and use of the algorithm.	The student decomposes incorrectly in one place value or does not include the remainder.	The student correctly decomposes and divides using the place value disks and provides a numerical answer of 142 with a remainder of 1.
5 **4.NBT.6**	The student answers fewer than two parts correctly, showing little to no evidence of place value strategies.	The student correctly solves two parts, showing little evidence of place value strategies.	The student correctly solves three parts with understanding of place value strategies, or the student correctly solves all four parts but does not show solid evidence of place value understanding.	The student solves all parts correctly using any place value strategy: a. 1,772 b. 761 with a remainder of 4 c. 1,624 d. 731
6 **4.MD.3** **4.OA.1** **4.OA.2** **4.OA.3** **4.NBT.5** **4.NBT.6**	The student incorrectly answers two or more of the four parts, showing little to no reasoning.	The student correctly answers two of four parts, showing some reasoning.	The student answers all four parts correctly but shows little reasoning in Part (a), or the student answers three of four parts correctly showing solid reasoning and understanding mathematically.	The student correctly answers all four parts, showing solid evidence of place value understanding: a. 1,638 square meters of flooring (estimate 40 × 40 = 1,600 square m). It is a reasonable because the answer and estimate have a difference of only 38 square meters. b. 528 more small posters than large posters.

©2015 Great Minds. eureka-math.org
G4-M3-TE-B2-1.3.1-01.2016

A Progression Toward Mastery

				c. 48 packages. d. Equations of $1 \times 28 = 28$ $28 \times 1 = 28$ $2 \times 14 = 28$ $14 \times 2 = 28$ $4 \times 7 = 28$ $7 \times 4 = 28$ Combinations of 17, 1, 28 17, 28, 1 17, 2, 14 17, 14, 2 17, 4, 7 17, 7, 4

Module 3:   Multi-Digit Multiplication and Division

©2015 Great Minds. eureka-math.org
G4-M3-TE-B2-1.3.1-01.2016

Name ___Jack___   Date _____

1. What is the greatest multiple of 7 that is less than 60?

   7, 14, 21, 28, 35, 42, 49, (56), 63   56 is the greatest multiple of 7 that is less than 60.

2. Identify each number as prime or composite. Then list all of its factors.

   a. 3 ___prime___   ___1, 3___

   b. 6 ___composite___   ___1, 2, 3, 6___

   c. 15 ___composite___   ___1, 3, 5, 15___

   d. 24 ___composite___   ___1, 2, 3, 4, 6, 8, 12, 24___

   e. 29 ___prime___   ___1, 29___

3. Use any place value strategy to divide.

   a. $3,600 \div 9$

   $$36 \text{ hundreds} \div 9 = 4 \text{ hundreds}$$
   $$= 400$$

   b. 96 pencils come in a box. If 4 teachers share 3 boxes equally, how many pencils does each teacher receive?

   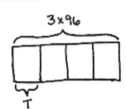

   $\begin{array}{r} 96 \\ \times 3 \\ \hline 288 \end{array}$

   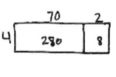

   $\begin{array}{r} 2 \\ 70 \\ 4\overline{)288} \\ -280 \\ \hline 8 \\ -8 \\ \hline 0 \end{array}$

   70 + 2 = 72
   Each teacher receives 72 pencils.

4. $427 \div 3$

   a. Solve by drawing place value disks:

   b. Solve numerically:

hundreds	tens	ones

←remainder

} 1 hundred
4 tens = 142
2 ones

with a remainder
of 1

$142 \ R1$

$3\overline{)427}$
-3
$\overline{12}$
-12
$\overline{07}$
-6
$\overline{1}$

✓ 142
$\times \ 3$
$\overline{426}$

$426+1=427$

5. Use any place value strategy to multiply or divide.

   a. $5316 \div 3$

$1,772$
$3\overline{)5316}$
-3
$\overline{23}$
-21
$\overline{21}$
-21
$\overline{06}$
-6
$\overline{0}$

✓ 1,772
$\times \ 3$
$\overline{5,316}$

   b. $3,809 \div 5$

$761 \ R4$
$5\overline{)3809}$
-35
$\overline{30}$
-30
$\overline{09}$
-5
$\overline{4}$

✓ 761
$\times \ 5$
$\overline{3,805}$

$3,805+4=3,809$

   c. 29×56

	50	6
9	450	54
20	1,000	120

56
$\times 29$
$\overline{54}$
450
120
$+1000$
$\overline{1,624}$

   d. 17×43

	40	3
7	280	21
10	400	30

43
$\times 17$
$\overline{21}$
280
30
$+400$
$\overline{731}$

Module 3:   Multi-Digit Multiplication and Division

EUREKA
MATH™

Directions: Solve using a model or equation. Show your work and write your answer as a statement.

6. A new grocery store is opening next week.

 a. The store's rectangular floor is 42 meters long and 39 meters wide. How many square meters of flooring do they need? Use estimation to assess the reasonableness of your answer.

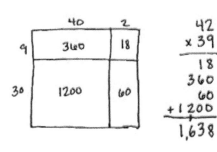

$$42 \times 39 \approx 40 \times 40$$
$$40 \times 40 = 1600$$

They need 1,638 square meters of flooring. My answer is reasonable because it is close to my estimate of 1,600 square meters.

 b. The store ordered small posters and large posters to promote their opening. 12 times as many small posters were ordered as large posters. If there were 48 large posters, how many more small posters were ordered than large posters?

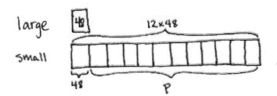

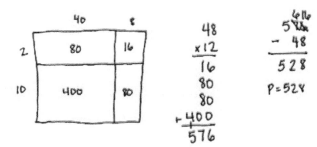

528 more small posters were ordered than large posters.

c. Uniforms are sold in packages of 8. The store's 127 employees will each be given 3 uniforms. How many packages will the store need to order?

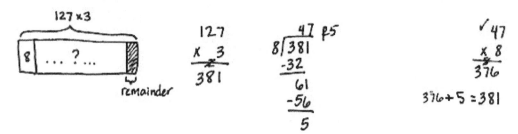

$$\begin{array}{r} 127 \\ \times\ \ 3 \\ \hline 381 \end{array}$$

$$\begin{array}{r} 47\ R5 \\ 8\overline{)381} \\ -32\ \ \ \\ \hline 61 \\ -56 \\ \hline 5 \end{array}$$

$$\begin{array}{r} \checkmark 47 \\ \times\ 8 \\ \hline 376 \end{array}$$

$376 + 5 = 381$

The store needs to order 48 packages. If they order 47 packages, only 376 uniforms will come and they will need 5 more uniforms.

d. There are 3 numbers for the combination to the store's safe. The first number is 17. The other 2 numbers can be multiplied together to give a product of 28. What are all of the possibilities for the other two numbers? Write your answers as multiplication equations, and then write all of the possible combinations to the safe.

$28 = 1 \times 28$
$28 = 28 \times 1$
$28 = 2 \times 14$
$28 = 14 \times 2$
$28 = 4 \times 7$
$28 = 7 \times 4$

The combination possibilities are:

17, 1, 28
17, 28, 1
17, 2, 14
17, 14, 2
17, 4, 7
17, 7, 4

Module 3:   Multi-Digit Multiplication and Division

EUREKA
MATH™

Answer Key

Eureka Math
Grade 4
Module 3

Special thanks go to the Gordon A. Cain Center and to the Department of Mathematics at Louisiana State University for their support in the development of *Eureka Math*.

For a free *Eureka Math* Teacher Resource Pack, Parent Tip Sheets, and more please visit www.Eureka.tools

Answer Key

GRADE 4 • MODULE 3

Multi-Digit Multiplication and Division

Lesson 1

Problem Set

1. a. 63 sq units; 32 units
   b. 54 sq units; 30 units
2. a. 22 cm; 30 sq cm
   b. 22 cm; 24 sq cm
3. a. 530 m
   b. 450 cm or 4 m 50 cm

4. a. 10 cm
   b. 7 cm
5. a. 40 cm
   b. 250 cm
6. a. 6 cm; 4 cm
   b. 12 m; 2 m

Exit Ticket

1. 16 sq cm; 20 cm
2. 892 m

Homework

1. a. 40 sq units; 26 units
   b. 35 sq units; 24 units
2. a. 20 cm; 21 sq cm
   b. 26 cm; 36 sq cm
3. a. 450 m
   b. 510 cm or 5 m 10 cm

4. a. 10 cm
   b. 5 m
5. a. 50 cm
   b. 350 m
6. a. 8 cm; 4 cm
   b. 3 m; 12 m

EUREKA
MATH™

Lesson 2

Problem Set

1.   a.   Width 4 ft, length 12 ft
      b.   32 ft
2.   a.   Diagram drawn; width 5 in, length 30 in
      b.   70 in; 150 sq in
3.   a.   6 cm
      b.   Diagram drawn; width 18 cm, length 7 cm
      c.   50 cm

4.   a.   Diagram drawn and labeled; 18 ft
      b.   Diagram drawn and labeled; 36 ft
      c.   The perimeter of the second rectangle is twice the first rectangle.
      d.   80 sq ft
      e.   4
      f.   When the side lengths are doubled, the perimeter will double but the area will quadruple.

Exit Ticket

1.   a.   Width 2 ft, length 12 ft
      b.   28 ft
2.   a.   Diagram drawn; width 4 ft, length 12 ft
      b.   32 ft; 48 sq ft

Homework

1.   a.   Width 7 ft, length 21 ft
      b.   56 ft
2.   a.   Diagram drawn; width 3 in, length 12 in
      b.   30 in; 36 sq in
3.   a.   4 cm
      b.   Diagram drawn; width 9 cm, length 12 cm
      c.   42 cm

4.   a.   Diagram drawn and labeled; 16 ft
      b.   Diagram drawn and labeled; 32 ft
      c.   The perimeter of the living room rug is double the perimeter of the bedroom rug.
      d.   60 sq ft
      e.   4
      f.   When the side lengths are doubled, the perimeter will double but the area will quadruple.

Lesson 3

Sprint

Side A

1.	4	12.	49	23.	7	34.	4
2.	2	13.	64	24.	9	35.	8
3.	9	14.	8	25.	5	36.	49
4.	3	15.	100	26.	8	37.	3
5.	25	16.	10	27.	16	38.	9
6.	5	17.	9	28.	4	39.	64
7.	1	18.	81	29.	8	40.	4
8.	1	19.	5	30.	25	41.	7
9.	4	20.	9	31.	3	42.	81
10.	16	21.	4	32.	9	43.	6
11.	7	22.	4	33.	36	44.	100

Side B

1.	25	12.	36	23.	8	34.	3
2.	5	13.	81	24.	9	35.	9
3.	4	14.	9	25.	3	36.	49
4.	2	15.	100	26.	7	37.	4
5.	9	16.	10	27.	16	38.	7
6.	3	17.	7	28.	2	39.	64
7.	1	18.	49	29.	7	40.	3
8.	1	19.	4	30.	25	41.	8
9.	4	20.	8	31.	4	42.	81
10.	16	21.	4	32.	8	43.	7
11.	6	22.	5	33.	36	44.	100

Module 3:   Multi-Digit Multiplication and Division

©2015 Great Minds. eureka-math.org
G4-M3-TE-B2-1.3.1-01.2016

EUREKA
MATH

Problem Set

1. 70 ft
2. 32 sq ft
3. 5 ft
4. 36 sq ft

Exit Ticket

Poster: Length 9 in, width 3 in

Banner: Length 10 in, width 2 in

Homework

1. 44 in
2. 11 sq cm
3. 3 ft
4. 32 sq in

Lesson 4

Problem Set

1. Disks drawn; 500; 500; 5 hundreds

2. Disks drawn; 5,000; 5,000; 5 thousands

3. a. 60
   b. 100
   c. 6
   d. 40
   e. 100
   f. 1,000
   g. 9,000
   h. 90
   i. 9

4. Disks drawn; 120; 12 tens

5. Disks drawn; 1,800; 1,800; 18 hundreds

6. Disks drawn; 25,000; 25,000; 25 thousands

7. 10; 10; 120

8. 2, 100; 6, 100; 600

9. 4, 4, 1,000; 16, 1,000; 16,000

10. 5, 4, 1,000; 20, 1,000; 20,000

Exit Ticket

a. 50

b. 100

c. 5

d. 20

e. 100

f. 200

g. 1,800

h. 320

i. 48

j. 240

k. 3,000

l. 40,000

        Module 3:   Multi-Digit Multiplication and Division

EUREKA
MATH™

Homework

1. Disks drawn; 700; 700; 7 hundreds

2. Disks drawn; 7,000; 7,000; 7 thousands

3. a. 80

   b. 100

   c. 8

   d. 30

   e. 1,000

   f. 100

   g. 4,000

   h. 40

   i. 4

4. Disks drawn; 150; 15 tens

5. Disks drawn; 1,700; 1,700; 17 hundreds

6. Disks drawn; 36,000; 36,000; 36 thousands

7. 10; 10; 160

8. 4, 100; 8, 100; 800

9. 5, 5, 1,000; 25, 1,000; 25,000

10. 7, 6, 1,000; 42, 1,000; 42,000

Lesson 5

Problem Set

1. Disks drawn; 6; 3, 6; 6
2. Disks drawn; 60; 3, 6 tens; 60
3. Disks drawn; 600; 3 hundreds, 6 hundreds; 600
4. Disks drawn; 6,000; 2, 3 thousands, 6 thousands; 6,000
5. a. 140
   b. 180
   c. 1,200
   d. 1,600
   e. 210
   f. 360
   g. 1,600
   h. 32,000
   i. 150
   j. 300
   k. 2,000
   l. 40,000

6. 180 balloons
7. 180 baseball cards
8. 3 fish

Exit Ticket

1. Disks drawn; 800; 2 hundreds, 8 hundreds; 800
2. Disks drawn; 8,000; 4, 2 thousands, 8 thousands; 8,000
3. a. 90
   b. 160
   c. 2,400
   d. 1,800
   e. 640
   f. 120
   g. 3,000
   h. 40,000
4. 210 hours

EUREKA
MATH™

Homework

1. Disks drawn; 10; 2,10; 10

2. Disks drawn; 100; 2, 10 tens; 100

3. Disks drawn; 1,000; 2 hundreds, 10 hundreds; 1,000

4. Disks drawn; 10,000; 5, 2 thousands, 10 thousands; 10,000

5. a. 180

   b. 420

   c. 4,900

   d. 2,700

   e. 810

   f. 280

   g. 3,600

   h. 48,000

   i. 350

   j. 400

   k. 1,000

   l. 30,000

6. 1,800 chicken nuggets

7. 240 stickers

8. 3 flowers

Lesson 6

Problem Set

1. Disks drawn; 800; 800; 800
2. Area model drawn; 8 hundreds
3. Area model drawn; 12 hundreds; 1,200
4. Area model drawn; 10 hundreds; 1,000
5. 400; 4

6. 1,200; tens, 12
7. 1,400; 7, 2, hundreds
8. 2,100; 7 tens, 3 tens, 21
9. 3,600 seats
10. $4,000

Exit Ticket

1. Disks drawn; 600; 600; 600
2. Area model drawn; 6 hundreds
3. 1,200 pages

Homework

1. Disks drawn; 1,800; 1,800; 1,800
2. Area model drawn; 18 hundreds
3. Area model drawn; 4 hundreds; 400
4. Area model drawn; 24 hundreds; 2,400
5. 1,000; 10
6. 1,500; tens, 15
7. 1,200; 6, 2, hundreds
8. 2,800; 4 tens, 7 tens, 28
9. 3,600 seconds
10. 2,000 pieces of paper

Module 3:   Multi-Digit Multiplication and Division

EUREKA
MATH™

Lesson 7

Sprint

Side A

1.	6	12.	900	23.	35	34.	54,000
2.	60	13.	9,000	24.	3,500	35.	8,100
3.	600	14.	12,000	25.	24	36.	64,000
4.	6,000	15.	1,200	26.	240	37.	490
5.	6,000	16.	120	27.	36	38.	3,600
6.	8	17.	15	28.	36,000	39.	5,600
7.	80	18.	1,500	29.	42	40.	63,000
8.	800	19.	14	30.	4,200	41.	1,000
9.	8,000	20.	140	31.	72	42.	300
10.	9	21.	16	32.	720	43.	20,000
11.	90	22.	16,000	33.	54	44.	4,000

Side B

1.	8	12.	600	23.	45	34.	54,000
2.	80	13.	6,000	24.	4,500	35.	6,400
3.	800	14.	12,000	25.	32	36.	81,000
4.	8,000	15.	1,200	26.	320	37.	4,900
5.	8,000	16.	120	27.	27	38.	360
6.	9	17.	15	28.	27,000	39.	5,600
7.	90	18.	150	29.	42	40.	63,000
8.	900	19.	12	30.	4,200	41.	100
9.	9,000	20.	120	31.	56	42.	3,000
10.	6	21.	16	32.	560	43.	2,000
11.	60	22.	1,600	33.	54	44.	40,000

Module 3:   Multi-Digit Multiplication and Division

Problem Set

1. Disks drawn and partial products recorded

    a. Answer provided

    b. 2×4 tens + 2×3 ones; 86

    c. 3×4 tens + 3×3 ones; 129

    d. 4×4 tens + 4×3 ones; 172

2. Disks drawn and partial products recorded

    a. 72

    b. 183

    c. 336

Exit Ticket

1. Disks drawn and partial products recorded; 246

2. Disks drawn and partial products recorded; 217

Homework

1. Disks drawn and partial products recorded

    a. 3×2 tens + 3×4 ones; 72

    b. 3×4 tens + 3×2 ones; 126

    c. 4×3 tens + 4×4 ones; 136

2. Disks drawn and partial products recorded

    a. 108

    b. 210

3. No; explanations will vary.

©2015 Great Minds. eureka-math.org
G4-M3-TE-B2-1.3.1-01.2016

EUREKA
MATH

Lesson 8

Problem Set

1. Disks drawn and partial products recorded

    a. 2, 1, 3; 213

    b. 2×2 hundreds + 2×1 ten + 2×3 ones; 426

    c. 3×2 hundreds + 3×1 ten + 3×4 ones; 642

    d. 3×1 thousand + 3×2 hundreds + 3×5 tens + 3×4 ones; 3,762

2. Disks drawn and partial products recorded

    a. 636

    b. 8,072

    c. 7,638

    d. 4,221

3. 720 bagels

Exit Ticket

1. Disks drawn and partial products recorded; 2,052

2. Disks drawn and partial products recorded; 3,162

Homework

1. Disks drawn and partial products recorded

    a. 4 hundreds, 2 tens, 4; 848

    b. 3×4 hundreds + 3×2 tens + 3×4 ones; 1,272

    c. 4×1 thousand + 4×4 hundreds + 4×2 tens + 4×4 ones; 5,696

2. Disks drawn and partial products recorded

    a. 1,234

    b. 3,210

    c. 9,102

3. a. 966 m

    b. 2,898 m

Lesson 9

Problem Set

1. a. 136; 136
    b. 672; 672
2. a. 753
    b. 810
    c. 2,736
    d. 1,620
    e. 1,580
    f. 2,352

3. 602
4. 4,113
5. 90 cm
6. $952
7. 1,008 g

Exit Ticket

1. a. 5,472
    b. 4,018
2. 92 years old

Homework

1. a. 92; 92
    b. 1,260; 1,260
2. a. 928
    b. 852
    c. 2,198
    d. 1,320
    e. 4,056
    f. 3,456

3. 432
4. 1,050 points
5. $477
6. $1,316
7. 512 pages

Module 3:   Multi-Digit Multiplication and Division

EUREKA
MATH™

Lesson 10

Problem Set

1. a. 126

   b. 252

   c. 2,586

   d. 1,293

   e. 18,636

   f. 9,318

   g. 17,236

   h. 34,472

2. 1,095 days

3. 1,848 m

4. 42,240 ft

Exit Ticket

1. a. 14,088

   b. 11,753

2. 4,820 sunflowers

Homework

1. a. 123

   b. 369

   c. 1,001

   d. 2,002

   e. 8,192

   f. 16,384

   g. 32,768

   h. 32,768

2. 768 fluid oz

3. 2,748 days

4. 8,192 megabytes

©2015 Great Minds. eureka-math.org
G4-M3-TE-B2-1.3.1-01.2016

Lesson 11

Problem Set

1. Standard algorithm, partial products method, and area model used

   a. 1,700; 400, 20, 5

   b. 3,738; 500, 30, 4; 7, 500, 7, 30, 7, 4

   c. 1,672; 8, 200, 9; 8, 200, 8, 9

2. 774; partial products method used

3. 1,868; tape diagram drawn

4. 35,917

5. 8,415

6. 23,850 pounds

Exit Ticket

1. 11,236

2. 6,075 pages

Homework

1. Standard algorithm, partial products method and area model used

   a. 2,416; 300, 2

   b. 1,080; 200, 10, 6; 5, 200, 5, 10, 5, 6

   c. 5,337; 9, 500, 90, 3; 9, 500, 9, 90, 9, 3

2. 1,900 people; partial products method used

3. 2,304; tape diagram drawn

4. 18,759

5. 21,511

6. 18,744 pounds

Module 3: Multi-Digit Multiplication and Division

©2015 Great Minds. eureka-math.org
G4-M3-TE-B2-1.3.1-01.2016

Lesson 12

Problem Set

1. 657¢ or $6.57

2. 11,508 L

3. 589 marbles

4. a. Equations will vary.

   b. Word problems and units will vary; 3,262

Exit Ticket

872 beads

Homework

1. 644 stickers

2. 12,236 copies

3. 285 bars

4. a. Equations will vary.

   b. Word problems will vary; 3,142 m

Lesson 13

Sprint

Side A

1. 4	12. 115	23. 63	34. 6,339
2. 40	13. 9	24. 363	35. 6,393
3. 44	14. 120	25. 84	36. 6,933
4. 2	15. 129	26. 284	37. 96
5. 40	16. 8	27. 484	38. 175
6. 42	17. 140	28. 684	39. 162
7. 6	18. 148	29. 884	40. 378
8. 90	19. 6	30. 9	41. 500
9. 96	20. 180	31. 39	42. 642
10. 15	21. 186	32. 639	43. 10,426
11. 100	22. 189	33. 3,639	44. 8,540

Side B

1. 6	12. 125	23. 84	34. 4,226
2. 60	13. 16	24. 484	35. 4,262
3. 66	14. 120	25. 48	36. 4,622
4. 2	15. 136	26. 248	37. 92
5. 60	16. 8	27. 448	38. 265
6. 62	17. 180	28. 648	39. 135
7. 9	18. 188	29. 848	40. 216
8. 60	19. 6	30. 6	41. 645
9. 69	20. 120	31. 26	42. 500
10. 25	21. 126	32. 426	43. 10,624
11. 100	22. 129	33. 2,426	44. 4,940

Module 3:   Multi-Digit Multiplication and Division

EUREKA MATH

Problem Set

1. $748

2. 216 lb

3. 1,362 lb

4. 7,183 pages

Exit Ticket

1. $1,512

2. $1,920

3. David; $408

Homework

1. $534

2. $245

3. 1,972 seats

4. 5,191 reams of paper

Lesson 14

Problem Set

1. 9 pairs; yes; 1 sock

2. 4 bows; yes; 4 in

3. 5 chairs; yes; 2 chairs

4. 5 days

5. 72 apples; 4 apples

6. 7 vans

Exit Ticket

8 groups; 9 chaperones

Homework

1. 8 booklets; yes; 1 sheet

2. 8 booklets; yes; 2 in

3. 4 groups; 5 students

4. 8 days; Day 9

5. 8 rows; 3 soldiers

6. 9 groups; 6 students

Module 3:   Multi-Digit Multiplication and Division

EUREKA
MATH™

Lesson 15

Problem Set

Array and area model drawn for each solution

1. 3, 0; yes

2. 3, 1; no, one small square outside of the larger rectangle

3. Quotient 9, Remainder 2

4. Quotient 4, Remainder 2

5. Quotient 10, Remainder 3

6. Quotient 8, Remainder 3

Exit Ticket

Array and area model drawn for each solution

1. Quotient 5, Remainder 2

2. Quotient 5, Remainder 2

Homework

Array and area model drawn for each solution

1. 6, 0; yes

2. 6, 1; no, one small square outside of the larger rectangle

3. Quotient 6, Remainder 2

4. Quotient 5, Remainder 4

5. Quotient 6, Remainder 1

6. Quotient 5, Remainder 6

©2015 Great Minds. eureka-math.org
G4-M3-TE-B2-1.3.1-01.2016

Lesson 16

Problem Set

1. Disks drawn 3R 1; 3; 1; 6; 7

2. Disks drawn 13R 1; 13; 1; $13 \times 2 = 26$, $26 + 1 = 27$

3. Disks drawn 3R 2; 2; 2; $2 \times 3 = 6$, $6 + 2 = 8$

4. Disks drawn 12R 2; 12; 2; $12 \times 3 = 36$, $36 + 2 = 38$

5. Disks drawn 1R 2; 1; 2; $4 \times 1 = 4$, $4 + 2 = 6$

6. Disks drawn 21R 2; 21; 2; $4 \times 21 = 84$, $84 + 2 = 86$

Exit Ticket

1. Disks drawn 1R 2; 1; 2; $1 \times 3 = 3$, $3 + 2 = 5$

2. Disks drawn 21R 2; 21; 2; $3 \times 21 = 63$, $63 + 2 = 65$

Homework

1. Disks drawn 2R 1; 2; 1; 6, $6 + 1 = 7$

2. Disks drawn 22R 1; 22; 1; $22 \times 3 = 66$, $66 + 1 = 67$

3. Disks drawn 2R 1; 2; 1; $2 \times 2 = 4$, $4 + 1 = 5$

4. Disks drawn 42R 1; 42; 1; $42 \times 2 = 84$, $84 + 1 = 85$

5. Disks drawn 1R 1; 1; 1; $1 \times 4 = 4$, $4 + 1 = 5$

6. Disks drawn 21R 1; 21; 1; $4 \times 21 = 84$, $84 + 1 = 85$

EUREKA
MATH™

Lesson 17

Problem Set

1. Disks drawn; 2; 1; 4, 2 × 2 = 4, 4 + 1 = 5
2. Disks drawn; 25; 0; 2 × 25 = 50
3. Disks drawn; 2; 1; 3 × 2 = 6, 6 + 1 = 7
4. Disks drawn; 25; 0; 3 × 25 = 75
5. Disks drawn; 2; 1; 4 × 2 = 8, 8 + 1 = 9
6. Disks drawn; 23; 0; 23 × 4 = 92

Exit Ticket

1. Disks drawn; 1; 1; 4 × 1 = 4, 4 + 1 = 5
2. Disks drawn; 14; 0; 14 × 4 = 56

Homework

1. Disks drawn; 3; 1; 3 × 2 = 6, 6 + 1 = 7
2. Disks drawn; 36; 1; 2 × 36 = 72, 72 + 1 = 73
3. Disks drawn; 1; 2; 1 × 4 = 4, 4 + 2 = 6
4. Disks drawn; 15; 2; 4 × 15 = 60, 60 + 2 = 62
5. Disks drawn; 2; 2; 3 × 2 = 6, 6 + 2 = 8
6. Disks drawn; 28; 0; 3 × 28 = 84

Lesson 18

Problem Set

1. $23; 23 \times 2 = 46$
2. $32; 32 \times 3 = 96$
3. $17; 17 \times 5 = 85$
4. $13; 13 \times 4 = 52$
5. $17 R2; 17 \times 3 = 51, 51 + 2 = 53$
6. $23 R3; 23 \times 4 = 92, 92 + 3 = 95$

7. $14 R5; 14 \times 6 = 84, 84 + 5 = 89$
8. $16; 16 \times 6 = 96$
9. $20; 20 \times 3 = 60$
10. $15; 15 \times 4 = 60$
11. $11 R7; 11 \times 8 = 88, 88 + 7 = 95$
12. $13 R4; 13 \times 7 = 91, 91 + 4 = 95$

Exit Ticket

1. $13 R2; 13 \times 7 = 91, 91 + 2 = 93$
2. $12 R3; 12 \times 8 = 96, 96 + 3 = 99$

Homework

1. $42; 42 \times 2 = 84$
2. $21; 21 \times 4 = 84$
3. $16; 16 \times 3 = 48$
4. $16; 16 \times 5 = 80$
5. $15 R4; 15 \times 5 = 75, 75 + 4 = 79$
6. $22 R3; 22 \times 4 = 88, 88 + 3 = 91$

7. $15 R1; 15 \times 6 = 90, 90 + 1 = 91$
8. $13; 13 \times 7 = 91$
9. $29; 29 \times 3 = 87$
10. $14 R3; 14 \times 6 = 84, 84 + 3 = 87$
11. $11 R6; 11 \times 8 = 88, 88 + 6 = 94$
12. $15 R4; 15 \times 6 = 90, 90 + 4 = 94$

EUREKA
MATH™

Lesson 19

Sprint

Side A

1.	10	12.	21	23.	34	34.	17
2.	2	13.	1	24.	32	35.	10
3.	12	14.	20	25.	43	36.	20
4.	10	15.	21	26.	31	37.	15
5.	2	16.	1	27.	22	38.	18
6.	12	17.	20	28.	33	39.	10
7.	10	18.	21	29.	22	40.	13
8.	2	19.	8	30.	33	41.	15
9.	12	20.	10	31.	10	42.	20
10.	1	21.	12	32.	20	43.	19
11.	20	22.	14	33.	15	44.	17

Side B

1.	10	12.	31	23.	43	34.	16
2.	3	13.	1	24.	23	35.	10
3.	13	14.	30	25.	34	36.	20
4.	10	15.	31	26.	32	37.	15
5.	3	16.	2	27.	22	38.	19
6.	13	17.	10	28.	33	39.	10
7.	20	18.	12	29.	22	40.	12
8.	1	19.	10	30.	44	41.	14
9.	21	20.	12	31.	10	42.	20
10.	1	21.	14	32.	20	43.	18
11.	30	22.	16	33.	15	44.	16

EUREKA
MATH™

Module 3:   Multi-Digit Multiplication and Division

563

©2015 Great Minds. eureka-math.org
G4-M3-TE-B2-1.3.1-01.2016

Problem Set

1. Equation accurately modeled; remainder circled

2. Remainder is greater than divisor; explanations will vary.

3. Equation accurately modeled; 1 remaining ten is decomposed into 10 ones.

4. a. Picture accurately models division; yes

    b. Explanations will vary.

5. Answers will vary.

Exit Ticket

1. Disks drawn; 16; yes; 1

2. No; she can fill 11 pages completely; explanations will vary.

Homework

1. Equation accurately modeled; remainder circled

2. Remainder is greater than divisor; explanations will vary.

3. Equation accurately modeled; 2 remaining tens are decomposed into 20 ones.

4. a. Picture accurately models division; yes

    b. Explanations will vary.

5. Answers will vary.

©2015 Great Minds. eureka-math.org
G4-M3-TE-B2-1.3.1-01.2016

Lesson 20

Problem Set

1. a. $72 \div 4 = 18$

   b. Whole: 72; parts: 40 and 32; 40, 4, 32, 4, 10, 8, 18

2. 15; whole: 45; parts: 30 and 15; $(30 \div 3) + (15 \div 3) = 10 + 5 = 15$; area model and number bond drawn

3. 16; whole: 64; parts: 40 and 24; area model and number bond drawn; solved with distributive property or standard algorithm

4. 23; solved with area model; explanations will vary.

5. 12; solved with area model and standard algorithm

Exit Ticket

1. $72 \div 3 = 24$

2. 14; solved with area model, number bond, and written method

Homework

1. a. $54 \div 3 = 18$

   b. Whole: 54; parts: 30 and 24; 30, 3, 24, 3, 10, 8, 18

2. 14; whole: 42; parts: 30 and 12; $(30 \div 3) + (12 \div 3) = 10 + 4 = 14$; area model and number bond drawn

3. 15; whole: 60; part: 40; part: 20; area model and number bond drawn; solved with distributive property or standard algorithm

4. 18; solved with area model; explanations will vary.

5. 16; solved with area model and standard algorithm

Lesson 21

Sprint

Side A

1.	4	12.	1 R1	23.	3	34.	1 R4
2.	4 R1	13.	2 R1	24.	3 R1	35.	1
3.	1	14.	2 R2	25.	1	36.	1
4.	1 R1	15.	3	26.	1 R1	37.	3 R1
5.	1 R2	16.	1 R2	27.	1 R2	38.	3 R3
6.	1 R3	17.	1 R3	28.	1 R3	39.	3 R3
7.	1 R2	18.	1	29.	1	40.	3 R3
8.	2	19.	1 R1	30.	1 R1	41.	3 R5
9.	2	20.	1	31.	2	42.	7 R1
10.	2 R1	21.	1 R1	32.	2 R1	43.	8 R5
11.	1	22.	1	33.	3	44.	9 R1

Side B

1.	1 R1	12.	1 R1	23.	2	34.	4 R1
2.	1	13.	1	24.	2 R1	35.	4
3.	1 R3	14.	1 R1	25.	2	36.	4 R5
4.	1 R2	15.	1 R1	26.	2 R1	37.	5 R5
5.	1	16.	1 R2	27.	3	38.	2 R5
6.	1 R1	17.	1	28.	2 R2	39.	6 R6
7.	1 R3	18.	1 R1	29.	1 R4	40.	6 R3
8.	1 R2	19.	3	30.	1	41.	7 R5
9.	1 R2	20.	3 R1	31.	1 R1	42.	8 R5
10.	2	21.	1 R3	32.	1	43.	7 R5
11.	1	22.	1 R2	33.	1	44.	7 R7

EUREKA MATH™

Problem Set

1. 18 R1; answer includes area model, long division, and distributive property

2. 25 R1; answer includes area model, long division, and distributive property

3. a. $53 \div 4 = 13$ R1

    b. $(40 \div 4) + (12 \div 4) = 10 + 3 = 13$

4. 16; answer includes area model and long division or distributive property

5. 16 R1; answer includes area model and long division or distributive property

6. 14; answer includes area model and long division or distributive property

7. 14 R2; answer includes area model and long division or distributive property

8. 13 R1; answer includes area model and long division or distributive property

9. 26 R1; answer includes area model and long division or distributive property

10. 12 groups; 1 student

Exit Ticket

1. $59 \div 2 = 29$ R1

2. 23 R1; answer includes area model, long division, and distributive property

Homework

1. 17 R1; answer includes area model, long division, and distributive property

2. 26 R1; answer includes area model, long division, and distributive property

3. a. $98 \div 4 = 24$ R2

    b. $(40 \div 4) + (40 \div 4) + (16 \div 4) = 10 + 10 + 4 = 24$

4. 14; answer includes area model and long division or distributive property

5. 14 R1; answer includes area model and long division or distributive property

6. 13; answer includes area model and long division or distributive property

7. 13 R2; answer includes area model and long division or distributive property

8. 12 R1; answer includes area model and long division or distributive property

9. 24 R1; answer includes area model and long division or distributive property

10. 24 lunch trays; 1 lunch tray

Lesson 22

Problem Set

1. a. Answer provided

 b. $1 \times 6 = 6$, $2 \times 3 = 6$; 1, 2, 3, 6; C

 c. $1 \times 7 = 7$; 1, 7; P

 d. $1 \times 9 = 9$, $3 \times 3 = 9$; 1, 3, 9; C

 e. $1 \times 12 = 12$, $2 \times 6 = 12$; $3 \times 4 = 12$; 1, 2, 3, 4, 6, 12; C

 f. $1 \times 13 = 13$; 1, 13; P

 g. $1 \times 15 = 15$, $3 \times 5 = 15$; 1, 3, 5, 15; C

 h. $1 \times 16 = 16$, $2 \times 8 = 16$, $4 \times 4 = 16$; 1, 2, 4, 8, 16; C

 i. $1 \times 18 = 18$, $2 \times 9 = 18$, $3 \times 6 = 18$; 1, 2, 3, 6, 9, 18; C

 j. $1 \times 19 = 19$; 1, 19; P

 k. $1 \times 21 = 21$; $3 \times 7 = 21$; 1, 3, 7, 21; C

 l. $1 \times 24 = 24$, $2 \times 12 = 24$, $3 \times 8 = 24$, $4 \times 6 = 24$; 1, 2, 3, 4, 6, 8, 12, 24; C

2. For 25: (1, 25); (5, 5); composite; more than 2 factors

 For 28: (1, 28); (2, 14); (4, 7); composite; more than 2 factors

 For 29: (1, 29); prime; only 2 factors

3. a. 2, 3, 5, 7, 11, 13, 17, 19

 b. 2 is a prime and even number.

4. Incorrect; 3 is not a factor of 28.

Exit Ticket

 a. $1 \times 9 = 9$, $3 \times 3 = 9$; 1, 3, 9; C

 b. $1 \times 12 = 12$, $2 \times 6 = 12$; $3 \times 4 = 12$; 1, 2, 3, 4, 6, 12; C

 c. $1 \times 19 = 19$; 1, 19; P

EUREKA
MATH™

Homework

1. a. Answer provided

    b. $1 \times 10 = 10$, $2 \times 5 = 10$; 1,2, 5, 10; C

    c. $1 \times 11 = 11$; 1, 11; P

    d. $1 \times 14 = 14$, $2 \times 7 = 14$; 1, 2, 7, 14; C

    e. $1 \times 17 = 17$; 1, 17; P

    f. $1 \times 20 = 20$, $2 \times 10 = 20$, $4 \times 5 = 20$; 1, 2, 4, 5, 10, 20; C

    g. $1 \times 22 = 22$, $2 \times 11 = 22$; 1, 2, 11, 22; C

    h. $1 \times 23 = 23$; 1, 23; P

    i. $1 \times 25 = 25$, $5 \times 5 = 25$; 1, 5, 25; C

    j. $1 \times 26 = 26$; $2 \times 13 = 26$; 1, 2, 13, 26; C

    k. $1 \times 27 = 27$, $3 \times 9 = 27$; 1, 3, 9, 27; C

    l. $1 \times 28 = 28$, $2 \times 14 = 28$, $4 \times 7 = 28$; 1, 2, 4, 7, 14, 28; C

2. For 19: (1, 19); prime; only 2 factors

    For 21: (1, 21); (3, 7); composite; more than 2 factors

    For 24: (1, 24); (2, 12); (3, 8); (4, 6); composite; more than 2 factors

3. a. 1, 3, 5, 7, 9, 11, 13, 15, 17, 19

    b. 9 and 15 are odd and composite

4. Correct; 3 is a factor of 27

Lesson 23

Problem Set

1. Explanations may vary.

    a. Yes

    b. No

    c. Yes

    d. Yes

    e. Yes

    f. Yes

    g. No

    h. No

2. a. 4; 4; 4; 24

    b. 9; 3; 3; 3; 36

3. $(4 \times 2) \times 7 = 4 \times (2 \times 7) = 4 \times 14 = 56$

    $(4 \times 2) \times 9 = 4 \times (2 \times 9) = 4 \times 18 = 72$

    $(4 \times 2) \times 10 = 4 \times (2 \times 10) = 4 \times 20 = 80$

4. Explanations may vary.

Exit Ticket

1. Explanations may vary.

    a. Yes

    b. No

    c. Yes

    d. Yes

2. Explanations may vary.

Homework

1. Explanations may vary.

    a. Yes

    b. No

    c. Yes

    d. Yes

    e. Yes

    f. Yes

    g. No

    h. No

2. a. 3; 3; 3; 4; 12

    b. 6; 2; 2; 2; 30

3. $(5 \times 2) \times 7 = 5 \times (2 \times 7) = 5 \times 14 = 70$

    $(5 \times 2) \times 8 = 5 \times (2 \times 8) = 5 \times 16 = 80$

    $(5 \times 2) \times 9 = 5 \times (2 \times 9) = 5 \times 18 = 90$

4. Explanations may vary.

EUREKA
MATH™

Lesson 24

Problem Set

1. a. 100, 105, 110, 115, 120, 125, 130, 135, 140, 145, 150, 155, 160, 165, 170, 175, 180, 185, 190, 195, 200, 205, 210, etc.

   b. 20, 24, 28, 32, 36, 40, 44, 48, 52, 56, 60, 64, 68, 72, 76, 80, 84, 88, 92, 96, 100, 104, 108, 112, 116, 120, etc.

   c. 36, 42, 48, 54, 60, 66, 72, 78, 84, 90, 96, 102, 108, 114, 120, 126, 132, 138, 144, 150, 156, 162, 168, 174, 180, etc.

2. 1, 2, 3, 4, 6, 8, 12, 24

3. a. Yes; yes

   b. No; no

   c. Yes; yes

4. Yes; explanations will vary.

5. a. Multiples of 2 circled red; 0, 2, 4, 6, 8

   b. Multiples of 3 shaded green; answers will vary; sums are multiples of 3 or divisible by 3.

   c. Multiples of 5 circled blue; 0, 5

   d. Multiples of 10 crossed out; zero in the ones place

Exit Ticket

1. 55; 66; 77; 88; 99

2. 21, 35, 42, 49, 56, 63, 70

3. a. 1, 2, 3, 6, 9, 18

   b. 1, 2, 3, 6, 9, 18

   c. Yes; explanations will vary.

Homework

1. a. 75, 80, 85, 90, 95, 100, 105, 110, 115, 120, 125, 130, 135, 140, 145, 150, 155, 160, 165, 170, 175, 180, 185, etc.

    b. 40, 44, 48, 52, 56, 60, 64, 68, 72, 76, 80, 84, 88, 92, 96, 100, 104, 108, 112, 116, 120, 124, 128, 132, 136, 140, etc.

    c. 24, 30, 36, 42, 48, 54, 60, 66, 72, 78, 84, 90, 96, 102, 108, 114, 120, 126, 132, 138, 144, 150, etc.

2. 1, 2, 3, 5, 6, 10, 30

3. a. Yes; yes

    b. Yes; no

    c. No; no

4. No; explanations will vary.

5. a. Multiples of 6 underlined; 0, 2, 4, 6, 8

    b. Multiples of 4 identified; 2, 6

    c. 0, 4, 8; answers will vary.

    d. Multiples of 9 circled; sum is 9.

EUREKA
MATH™

Lesson 25

Problem Set

1. Chart completed per directions
2. a. 2, 3, 5, 7, 11, 13, 17, 19, 23, 29, 31, 37, 41, 43, 47, 53, 59, 61, 67, 71, 73, 79, 83, 89, 97
   b. Not multiples of any numbers except one and themselves
   c. Composite numbers
   d. Prime numbers

Exit Ticket

1. 4, 6, 8, 9, 10, 12, 14, 15, 16, 18, 20, 21, 22, 24, 25, 26, 27, 28, 30 crossed off
2. 2, 3, 5, 7, 11, 13, 17, 19, 23, 29, 31 circled
3. 1

Homework

1. Answers will vary.
2. Composite
3. Prime
4. 1; neither prime nor composite

Lesson 26

Problem Set

1. Disks accurately drawn

    a. 3; 3

    b. 30; 3 tens

    c. 300; 6 hundreds, 3 hundreds

    d. 3,000; 6 thousands, 3 thousands

2. Disks accurately drawn

    a. 4; 4

    b. 40; 12 tens, 4 tens

    c. 400; 12 hundreds, 4 hundreds

3. a. Answer provided

    b. 300; 6 hundreds ÷ 2 = 3 hundreds

    c. 200; 8 hundreds ÷ 4 = 2 hundreds

    d. 300; 9 hundreds ÷ 3 = 3 hundreds

    e. 50; 5

    f. 60; 24 tens ÷ 4 = 6 tens

    g. 90; 45 tens ÷ 5 = 9 tens

    h. 40; 20 tens ÷ 5 = 4 tens

    i. 900; 9

    j. 600; 24 hundreds ÷ 4 = 6 hundreds

    k. 800; 24 hundreds ÷ 3 = 8 hundreds

    l. 800; 40 hundreds ÷ 5 = 8 hundreds

4. 700 kg

5. 70 stickers

6. $400

Exit Ticket

1. a. 2

    b. 200; 12 hundreds ÷ 6 = 2 hundreds

    c. 300; 21 hundreds ÷ 7 = 3 hundreds

    d. 400; 32 hundreds ÷ 8 = 4 hundreds

2. 40 pennies

EUREKA
MATH™

Homework

1. Disks accurately drawn

    a. 2; 2

    b. 20; 2 tens

    c. 200; 6 hundreds, 2 hundreds

    d. 2,000; 6 thousands, 2 thousands

2. Disks accurately drawn

    a. 3; 3

    b. 30; 12 tens, 3 tens

    c. 300; 12 hundreds, 3 hundreds

3. a. Answer provided

    b. 300; 9 hundreds ÷ 3 = 3 hundreds

    c. 200; 4 hundreds ÷ 2 = 2 hundreds

    d. 100; 3 hundreds ÷ 3 = 1 hundred

    e. 50; 5

    f. 80; 16 tens ÷ 2 = 8 tens

    g. 80; 40 tens ÷ 5 = 8 tens

    h. 60; 30 tens ÷ 5 = 6 tens

    i. 400; 4

    j. 400; 16 hundreds ÷ 4 = 4 hundreds

    k. 600; 24 hundreds ÷ 4 = 6 hundreds

    l. 600; 30 hundreds ÷ 5 = 6 hundreds

4. 4,000 L

5. 70 mL

6. $600

Lesson 27

Sprint

Side A

1.	3	12.	11	23.	41	34.	71
2.	3	13.	13	24.	43	35.	73
3.	3	14.	17	25.	47	36.	79
4.	5	15.	19	26.	53	37.	83
5.	5	16.	23	27.	59	38.	2
6.	5	17.	19	28.	97	39.	17
7.	7	18.	29	29.	91	40.	5
8.	11	19.	31	30.	97	41.	59
9.	11	20.	37	31.	89	42.	31
10.	17	21.	2	32.	61	43.	2
11.	19	22.	2	33.	67	44.	43

Side B

1.	5	12.	13	23.	41	34.	71
2.	5	13.	11	24.	43	35.	73
3.	5	14.	17	25.	47	36.	67
4.	7	15.	19	26.	53	37.	59
5.	7	16.	23	27.	59	38.	2
6.	7	17.	19	28.	97	39.	19
7.	3	18.	29	29.	91	40.	5
8.	11	19.	31	30.	97	41.	59
9.	11	20.	37	31.	89	42.	41
10.	17	21.	2	32.	67	43.	2
11.	19	22.	2	33.	61	44.	67

EUREKA MATH™

Problem Set

1. Disks accurately drawn

   a. 162

   b. 172

   c. 161

   d. 183

2. Disks accurately drawn; algorithm accurately recorded

   a. 131

   b. 242

   c. 172

Exit Ticket

1. 141; Disks accurately drawn; algorithm accurately recorded

2. 141; Disks accurately drawn; algorithm accurately recorded

Homework

1. Disks accurately drawn

   a. 173

   b. 264

   c. 172

   d. 243

2. Disks accurately drawn; algorithm accurately recorded

   a. 162

   b. 151

   c. 241

©2015 Great Minds. eureka-math.org
G4-M3-TE-B2-1.3.1-01.2016

Lesson 28

Problem Set

1. a. 287

    b. 287

    c. 177

    d. 118

    e. 218 R1

    f. 118 R1

    g. 91 R2

    h. 91 R4

    i. 169 R2

    j. 238 R3

2. 145 bottles; yes; 1 bottle

Exit Ticket

1. a. 388   2. 32 servings

    b. 198 R2

Homework

1. a. 189

    b. 265

    c. 128

    d. 123

    e. 179 R2

    f. 172 R2

    g. 166

    h. 156 R3

    i. 155 R1

    j. 132 R3

2. 233 m

©2015 Great Minds. eureka-math.org
G4-M3-TE-B2-1.3.1-01.2016

Lesson 29

Problem Set

1. a. 418

   b. 394 R2

   c. 3474

   d. 2,237 R1

   e. 3,784 R1

   f. 2,523

   g. 1,591

   h. 1,514 R4

   i. 2,489 R2

   j. 2,489

2. 93 goats

Exit Ticket

1. a. 591

   b. 1,694 R2

2. 446 stamps

Homework

1. a. 616

   b. 616

   c. 3,142

   d. 3,293 R1

   e. 1,815

   f. 2,712 R1

   g. 2,822 R1

   h. 2,818 R2

   i. 1,234 R1

   j. 1,234 R3

2. 1,296 apples

EUREKA
MATH™

Lesson 30

Problem Set

1. 51
2. 234 R2
3. 209
4. 203 R1
5. 190
6. 1,280
7. 614
8. 1,341 R1
9. 2,078 R1
10. 3,002 R2
11. a. 1,043 R2

    b. Answers will vary.

Exit Ticket

1. 95
2. 2,346 R2

Homework

1. 81 R4
2. 251 R1
3. 207 R3
4. 200 R2
5. 240
6. 1,250
7. 412
8. 4,515 R1
9. 1,554 R2
10. 2,000

EUREKA
MATH™

Lesson 31

Sprint

Side A

1.	3	12.	300	23.	60	34.	40
2.	30	13.	500	24.	600	35.	80
3.	300	14.	700	25.	4	36.	800
4.	3,000	15.	900	26.	40	37.	80
5.	3	16.	90	27.	3	38.	700
6.	30	17.	2	28.	300	39.	80
7.	300	18.	3	29.	4	40.	900
8.	3,000	19.	30	30.	40	41.	90
9.	2	20.	300	31.	6	42.	80
10.	3	21.	5	32.	600	43.	900
11.	30	22.	6	33.	700	44.	800

Side B

1.	2	12.	50	23.	40	34.	60
2.	20	13.	70	24.	400	35.	70
3.	200	14.	700	25.	3	36.	700
4.	2,000	15.	900	26.	30	37.	70
5.	2	16.	90	27.	3	38.	600
6.	20	17.	3	28.	300	39.	800
7.	200	18.	4	29.	3	40.	70
8.	2,000	19.	40	30.	30	41.	800
9.	2	20.	400	31.	6	42.	90
10.	3	21.	5	32.	600	43.	800
11.	30	22.	4	33.	700	44.	80

EUREKA
MATH™

Module 3:   Multi-Digit Multiplication and Division

581

©2015 Great Minds. eureka-math.org
G4-M3-TE-B2-1.3.1-01.2016

Problem Set

1. 78 tables; number of groups unknown

2. 473 books; group size unknown

3. 501 sacks; number of groups unknown

4. 1,920 cookies; group size unknown

5. 603 miles; group size unknown

Exit Ticket

1. 143 cars; group size unknown

2. 178 sacks; number of groups unknown

Homework

1. 125 mL; group size unknown

2. 206 baggies; number of groups unknown

3. 70 miles; group size unknown

4. 219 strips; number of groups unknown

5. 1,164 Groblarx fruits; group size unknown

Module 3:   Multi-Digit Multiplication and Division

EUREKA
MATH™

Lesson 32

Problem Set

1. 31 seats

2. 8 bagels

3. 87 bags; 5 pieces of candy

4. 150 teams; 4 children

5. 1,014 kg; 5 kg

Exit Ticket

1. 121 students

2. 59 crayons

Homework

1. 48 guests

2. 500 pencils

3. 251 sacks

4. 36 muffins

5. 1,287 m

Lesson 33

Problem Set

1. a. $892 \div 4 = 223$

   b. Whole: 892; parts: 400, 400, 80, 12

   $(400 \div 4) + (400 \div 4) + (80 \div 4) + (12 \div 4) = 100 + 100 + 20 + 3 = 223$

2. a. 240; area model accurately drawn

   b. Answers will vary.

3. a. 258; area model accurately drawn

   b. Answers will vary.

   c. Algorithm accurately recorded

4. a. 792; area model accurately drawn

   b. Answers will vary.

   c. Algorithm accurately recorded

Exit Ticket

1. a. $747 \div 3 = 249$

   b. Whole: 747; parts: 600, 120, 27

   $(600 \div 3) + (120 \div 3) + (27 \div 3) = 200 + 40 + 9 = 249$

2. a. 684; area model accurately drawn

   b. Answers will vary.

   c. Algorithm accurately recorded

EUREKA
MATH™

Homework

1. a. 1,828 ÷ 4 = 457

    b. Whole: 1,828; parts: 1,600, 200, 28

    (1,600 ÷ 4) + (200 ÷ 4) + (28 ÷ 4) = 400 + 50 + 7 = 457

2. a. 204; area model accurately drawn

    b. Answers will vary.

3. a. 183; area model accurately drawn

    b. Answers will vary.

    c. Algorithm accurately recorded

4. a. 1,381; area model accurately drawn

    b. Answers will vary.

    c. Algorithm accurately recorded

©2015 Great Minds. eureka-math.org
G4-M3-TE-B2-1.3.1-01.2016

Lesson 34

Problem Set

1. Disks drawn accurately
   a. 3; 3; 720
   b. 43; 43; 1,720
   c. 10, 37; 37; 1,110
2. Disks drawn accurately
   a. 540
   b. 1,240
3. a. 1,360
   b. 2,150
4. a. 1,360
   b. 1,500

Exit Ticket

1. 2, 10, 41, 820
2. 1,920

Homework

1. Disks drawn accurately
   a. 2; 2; 680
   b. 34; 34; 1,020
   c. 10, 42; 42; 1,260
2. Disks drawn accurately
   a. 320
   b. 1,280
3. a. 630
   b. 2,520
4. a. 1,720
   b. 1,610

　　　Module 3:　　　Multi-Digit Multiplication and Division

©2015 Great Minds. eureka-math.org
G4-M3-TE-B2-1.3.1-01.2016

EUREKA
MATH™

Lesson 35

Problem Set

1. 40; 400; 440
2. 50; 2,000; 2,050
3. 180; 4,200; 4,380
4. Area model drawn; 2,560
5. Area model drawn; 3,780
6. 2,040
7. 2,040
8. 2,200
9. 4,400

Exit Ticket

1. 90; 2,700; 2,790
2. 240; 2,800; 3,040

Homework

1. 210; 300; 510;
2. 320; 2,000; 2,320
3. 400; 1,500; 1,900
4. Area model drawn; 1,140
5. Area model drawn; 880
6. 1,760
7. 2,640
8. 3,290
9. 5,200

Lesson 36

Problem Set

1. a. 4×2 , 4×10, 10×2, 10×10

    b. 2, 10, 2, 10

2. 308; area model and partial products accurately recorded

3. 800; area model and partial products accurately recorded

4. 1,470; area model and partial products accurately recorded

5. 462; partial products accurately recorded

6. 506; partial products accurately recorded

Exit Ticket

1. 1,118; area model and partial products accurately recorded

2. 935; area model and partial products accurately recorded

Homework

1. a. 3×2, 3×10, 10×2, 10×10

    b. 2, 10, 2, 10

2. 578; area model and partial products accurately recorded

3. 810; area model and partial products accurately recorded

4. 855; area model and partial products accurately recorded

5. 564; partial products accurately recorded

6. 2,139; partial products accurately recorded

7. 253; partial products accurately recorded

8. 506; partial products accurately recorded

EUREKA
MATH

Lesson 37

Problem Set

1. 4 × 2, 4 × 10, 10 × 2, 10 × 10; 8, 40, 20, 100, 168; 4 × 12, 10 × 12; 48, 120, 168
2. 2 × 3, 2 × 40, 30 × 3, 30 × 40; 6, 80, 90, 1,200, 1,376; 2 × 43, 30 × 43; 86, 1,290, 1,376
3. 7 × 15, 50 × 15; 105, 750, 855
4.
   a. 150, 6, 25; 1,000, 40, 25; 1,150
   b. 36, 2, 18; 1,080, 60, 18; 1,116
   c. 234, 1,560, 1,794
   d. 234, 1,560, 1,794

Exit Ticket

1. 3 × 2, 3 × 20, 40 × 2, 40 × 20; 6, 60, 80, 800, 946; 3 × 22, 40 × 22; 66, 880, 946
2. 5 × 64, 10 × 64; 320, 640, 960

Homework

1. 6 × 4, 6 × 30, 20 × 4, 20 × 30; 24, 180, 80, 600, 884; 6 × 34, 20 × 34; 204, 680, 884
2. 2 × 1, 2 × 40, 80 × 1, 80 × 40; 2, 80, 80, 3,200, 3,362; 2 × 41, 80 × 41; 82, 3,280, 3,362
3. 2 × 26, 50 × 26; 52, 1,300, 1,352
4.
   a. 204, 3, 68; 1,360, 20, 68; 1,564
   b. 147, 3, 49; 1,470, 30, 49; 1,617
   c. 80, 320, 400
   d. 54, 3,780, 3,834

Lesson 38

Problem Set

1. 3 × 54, 20 × 54; 3, 20; 162, 54; 1,080, 54; 1,242
2. 6 × 54, 40 × 54; 6, 40; 324, 6, 54; 2,160, 40, 54; 2,484
3. 5 × 47, 50 × 47; 5, 47, 50, 47; 235, 5, 47; 2,350, 50, 47; 2,585
4. 290, 5, 58; 2,320, 40, 58; 2,610
5. 410, 5, 82; 4,100, 50, 82; 4,510
6. 3,339
7. 6,132

Exit Ticket

1. 216, 3, 72; 2,880, 40, 72; 3,096
2. 1,855

Homework

1. 6 × 43, 20 × 43; 6, 20; 258, 43; 860, 43; 1,118
2. 7 × 63, 40 × 63; 7, 40; 441, 7, 63; 2,520, 40, 63; 2,961
3. 4 × 67, 50 × 67; 4, 67, 50, 67; 268, 4, 67; 3,350, 50, 67; 3,618
4. 208, 4, 52; 1,560, 30, 52; 1,768
5. 516, 6, 86; 4,300, 50, 86; 4,816
6. 2,808
7. 3,344
8. 3,969
9. 5,372

EUREKA
MATH™

This page intentionally left blank

This page intentionally left blank